CONTROL OF THE MIND

MAN AND CIVILIZATION

CONTROL OF THE MIND

a symposium edited by

Seymour M. Farber *Roger H. L. Wilson*

University of California
San Francisco Medical Center

McGRAW-HILL *New York* *San Francisco*
1961 *Toronto* *London*

CONTROL OF THE MIND

Library of Congress Catalogue Card 62-10849

II

This book is a record of the symposium Man and Civilization: Control of the Mind *held at the University of California San Francisco Medical Center, January 28, 29, and 30, 1961, produced in collaboration with Robert M. Featherstone, Seymour M. Lipset, and Alexander Simon, members of the program committee. Within the limits of space, it consists of the actual material as it was presented. To preserve spontaneity, the panels in particular have been presented in their original form with only minor editing. Thus we have as true a mirror as possible of this unusual symposium.*

CONTRIBUTORS

Francis C. Brown, LL.B., LL.M., President and Chairman of the Board, Schering Corporation; President, Schering Foundation, Bloomfield, New Jersey

Jonathan O. Cole, M.D., Chief, Psychopharmacology Service Center, National Institutes of Health, United States Public Health Service, Bethesda, Maryland

Very Reverend Martin C. D'Arcy, S.J., M.A., Formerly The Master of Campion Hall, Oxford; Provincial of English Province of Society of Jesus, London, England

William R. Dennes, D.Phil., LL.D., Ph.D., Mills Professor of Intellectual and Moral Philosophy and Civil Polity, University of California, Berkeley, California

Seymour M. Farber, M.D., Assistant Dean in Charge of Continuing Education in Medicine and the Health Sciences, University of California Medical Center, San Francisco, California

Robert M. Featherstone, Ph.D., Professor and Chairman of the Department of Pharmacology, University of California School of Medicine, San Francisco, California

Donald O. Hebb, Ph.D., Professor of Psychology, McGill University, Montreal, Canada

H. Stuart Hughes, Ph.D., Professor of History, Harvard University, Cambridge, Massachusetts

Aldous Huxley, Author, Los Angeles, California

Holgar Hydén, M.D., Professor and Chairman, Department of Histology, Faculty of Medicine, University of Göteborg, Sweden

Seymour S. Kety, M.D., Chief, Laboratory of Clinical Science, National Institute of Mental Health, Bethesda, Maryland

Arthur Koestler, Author, London, England

David Krech, Ph.D., Professor of Psychology, University of California, Berkeley, California

Harold D. Lasswell, Ph.D., Professor of Law and Political Science, Yale School of Law, Yale University, New Haven, Connecticut

Seymour M. Lipset, Ph.D., Professor of Sociology, University of California, Berkeley, California; Visiting Ford Research Professor of Political Science, 1960-61, Yale University, New Haven, Connecticut

C. A. Mace, M.A., D.Litt., Professor of Psychology, Birkbeck College, University of London, London, England

James G. Miller, M.D., Ph.D., Professor of Psychiatry and Psychology, Director, Mental Health Research Institute, University of Michigan, Ann Arbor, Michigan

Wilder Penfield, M.D., D.Litt., D.Sc., Guggenheim Fellow, Montreal Neurological Institute, Montreal, Canada

William E. Porter, Professor of Journalism, State University of Iowa, Iowa City, Iowa

Karl H. Pribram, M.D., Associate Professor of Psychiatry and Psychology, Stanford University School of Medicine, Stanford, California

Leo C. Rosten, Ph.D., Author; Ford Visiting Professor in Government Affairs, 1960-61, University of California, Berkeley, Calif.

John B. deC. M. Saunders, M.B., Ch.B., F.R.C.S. (Edin.), Provost, University of California Medical Center; Dean, School of Medicine; Professor of Anatomy and Lecturer in Medical History and Bibliography, San Francisco, California

Glenn T. Seaborg, Ph.D., Chancellor, University of California, Berkeley, California

Alexander Simon, M.D., Professor and Chairman of the Department of Psychiatry, University of California School of Medicine; Medical Superintendent, Langley Porter Neuropsychiatric Institute, San Francisco, California

Herbert A. Simon, Ph.D., Professor of Administration; Associate Dean, Graduate School of Industrial Administration, Carnegie Institute of Technology, Pittsburgh, Pennsylvania

Roger H. L. Wilson, M.D., Assistant Head of Continuing Education in Medicine, University of California Medical Center, San Francisco, California

PREFACE

The scriptural invitation to reason together, never safely neglected by any of the sciences, has an especial relevance and urgency for the sciences of the mind at this time. In the last decade or so there have been several major contributions to our understanding of brain function. These developments have transformed our conception of psychological research. Since its inception modern psychology has more or less consciously taken physics for its model science, and it has attempted to unify itself on this model. But most of these developments, as the present volume shows quite clearly, have originated in fields of study which would have been regarded a short time ago as quite outside the psychological field. Electronics has given us the computer as a model for the human thinking process, research in drugs has opened up the pharmacological approach to the study of brain function, and histology promises us, at any rate, a precise and scientific account of brain function on the physiological level. There is no longer any hope for the unified science we had expected; we must begin to think of psychology as a constellation of sciences rather like the biological sciences. At the same time, these developing disciplines have the utmost unity of subject matter; they are all directed to the understanding of one organic function. However, as these new disciplines for the study of the mind organize themselves, one thing is clear: that organization must include an unusually large number of interdisciplinary channels of communication.

But modern psychology must confront another difficulty. Every science, it seems, sooner or later gets into areas where major questions of value arise. Other sciences can generally evade the problems thus raised by restricting themselves to a purely instrumental role; how their discoveries are to be used is left to others. This recourse is not open to psychology, working as it does with the only organ in this world which makes such judgments of value. The psychologist is hence in a dilemma: he cannot in all conscience make these judgments himself, nor can he separate his field of research from the judgmental process which is implicit in it. What can he do? There is at present no answer to this question. But there is at least this course of action open to him. He can extend his interdisciplinary conversations to include those who are especially interested in problems of value judgments—theologians, philosophers, artists, for example.

This book, and the symposium of which it is a record, was designed to initiate both the smaller, technical sort of discussion and the larger philosophical one. It is admittedly imperfect, as all beginnings must be. It by no means includes all the voices which deserve a hearing on this subject, and perhaps the discussions are not focused upon the issues as sharply as they might be. But the speakers are without exception distinguished men in their respective fields who have valuable contributions to make. And one of the problems is that we must learn to speak together. It will take many such symposia, both at the University of California and elsewhere, to master the difficult art of conversing fruitfully with those from other disciplines.

One inescapable defect of this book is that it does not properly reflect the significant degree of interdisciplinary conversation that was achieved at the symposium. The last afternoon was given over entirely to a series of three-member discussion groups meeting simultaneously in different rooms. These discussion groups were informal and included an interchange of very significant comment from members of the audience. Considerations of space, unfortunately, have made it necessary to summarize these discussions. One must particularly lament the failure of this present volume to represent adequately the contribution of the audience to these problems, which, to some exent at any rate, belong to all mankind.

In the organization of an enterprise of this magnitude one inevitably incurs debts which cannot be paid, even by public acknowledgment. It would be unpardonable, however, to fail to acknowledge the indebtedness of the whole symposium to Francis C. Brown, President of the Schering Foundation and Schering Corporation, whose tact and perception was as invaluable as the financial assistance which he extended through the Schering Foundation. It is peculiarly fitting that an enterprise of this sort should have been supported, ultimately, by a pharmaceutical company—Schering, which has contributed so substantially to the physical and mental well-being of modern man.

It would be an impertinence and an impossibility to attempt to assess the services of Provost Saunders of the University of California San Francisco Medical Center to this first attempt at a new approach to one of man's central problems. And I trust that the many individuals, within the university and without, who willingly sacrificed many hours to a discussion of the problems presented by the symposium during the years of its planning will be sufficiently rewarded by this fruit of their combined suggestions. The staff of the University of California Extension Division of the San Francisco Medical Center is already too well aware, we suspect, of our dependence upon them for thanks to be necessary.

Seymour M. Farber
Roger H. L. Wilson

INTRODUCTION

John B. deC. M. Saunders

The present work has its genesis in an earlier discussion at the University of California San Francisco Medical Center on the pharmacological effects of certain drugs on the mind. The great technological skill and ingenuity of the modern chemist has provided the medical scientist and the physician with an abundant array of new chemical compounds of varying and diverse structure which influence the central nervous system to distort, accelerate, or depress the mental state and behavioral characteristics of the individual. The conference emphasized that many of these chemical agents possess a highly selective action on particular and discrete parts of the nervous system—so much so as to permit from an examination of their actions in man and animals an arrangement in order and rank. Those chemical agents thus offer, by a consideration of the relationships between chemical structure and biological action, the possibility of providing a vast array of drugs influencing the specific activity of the brain. Indeed, since such agents may either potentiate or attenuate one another, exhibit overlap in their actions, and demonstrate polarity in their effects on the brain, the very strong possibility is suggested of a full spectrum of chemical agents which can be used for the control of the mind in the majority of its activities. Further, these considerations draw attention to the fact that such agents have begun to offer a tool of exceptional importance for the fractionation or chemical dissection of nervous function in the first or analytical phase, which is prerequisite to an objective attack upon the greatest of all problems in the biology of man, that of the mind-brain relationship. The advances of the past 10 years in this and cognate fields of neurophysiology, neurobiochemistry, neuroendocrinology and the like have been tremendous, restoring to scientists an earlier confidence and optimism that despite great difficulties they are at the beginning of an approach which will modify enormously the existing multitude of explanatory systems on the nature of the mind and enable them to take the first step, feeble though it may be, toward a genuine understanding of the mind-brain relationship, which, as William James said some 60 years ago, would constitute the "scientific achievement before which all past achievements would pale."

Despite the new-grown optimism that the biologist and medical scientist are on the threshold leading to a fuller understanding of the mind as an expression of cerebral activity, there is, especially among thoughtful physicians, a deep sense of disquiet. Here at the command of mankind are drugs capable of producing, on the one hand, that calm and peaceful state of αταρζια so greatly sought by Epicurean philosophers and, on the other, psychic stimulants which may provoke the imagery of literary genius or visions of the mystic. It is coming to be recognized that, unfortunately, an increasing number of people in our society are, through the medium of these agents, seeking tranquility at the expense of effective living or as an escape from reality. As Professor Waggoner of the University of Michigan has recently put it, "With the widespread use of these drugs some individuals may lose the initiative and the responsiveness needed in our competitive culture, much of which comes from healthy anxiety." Here at our disposal, to be used wisely or unwisely, is an increasing array of agents that manipulate human beings. As an example of the possible magnitude of the problem, one needs only to be reminded of the vast and continuing consequences of the earliest cerebral depressant introduced into the social life of man in the hope of controlling the tyranny of mind and memory—alcohol. Thus the new techniques introduce social, ethical, and religious complications of great consequence. It is now possible to act directly on the individual to modify his behavior instead of, as in the past, indirectly through modification of the environment. This, then, constitutes a part of what Aldous Huxley has called "The Final Revolution," that is, the application to human affairs of technology both on the social and on the individual level. Huxley sees the possibility that through the "technicization" of persuasion by psychobiological means and pharmacological method, as well as by other technological means such as mass communication, within a generation or so it is possible to create for entire societies a sort of painless concentration camp of the mind, in which people will have lost their liberties in the enjoyment of a dictatorship without tears.

In this connection "technicization" thus poses a threat to our entire culture and is capable of making a mockery of Western civilization and the democratic tradition. Sir Charles Snow, presently Regents' Professor at the University of California, has drawn attention to the widening chasm which is developing with the scientific revolution. He has emphasized that the bond of a common language between science and the humanities has been broken, with mutual ignorance rapidly growing, so that we are in grave danger of losing the full benefits of science by a denial of the cultural wisdom of the past. New techniques of communication must be undertaken to bridge the expanding interval between the two worlds now apart: the scientific culture and the wisdom culture.

Therefore it seemed important and desirable to hold periodic conferences upon a wider and more representative scale, in which would be brought together members of the various scientific disciplines with leaders of religion, philosophy, government, history, law, and communication to examine the present outlook and to alert ourselves to the problems of the future and suggest appropriate courses of action. To initiate such a conference the problem of the control of the mind seemed of first importance.

It is perhaps not inappropriate to select a medical center for such a conference. The physician, by tradition and training, has always been a man of two worlds. His roots are scientific and his endeavors humanistic. Professionally he is aware of both the science and the art of medicine. He is the son of Apollo as well as of Asclepios. He is of many personalities—social, historical, political, cultural—since he must guide, counsel, and organize, to promote, protect, and restore the health of the community, but above all he stands with the individual. This was expressed by one of the masters of medicine, Claude Bernard: "*La science, c'est nous; l'art, c'est moi."* However, the physician has had a long experience in such conferences, for in that other immortal "Symposium" of Plato, there he was, the physician Eryximachus.

If I remember correctly, there is a story told by Scheherazade in *A Thousand and One Nights* which concerns a young man who was given a very beautiful and very wonderful magic feather. To protect the precious gift he wore it in his cap. However, one day he nearly lost it when his attention was diverted while listening to some persuasive orator in the market place. Thereafter he developed a habit of always feeling for the feather even though his cap was no longer on his head, and in doing so, he discovered that the gesture alone was capable of holding off the magical forces which surrounded him. I like to think that the parable refers to the eternal vigilance necessary for the preservation of a free mind.

We welcome the group of distinguished scholars represented here and look forward to their discussions as they examine the forces acting on the mind in our present society.

The introductory series of discussions might well be announced in the words of Francis Bacon from his *Proficience and Advancement of Learning:* "The first article on the culture of mind will regard the different natures or dispositions of men . . . so then an artificial [i.e., scientific] and accurate dissection may be made of men's minds and nature. . . ."

CONTENTS

PART ONE

THE MIND AND ITS INTEGRATION

Chairman: Alexander Simon

The symposium began with a series of three papers exploring the neurological, histological, and psychological problems arising out of attempts to define the concept of mind or deal with the numerous and puzzling corollaries to mind. The speakers are particularly concerned with the merits of monism or pluralism in relation to the mind-body problem, with the physical bases of memory and other mental processes, with the role of the emotions in the function of mind, and with the relation of mind and experience. Following delivery of the papers, the three speakers joined with a moderator for a panel discussion of the questions stimulated by their treatment of the subject matter. A transcription of the panel discussion has been edited and included in the text.

In the evening session, author Aldous Huxley addressed himself to the broad topic of "Human Potentialities" viewed in the light of modern thought. The paper is chiefly concerned with the possible long-range consequences, both social and individual, of modern developments in religion, physiology, pharmacology, psychology, and a number of related subject areas.

Wilder Penfield

THE PHYSIOLOGICAL BASIS OF THE MIND

One evening in the late eighteenth century an Italian woman stood in her kitchen watching the frogs' legs which she was preparing for the evening meal. "Look at those muscles move," she said to her husband. "They always seem to come alive when I hang them on the copper wire." Her husband looked. He was the Professor of Surgery in the University of Bologna, but he is known to us as the discoverer of electricity —Luigi Galvani. Here was the beginning of it all two hundred years ago. The cut end of the frog's nerve was in contact with the copper wire, and electric current produced by the contact was passing along the nerve to the muscle; as a result, the muscle was twitching and contracting.

Galvani did not understand just where the energy was coming from at first, but nevertheless, with his wife's help, he had here discovered the key to nerve conduction and to muscle action. Here was the basis of all animal movement, reflex and voluntary, in frog and man. You see, from the time of the Greek physician Galen, sixteen centuries before Galvani, men had considered that there was a spirit, or *anima*, within the body that carried mysterious messages to the hand and the foot and the tongue to move them.

From now on electric currents were to explain all this—how the frog could jump at the approach of danger, how we can put one foot before the other to walk or run, how we move our mouths and muscles of respiration in order to talk, how we move our eyes to read, how we turn our heads to listen. But it did not explain how the frog came to be aware of danger, nor does it answer the riddle of how we think. That is what you have asked me to explain at the start of this symposium.

All these body movements, some of them subject to the will and others quite involuntary, are executed as motor mechanisms initiated by electrical potentials that flash out along the nerves to the muscles and from the muscles back again to the central nervous system, which is housed within the spinal cord, and the brain. More than that, we know now that it is electrical potentials which speed from the sense organs—the eye, the ear, the nose, the tongue, and the skin—inward along the nerves to the brain. All sensory information from our bodies and from the world around us becomes available within the brain.

Thus neurophysiology has explained away the mysterious *anima*, the spirit of ancient days, quite successfully. But what about the remaining intangibles, the mind and consciousness and the soul? No, these things science has not explained, not yet. It is quite possible that it never will. So far, one conclusion seems clear to the neurophysiologist: there is no evidence of any mental activity unless some action is going on in the brain.

"And what," you might well ask, "is brain action?" Brain action consists in the traveling of electrical potentials along circuits formed by nerve-fiber bundles within the brain. The nerve fibers are branches from living nerve cells which form the gray matter of the brain. The gray matter is found in nuclei within the center of the brain and forms the cerebral cortex that covers the hemispheres. There are said to be 12 billion cells in one human brain. The branching nerve fibers that issue from them are capable of conducting currents, and each of these cells is capable of producing a small amount of electrical energy within itself. That energy can boost or block or alter the currents that pass and repass.

My teacher in undergraduate and graduate years was Sir Charles Sherrington. In his time, he was a great leader of neurophysiologists. Here is a description he gave of man's nervous system to a lay audience. It betrays the fact that he was really a poet as well as a scientist:

Picture to yourself a scheme of lines and nodal points gathered together at one end into a great ravelled knot, the brain, and at the other trailing off to a sort of stalk, the spinal cord. Imagine activity in this shown by little points of light. Of these some stationary points flash rhythmically, faster or slower. Others are travelling points streaming in serial lines at various speeds. The rhythmic stationary lights lie at the nodes. The nodes are both goals whither converge, and junctions whence diverge, the lines of travelling lights. Suppose we choose the hour of deep sleep. Then only in some sparse and out-of-the-way places are nodes flashing and trains of light points running. The great knotted headpiece lies for the most part quite dark. Occasionally at places in it lighted points flash or move but soon subside.

Should we continue to watch the scheme, we should observe after a time an impressive change which suddenly accrues. In the great head end, which had been mostly darkness, spring up myriads of lights, as though activity from one of these local places suddenly spread far and wide. The great topmost sheet of the mass, where hardly a light had twinkled or moved, becomes now a sparkling field of rhythmic flashing points with trains of travelling sparks hurrying hither and thither. It is as if the milky way entered upon some cosmic dance. Swiftly the head mass becomes an enchanted loom where millions of flashing shuttles weave a dissolving pattern, always a meaningful pattern though never an abiding one. The brain is waking and with it the mind is returning.

It was in 1950 that I was first invited to take part in a symposium discussion of the brain and the mind. That was a BBC series of broadcasts entitled The Physical Basis of Mind. Scientists and philosophers took part in it. The scientists were all physicians—two physiologists, two anatomists, a psychiatrist, a neurologist, and a neurosurgeon. They spoke first, and the three philosophers last so they could listen if they thought it worthwhile, to what the physicians said week by week before their turns should come.

The symposium was opened by Sherrington, who was ninety-three in that year. At the close of his talk he chuckled and remarked that 2,000 years ago Aristotle "was asking how the mind is attached to the body."

Let me turn now to the reports of the philosophers. Perhaps this may be as good a way as any other to let you see the problem of neurophysiology from without. A. J. Ayer, Professor of Philosophy in University College, London, quoted from the broadcast which Adrian, a psychologist from Cambridge, had made:

The part of the picture of the brain which may always be missing is, of course, the part which deals with the mind, the part which ought to explain how a particular pattern of nerve impulses can produce an idea: or the other way round, how a thought can decide which nerve cells are to come into action.

After quoting that, Ayer then asserted that if people would only abandon the ancient thinking of Descartes that mind and body are separate, the problem would become a philosophical one, and would no longer be a matter of scientific concern. He continued:

The picture we are given [by the scientists] is that of messengers travelling through the brain, reaching a mysterious entity called the mind, receiving orders from it, and then travelling on. But since the mind has no position in space—it is by definition not the sort of thing that can have position in space—it does not literally make sense to talk of physical signals reaching it.

How logical this philosopher's approach to the problem seems. And how impressively like the method of Socrates. Socrates used to leave his embarrassed pupils to find their own way out of a situation that he had shown to be absurd. But in this case the neurophysiologists already recognized the nature of the inconsistency. Therein lies the problem.

The "messages travelling through the brain" never do reach a place that we can discover where the mind is found. Say, rather, that electrical currents pass through differing circuits of the brain and that there is simultaneous change in the shapes of conscious thought. The passing of potentials and the concomitant change of thought are apparently identical in time, but as far as we can determine, there is no actual meeting. We are beginning to learn where the brain action is, but we know no "where" of mind. Nor can we see, as yet, that either one comes first, the change in thought or the movement of current. The riddle we must try to solve is this: What is the nature of the mind? How is it joined to action within the brain? To declare that these things are one, not two, does not make them so. But it does block the progress of research.

Gilbert Ryle, the Professor of Metaphysical Philosophy at Oxford, employed amused sarcasm rather than Socratic logic in his contribution to the symposium. It ended with this sweeping injunction:

The umbrella titles "Mind" and "Matter" obliterate the very differences that ought to interest us. Theorists should drop both these words. . . . "Mind" and "Matter" are echoes . . . [of the arguments of the philosophy of the past].

Neither of these philosophers suggested what words we should use when we talk with the men and women whose brain-mind or mind-brain problem we must continue to study. They did not trouble to advise us frankly whether to embrace the gospel of materialism which assumes that all is matter, energy, and automatic mechanism. (This would be in keeping with the philosophy of Karl Marx.) Neither did they suggest that we should adopt the ancient preaching of Bishop Berkeley that all is mind. This philosophy echoes still in the gentle teaching of Christian Science. Choosing this side of the shield we might be forced to abandon biological science as unnecessary—and thus leave everything in the hands of the philosophers and Mary Baker Eddy.

Viscount Samuel, the third philosopher, did give due consideration to the facts. He pointed out that neither the materialist nor the idealist point of view "has won general assent" during the discussion of this problem:

This is one of the oldest and most fundamental of the problems of philosophy—the relation between mind and matter. For centuries, philosophers of different schools have made strenuous efforts to resolve one into the other.

The whole effort to resolve mind into matter or else matter into mind is the outcome of what T. H. Green called "the philosophic craving for unity." . . . An essential duality in nature is the alternative that is left.

Lord Samuel continued with his discussion as follows:

Dr. Russel Brain [the neurologist] tells us that "all stimuli reach the brain as electrical patterns." . . . This discussion has helped to clarify the whole problem by establishing the fact that the meeting-place is not at the points where external stimuli impinge upon the nervous system; it is at the points where mind accepts and utilizes the sense-data offered by the brain. But the discussion has not been able to answer the question what it is that takes over at those points; and therefore it could not even begin to consider how the connection was made.

Then Samuel quoted what Sherrington had written elsewhere, as follows:

> That our being should consist of *two* fundamental elements offers, I suppose, no greater inherent improbability than that it should rest on one only. . . . We have to regard the relation of mind to brain as still not merely unsolved, but still devoid of a basis for its very beginning.

Then Samuel concluded:

> That, it seems, is where we are now at a standstill. Until science and philosophy can help us to move on from that position we cannot hope that the universe will, for us, be rationalized.

We must accept this statement still. We have no basis on which to begin to understand the relation of mind to the brain. But I believe that understanding will come in time with continued advance—not to us, but to our successors.

I must tell you then where physiology stands in its approach to this hoped-for basis of understanding. Some of you may know very little about the brain. Some of you are physicians, but you may have turned to other interests in medicine. Let me simplify; you will remember your lectures on neuroanatomy and what you saw in the dissecting room. You were impressed by this great cream-colored organ separated from the skull by the two mother membranes. First there was the *dura mater,* tough and shining and silver-white just beneath the bone of the skull, and under that the delicate transparent *pia mater,* covering the brain's rounded convolutions and bridging the fissures where you could see the clear cerebrospinal fluid that bathes the brain and floats it as though in a bath within the skull.

You remember the carpet of arteries and veins that nourish the cortex or gray matter so richly, and the drawings of the brain. There was the vertical fissure named for Rolando. The convolution in front of it was labeled *motor,* and you were told it controlled the opposite side of the face and the arm and leg. The convolution behind the fissure was marked *sensory,* and you knew it had to do with discriminative sensibility on the opposite side of the body, not pain sensation. The inflow of pain sense stopped in the thalamus, deep in the brain, without reaching the cortex.

The occipital lobes at the back of the head were labeled *visual,* and on the edge of the superior convolution of the temporal lobe was the margin of the *auditory* area, most of which was buried in the deep

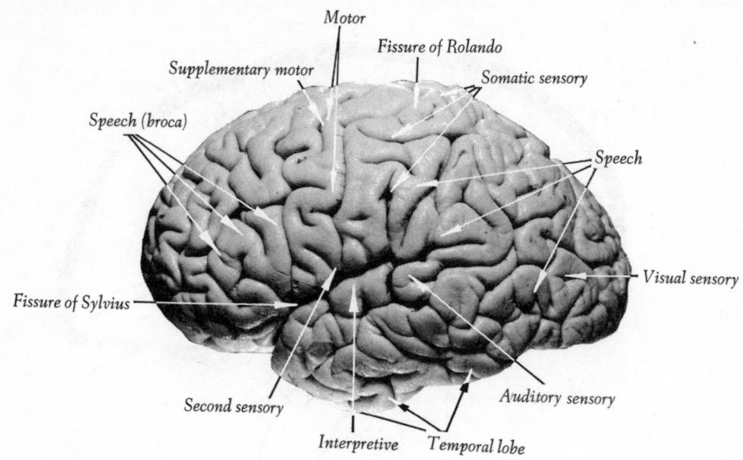

Figure 1 The human brain, showing the functional areas of the cortex [after Penfield and Roberts, 1959].

fissure of Sylvius. You were told, too, that somewhere hidden under the brain were small areas related to the sense of *smell* and also *taste*. On the left hemisphere the word *speech* was written in two places—one on the posterior part of the temporal lobe and one on the lower part of the frontal lobe.

You probably remember that Pavlov showed that removing areas of cortex made a dog forget what he had learned, and Lashley claimed a rat would learn again no matter which part of the cortex had been removed, as long as some was left. Lashley spent his life looking vainly for the "engram" in the animal brain, the local memory trace, knowing it must be somewhere. He never found it.

In the case of man, physiologists and anatomists were content to follow the sensory tracts from the skin and eye and ear and other sense organs on the outside of the body inward and up to the cortex. Then they followed the motor fibers down from the cortex to the muscles on the opposite side of the body.

The cerebral cortex was the end and the beginning, the top, the mysterious place where Mind might possibly have its existence, like the gods on Mount Olympus. What happened between sensory arrival at the cortex and motor emission was a mystery. Neurologists talked

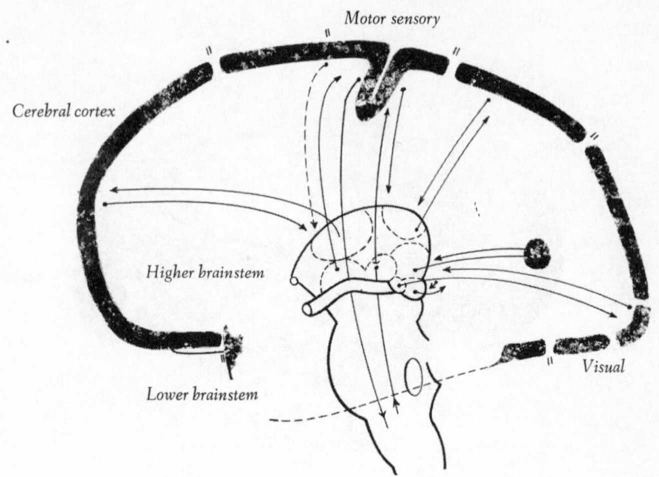

Figure 2 Diagram of connections between the brainstem and the cerebral cortex, illustrating the probable functional interaction of the areas of cortex with the corresponding portions of the diencephalon from which each area of cortex is a developmental projection [*after Penfield and Jasper, 1954*].

vaguely of "association" fibers that did something by connecting the nerve cells of the cortex with each other.

Let me make an addition to that picture which is partly hypothesis and partly proven. First, the sensory pathways do not end on the cortex. The high road of elaborative sensory conduction goes to the cortex and then returns directly into the thalamic centers (Figure 2), where the pain pathway had ended directly without such a detour to the cortex.

Second, the stream of electrical impulses that controls the voluntary muscles does not begin in the cortex. It begins somewhere near where the sensory tracts seem to end in the underlying brainstem (Figure 2). From the brainstem, it flows out to the motor gyrus of the cortex on both sides and then on to the muscles.

Third, there must be, in what we may call the higher portion of the brainstem (Figure 3), a system of nerve tracts and cell collections which are connected symmetrically with the cerebral cortex on either side. Many of these connections, like the stems of lily pads, provided the pads of cortex with functional control or connection.

Now let us turn to the mental processes which are called perception, memory of past experience, memory of words, memory of concepts, interpretation of present experience, the directing and focusing of attention that selects and excludes material for thought, decision of action. All those things, those psychological processes, must be subserved by the coordinating and integrating currents that pass over the connections of this central system. If there is truly a neuronal mechanism that serves effectively as the basis of conscious thought, the mechanism must use these paths.

When there is damage to, or interference with, the higher brainstem, whether due to indirect concussion or direct injury, or tumor pressure, or vascular "stroke," the result is inevitably the loss of consciousness. If the neuronal activity which coordinates and integrates brain action and makes conscious thought possible takes place here, then this loss of consciousness is to be expected. On the other hand, large areas of cortex can be removed on one or both sides without loss of consciousness.

These connections that pass through the higher brainstem and unite the two hemispheres, and which seem to be indispensable for

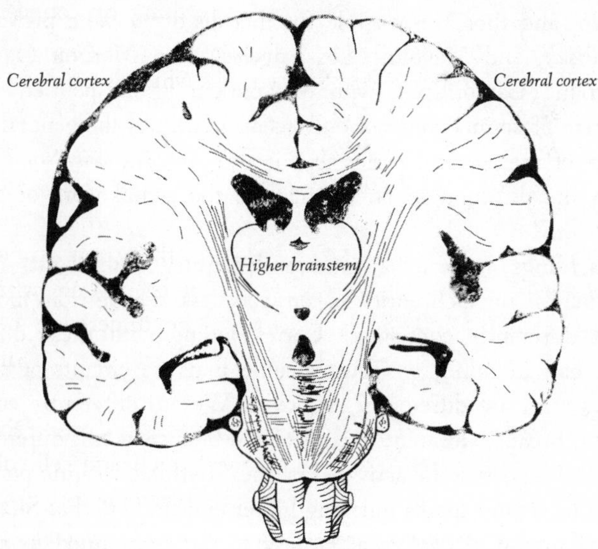

Figure 3 Vertical cross section of the human brain [after Penfield and Roberts, 1959].

conscious thinking, may be called the *centrencephalic system*. Some of the pathways are known and many only surmised.

Do not jump to the conclusion that I am suggesting the brainstem to be the location of an entity called mind or consciousness. One distinguished neurologist has already made that mistake and wasted some breath on it. That would be just as erroneous as to suggest that consciousness sits in the cortex or that it has a position in space anywhere. What we may assume is this:

The functional action going on in some part of the cortex of one or both hemispheres together with some part of the brainstem makes possible conscious mental processes or states of mind. It is through the centrencephalic system of connections that the coordination of brain action is carried out.

In 1953 I took part in a second symposium on the brain-mind problem. It was called the Laurentian Symposium on Brain Mechanisms and Consciousness. This time the discussants were all physicians from various parts of the world and included Prof. Donald O. Hebb. Some progress was made, partly due to the fact that the reticular activating system, a system of connecting fibers, had been recently discovered in the brain, and those responsible for this discovery were present: Moruzzi (Pisa), and Magoun (Los Angeles), and Morison (Harvard).

Adrian (Cambridge), who was present again, pointed out that this system of connections not only seems to control the general level of vigilance of the cerebral cortex, but it also probably has "something to do with the direction of attention, with the actual work of the conscious brain."

Hughlings Jackson, a nineteenth-century neurologist, observed that "There is no such entity as consciousness; we are from moment to moment differently conscious." Corresponding with these differences Jackson had in mind, we must assume that the circuits of the integrating system are differently employed. We are differently conscious, no doubt, because different circuits of the brainstem and different areas of the cerebral cortex are activated by the "rhythmic flashing points with trains of travelling sparks hurrying hither and thither" that Sherrington described in the physiological fantasy of the "enchanted loom where millions of flashing shuttles weave a dissolving pattern, always a meaningful pattern, though never an abiding one."

Time was when the brain was considered to be the "organ of the mind," functioning as a whole during all conscious states. Such a point of view is no longer tenable. Modern advances in knowledge lead us to ever-increasing localization of function within the brain. We are differently conscious from moment to moment, and concomitant with that there is a differing pattern of neuron activation.

When a man is using words, for example—it may be during speech or writing, or listening to speech or reading, or indeed, at times when words are used in quiet thinking—there must always be utilization of the speech areas in the left cerebral cortex and in the underlying thalamic nucleus of the left, the dominant, hemisphere. However, a man can play the piano with both hands or drive a car or understand the nature of an experience without calling on that speech mechanism at all.

As a neurosurgeon, I have found it necessary, as many neurosurgeons have, to remove large areas of cerebral cortex on one side from a patient while he was still conscious, using local anesthesia. As long as the brainstem is not molested, the patient remains conscious and, curiously enough, is not aware of any change until he turns his attention to a proposition that calls for specific use of the removed portion of his cerebral cortex. Then he may discover, for example, that he cannot feel accurately what he touches with the left hand or that, although he still sees to the right, he no longer sees objects on the left. These are not experiments but parts of some procedure which is a part of urgent treatment.

Jung of Freiburg has urged that the essential element in consciousness is the focusing of attention, the selecting of certain things as though a beam of light were focused upon them. I like this emphasis because it gives the neurophysiologist something to search for: the directional mechanism of attention. The searchlight might be thought of as situated in the higher brainstem. To focus attention, a man somehow selects certain circuits of the brain and activates them.

Now let me turn for a moment to some of the faculties of the mind. Take memory, for example, which has its different forms. It may be shown that man has functionally separable neuronal mechanism for (1) memory of current experience, (2) memory of words, and (3) memory of generalizations or concepts. These separations may be demonstrated occasionally on the operating table when the patient is fully conscious and the brain is exposed.

A large part of the gray matter that covers the temporal lobe may be called interpretive cortex (Figure 1). Functionally it may be considered to belong to a different integrative level than the so-called sensory cortex and motor cortex because it deals with the records of experience which have already passed through the mind. When a gentle electrical current is applied to this area of cortex the patient may, for example, exclaim suddenly, "I hear my mother and brother talking." In that particular case, when the surgeon stopped and asked, the patient explained that they were in the living room at home and she seemed to be there with them, seeing and hearing the same things that she heard and saw in some past strip of time. And yet, at the same time, she was aware of the fact that she was in the operating room on the operating table.

Many different past experiences have been recalled thus by the electrode, sometimes from a recent, and sometimes from a far-distant, past. For example, the recall may have summoned a time of listening to an orchestra, a time of hearing and seeing a man at the piano in a café, a time of laughing conversation with friends, a time of standing on the street corner at "Jacob and Worthington, South Bend, Indiana," a time of lying in the delivery room at childbirth, and many other personal experiences.

These flashbacks from the past carry far more detail than any person could summon voluntarily. Sometimes, instead of this type of experiential recall, the patient makes a sudden reinterpretation of the present time and situation, a false interpretation. For example, he may say suddenly, "I feel as though this had all happened before," or "I am afraid," as though the environment were all at once threatening.

We conclude that, in the interpretive cortex, it is possible to activate electrically a functional unit that operates under normal conditions as a subconscious reflex. You have all had the sudden feeling of familiarity. After this reflex signal, a bit of your own past comes back. It is apparent that in any normal individual, when the present experience resembles strikingly an experience from the past, that past is summoned reflexly, automatically. A man is not aware of the summoning until the interpretation, for example, that the situation is familiar or dangerous, flashes up in consciousness. That happens even before the previously similar recollection can be identified. Presently, the subject discovers that the data from the past has come within voluntary reach. The man, or the place, you saw last perhaps 15 years ago, comes back to you sufficiently so you can check off the changes which time has wrought in him, or in it.

Here is a unitary functional mechanism that is located in the cortex, at least in part. This is the record of the things that were once within the spotlight of a man's attention, not the things he ignored, but the things he was aware of in a previous period of time. The trace or engram or neuron record is not located in temporal cortex, I suspect, but is at a distance, where it can be reached and activated from the cortex. Exactly where, we cannot yet be quite sure.

Speech, likewise, has a separable mechanism. In this case, the electric current can be used in a different way to paralyze rather than to activate. The cortical speech mechanism may be blocked selectively when an electrode is placed on a speech convolution (Figure 1). The current interferes with its use, but the patient is not aware of this interference unless he happens to want to speak. Then he discovers to his astonishment that he cannot capture words. One patient was being shown a picture of a butterfly when the electrode was applied to the speech area. He was silent. After the electrode had been withdrawn he was asked about this. He explained that he could not get the word "butterfly" so he tried for "moth." But that word, too, would not come.

Thus, it is apparent that his capacity to recognize and perceive the nature of the object shown him was intact. The memories of the concept of butterfly and the concept of moth were also intact. Somehow, within the circuits that form the basis of the mind, he had presented those concepts, one after the other, to the speech mechanism with a negative result. Here is an example of the operation of the mind. Action in the brain accompanied the thought part way, but when words were called for, the brain failed. He expected an automatic response, expected the word to flash up in consciousness reflexly. It was not that his lips and tongue were paralyzed. It was the idea of the word that was not forthcoming.

There are, as you see, many demonstrable mechanisms. They work for the purposes of the mind automatically when called upon.

These mechanisms that we have begun to understand constitute part, at least, of the *physiological basis of the mind.* But what agency is it that calls upon these mechanisms, choosing one rather than another? Is it another mechanism, or is there in the mind something of different essence?

Here we have come to what Samuel called the "meeting place." We may not call it a place, and yet we grope our way back to the idea of the *neighborhood of brain action.* This is as far as science can carry us now. It will go further in the years to come, much further, and I believe, though I cannot prove it, that the truth which we "know in part" will be revealed in full to man through man's continuing effort. Some day "the universe will for us be rationalized."

Surely we are nearer the goal than Aristotle was, and yet, after all this progress, when we try to see the actual link between the patterning of electrical impulses in the brain and a change in the mind of man, we are still in the dark—as much in the dark as Aristotle when he asked so long ago, "How is the mind attached to the body?"

In conclusion, it must be said that there is as yet no scientific proof that the brain can control the mind or fully explain the mind. The assumptions of materialism have never been substantiated. Science throws no light on the nature of the spirit of man or God.

Those who study the brain can only carry on, studying its mechanisms with an open mind. They must strive to prove how nerve impulse and thought could be one or, on the other hand, to discover the nature of the mind as a separate element and so make dualism scientific. I suspect that when men no longer "see through a glass darkly," but "face to face," they will discover that underlying truth can harmonize divergent faiths. True monism may well make room for what we call the machine, the mind, and the spirit of man and God.

Meanwhile, we must all live private lives, laymen and scientists alike. We must run our course before an answer can come from science, and every thinking man must adopt of himself a faith to live by. He may take the best from man's ancient faiths. He must make the assumptions he considers reasonable as to the creation of the world and mankind.

Last summer in London, at the three-hundredth anniversary of the founding of the Royal Society, the oldest scientific body in the world, President Sir Cyril Hinshelwood made this statement:

> The men of science themselves, as far as can be judged, have numbered about the same proportion of religious believers as the generality of people. Nor have they been conspicuously less well endowed with kindness or morality.

In attempting to describe a physiological basis of the mind here before this great symposium devoted to a study of the control of the mind, my predicament is like that of a certain astronomer who was invited to inaugurate the proceedings of a religious gathering by describing God's handiwork in outer space. There is a relationship, but it is difficult to define.

I have attempted to analyze the microcosm of forces and structures in the human brain. It is just as much God's handiwork as the stars and planets that move in outer space and just as vast in its complication. It should inspire in us no less awe than the macrocosm we call the firmament.

There is within us, each of us, a greater wonder than that—the human brain. It holds a mirror up to the mind of man so man may see the stars and look into the future. He may turn, as we do here and now, to examine the civilization he has himself created. And finally, using the brain to study the brain, man may succeed where the computing machine would inevitably fail. He may discover the nature of his own mind, and God's.

Holgar Hydén

BIOCHEMICAL ASPECTS OF BRAIN ACTIVITY

The outer world is consciously experienced through the sensory part of the nervous system, and the information received is stored by memory mechanisms for future use.

Behind the biochemical processes now known to occur in the central nervous system is a long evolution. Not even the general features of this evolution are known, let alone any details. As a background to the experimental results concerning the biochemical processes themselves, I would like to make some general comments and pose some questions which are now possible to tackle.

The point at which nerve cells or neurons began to form and exert an integrated activity as a nervous system occurred early in the history of development. The outer stimuli impinging upon the nervous system formed a prerequisite, as they do today, for the maintenance of the nervous function. One unchanging stimulus, for example, is the force of gravity, which maintains a high activity in the gravity-responding brain centers throughout the life cycle. Some of the data to be discussed in this paper deal with processes occurring in these centers and their response to stimuli required for the nervous system to perform its function. This last aspect has especially been stressed by Stanley-Jones [1]. At our laboratory we have found that if an individual is deprived of a particular type of sensory stimulation, the neurons comprising that sensory part do not develop biochemically, even though they may appear structurally the same. In rabbits born and reared in complete darkness up to

12 weeks the ganglion cells of the retina were found to be to a high degree deficient of protein and ribonucleic acid, their water content was increased [2], and they failed to develop fully from a functional standpoint.

The fully developed nervous system is securely anchored in the genetic control mechanism of the brain cells, which is also part of the individual and is characteristic of the species. In that connection a unique feature of the nerve cells can be pointed out. Somatic cells divide; some divide rapidly over short intervals, others over longer intervals, but they all divide. The unique feature of the nerve cells is that they do not divide. Apart from the fact that quite a number of neurons atrophy in later life, a man is born and dies with the same nerve cells.

Why do nerve cells differ from other cells? One main reason is the necessity to keep the accumulating experiences of the memory store of each neuron ready for immediate use throughout the life cycle. This specialized task of the nerve cells is linked with the intricate form, characterized by long, branching processes, acquired by the neurons during their evolution. We shall therefore discuss a possible memory mechanism and its substrate in the neuron.

The development of the human brain, with its large forebrain and abundant cortex, took place during 500 to 1,000 million years. That means that the mutation pressure must have been high on this planet and the active surroundings favorable for the selection of homonoid mutations. Perhaps a belt of high radiation intensity passed our Milky Way during that stage.

The dependence of the central nervous system on outer stimuli for the maintenance of the function also brings up the question of the utilization of energy in the neurons and the other brain cells—a question which, of course, has wider implications. The development of the human brain and the resulting activities of the mind might be taken as expressions of differentiated life on this planet, but the driving energy of that life can nevertheless be regarded as infinitesimal against the background of the universe exchange and the transformation of energy. When the photons of the suns interact with planetary particles, high-energy electrons are formed. In the passage of these electrons to their ultimate fusion with acceptors, accompanied by loss of energy, life is allowed to exist energetically as something to the left of the main road.

Brain tissue does have some highly specialized properties. The electrical phenomena associated with the nerve impulse are characteristic of the neurons, and much of our knowledge about the function of the brain is derived from the work of the electrophysiologists. One reason for the success of these studies has been the ease of access to the characteristic signals and the fact they can be translated into visual form. Recording instruments have been available almost from the days of Galvani, and these instruments have become progressively more refined with the passage of time. Since there is a tendency in biology and medicine to increase the resolving power of the tools in order to get down to the cellular level, the electronic equipment for the study of action potentials is now highly complex.

Another conspicuous feature of the brain cells is their capacity to produce nucleic acids and proteins on a large scale. This activity seems to be as characteristic of the neurons as is the generation of bioelectrical potentials and is intimately linked with the specialized nervous function. These biochemical processes are not as readily accessible for a study as are the electrical phenomena. Thanks to new methods, however, more information is now beginning to accumulate. Chemical changes accompanying increased brain activity will be discussed later, but this raises the question of the structural complexity of the nervous tissue.

The brain is composed of two main types of cells: nerve cells with their processes and glia cells surrounding the nerve cells. While the neurons do not divide, the glia cells do. The glia cells are more than 10 times as numerous as the nerve cells. They are closely associated with the nerve cells, and they change their activity concomitantly with changing functional demands; in other words, they also respond to external stimuli. This situation raises some clearly defined issues:

1. Why do the nerve cells not divide?

2. What is the purpose of the conspicuous protein production in the nerve cells?

3. What is the nature and purpose of the close association between nerve cells and glia cells?

4. Can a molecular change in the brain at the cellular level be utilized to modify the mind? This question was raised as a result of some experiments we made to induce a molecular change in the nervous system.

In general, the synthetic activity is high in the central nervous system, as is the rate of metabolic processes, but the reactive changes are not evenly distributed throughout the brain. This is to be expected when we consider that the nervous system is characterized by a structural complexity unparalleled by any other organ in the body.

Beginning with everyday experiences, it is clear that the nervous system can do much more than respond to stimulation with reflexes and conditioned reflexes. Konrad Lorentz [3] remarked that if an experiment is designed to show reflex activity, the poor brain never gets an opportunity to show that it can do more than just react to the stimulation. Such an experiment, even though successful, can do no more than merely confirm the hypothesis.

An intimate morphological relation exists between the glia and nerve cells. Even the long conducting process, the axon, is surrounded by a type of glia cell, the so-called Schwann cell, and no part of the neuron is left exposed. Every part of the neuron is either covered by the delicate glia membranes or its surface is taken up by the nerve endings from another neuron, forming a so-called synapse. Figure 1 demonstrates schematically this intimate relationship between glia and neuron.

To give intelligible information in biochemical and biophysical analyses, the two cell types must be separated from each other. The nerve cells and the glia cells are collected from the fresh tissue and separated from one another by hand under a microscope [4,5]. Very small and accurate movements are needed; let us assume that the line drawn to write a letter *a* does not deviate more than 20 microns when a large number of *a*'s are written; work of this precision is demanded to obtain fresh living nerve cells and glia cells. These cells can be cultivated, or different types of biochemical analyses can be performed on them. For example, the big nucleic acid molecules can be extracted from each cell, and the amount of nucleic acid in each cell can be determined. Each nerve cell or glia cell sample of the same volume as that of the nerve cell can be put into a small so-called microdiver, so that its enzyme activity can be determined.

Figure 2 shows a fresh living nerve cell photographed in the phase-contrast microscope. In the nucleus is the dense nucleolus. The dendritic processes can be seen projecting from the cell body. The dense particles on the surface of the cell represent the points of contact be-

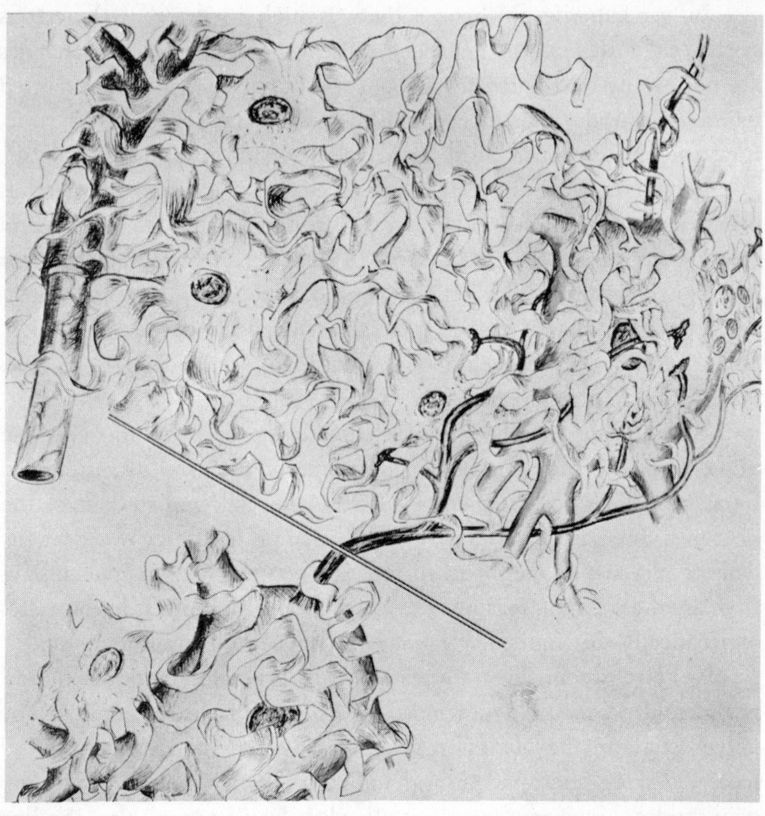

Figure 1 Schematic drawing showing the complicated structural relationship between the capillaries, the glia, and the neuron. To the left is seen a neuron, the left part of which has been partly uncovered from the glia membranes to show the synaptic knobs on the cell surface. The glia close to the neuron are oligodendroglia cells and those ensheathing the capillary to the right are astrocytes.

tween this nerve cell and many others, the so-called synapses. Figure 3 demonstrates two nerve cells of the same type as those in Figure 2. Immediately after isolation they were photographed near the absorption maximum of the nucleic acids, at 2570 Å. The dark areas within the cell are rich in ribonucleic acids.

Figure 4, upper row, demonstrates three Deiters' nerve cells from

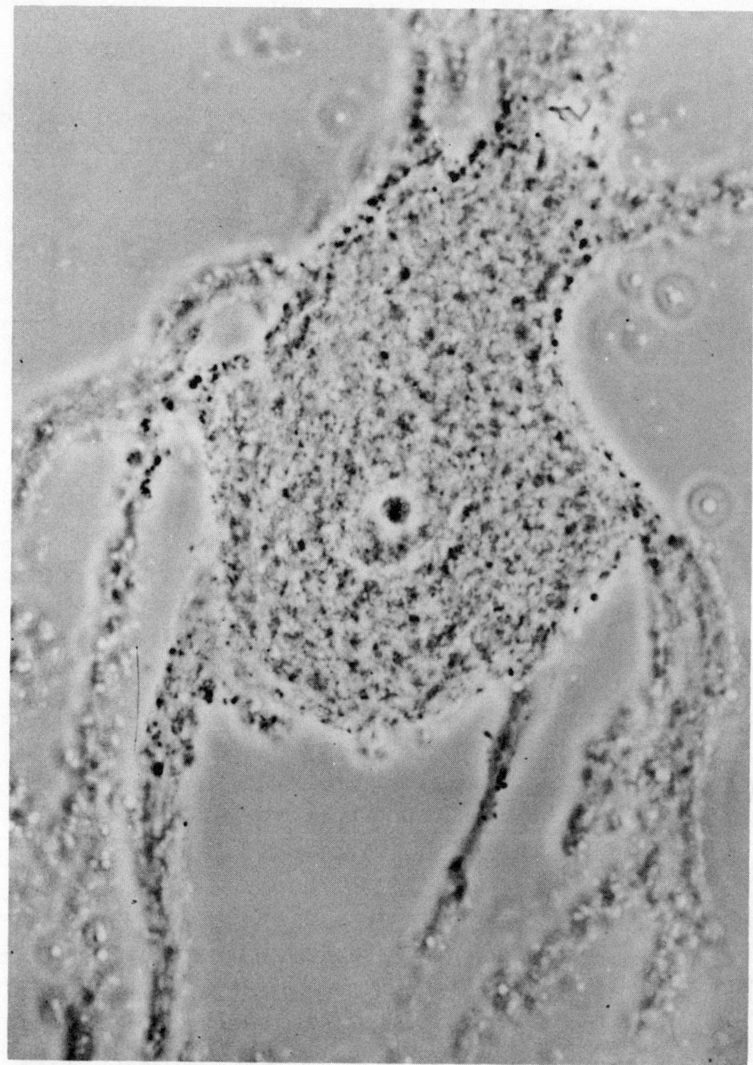

Figure 2

the lateral vestibular nucleus in the brainstem. They were dissected out freehand, cleaned from the surrounding oligodendroglia, and photographed in the phase-contrast microscope. In the lower row are three collections of glia cells, each of which originally surrounded the nerve

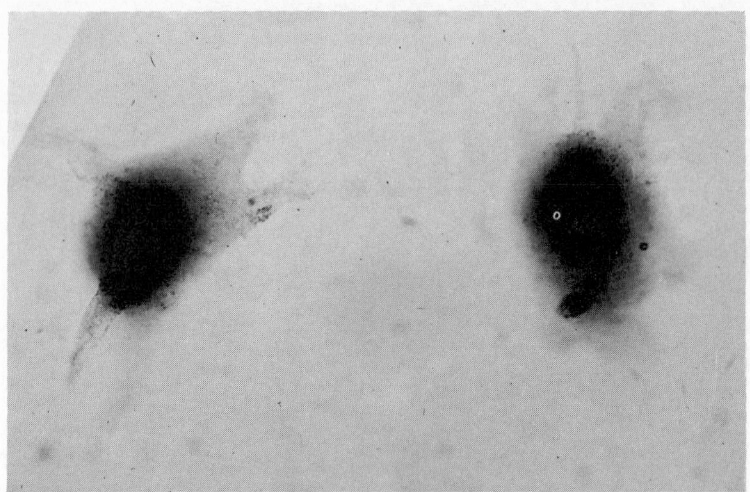

Figure 3

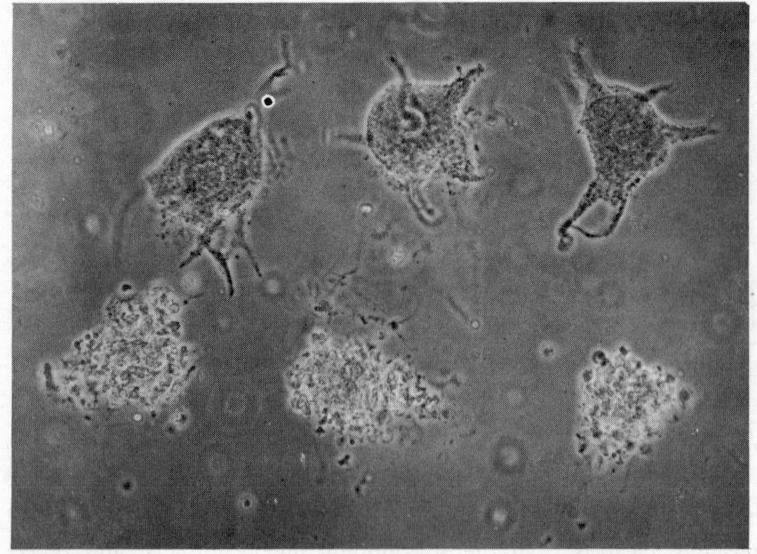

Figure 4

cell above. The volume and weight of the two types of samples are the same.

The volume varies greatly from one neuron to another. In the case of a medium-sized or a big neuron, the volume of the conducting process, the axon, is greater than the volume of the whole nerve cell body, including its processes. The weight of the nerve cell also varies. For chemical analysis it should be realized that amounts of a millionth of a millionth of a gram must be determined; a micromicrogram is the unit. Owing to the introduction of suitable methods [5–12], the nerve cells constituting a center within the brain can be analyzed statistically.

The nerve cells are characterized by nucleic acids, of which there are two types: desoxyribonucleic acid (DNA), which is typical of the chromosomes and has a genetic effect, and ribonucleic acid (RNA), which is highly characteristic of the nerve cell body. RNA mediates the synthesis of cell protein and changes rapidly with variation in the brain activity. It is composed of four nitrogenous bases; their sequence along the backbone of the molecule makes the molecule specific.

High-resolution electron micrographs have shown that in a nerve cell precipitated and extracted during the treatment preceding its sectioning the RNA is situated close to delicate, three-layered membranes in the form of small particles. These structures compose the so-called endoplasmic reticulum, or cytomembranes.

According to present knowledge, the protein synthesis occurs at the RNA-rich sites in the cytoplasm, and the RNA directs the order in which the amino acids are lined up in the manufacture of the protein; thus RNA controls this specificity. RNA exists also in the cell nucleus and is especially synthesized and active in the small nucleolus. Although it is true that the genetically active DNA of the nucleus, linked up with the chromosomes, determines the type of cell with respect to its daily activity, the immediate role in the complicated protein synthesis is played by the RNA of the cell.

Table 1 demonstrates the widely different amounts of RNA in different types of nerve cells. It can be added that the oligodendroglia contains 125 micromicrograms of RNA compared with 1,550 micromicrograms per Deiters' nerve cell determined on the basis of the same volume.

Table 2 shows the composition of the RNA contained in the

Table 1 RNA content in different types of nerve cells

Type of nerve cell	RNA, micro-micrograms per cell, mean values	Concentration, weight per volume	
		Carnoy-fixed cells, per cent	Fresh cells, per cent
Retinal ganglion cells, rabbit	20–110	1.2–2.0	—
Ganglion cells of the supra-optical nucleus, rabbit	70	2.4	—
Spinal ganglion cells, rabbit	1,070	—	0.5
Hypoglossal cells, rabbit	200	3.5	1.5
Anterior horn cells, rabbit	530	2.5	—
Anterior horn cells, man 40 to 50 years	670	—	—
Anterior horn cells, man 60 to 70 years	540	—	—
Deiters' cells, rabbit			
Large type	1,550	—	1.3
Small type	700	—	1.5

Table 2 Deiters' nerve cells and their oligodendroglial cells in the rabbit; microelectrophoretic analysis of the RNA; nerve cell 1,550 micromicrograms of RNA per cell, glia 125 micromicrograms of RNA per sample; purine and pyrimidine bases as molar proportions in per cent of the sum

	Nerve cell	Glia	P
Adenine	19.7	20.8	
Guanine	33.5	28.8	0.001[xxx]
Cytosine	28.8	31.8	0.01[xx]
Uracil	18.0	18.6	

Deiters' nerve cells and their glia. The RNA of the nerve cell contains more guanine and less cytosine than do the glia.

Finally, to complete the picture of the Deiters' nerve cells, Table 3 gives some data on the dry weight, protein, and lipid content per cell.

Table 3 Example of the chemical composition of a Deiters' nerve cell: total dry weight 21.700 micromicrograms, volume 94.000 cubic microns [from Hydén, 25]

Component	*Nucleolus*	*Nucleoplasm*	*Cytoplasm*	*Dendrites*
Total dry weight	100 $\mu\mu g$	800 $\mu\mu g$	20.800 $\mu\mu g$	—
Dry weight per volume	0.38 $\mu\mu g/\mu^3$	0.21 $\mu\mu g/\mu^3$	0.23 $\mu\mu g/\mu^3$	0.20–0.10 $\mu\mu g/\mu^3$
RNA total	—	—	1.200 $\mu\mu g$	100 $\mu\mu g$
RNA concentration, weight per volume	1.5%	0.5%	1.2–1.5%	—
RNA concentration, per cent of dry protein	—	—	7%	—
Proteins, total	—	650 $\mu\mu g$	16.600 $\mu\mu g$	—
Protein concentration, weight per volume	—	16%	20%	—
Protein, weight per cell weight	—	—	75%	—
Lipid fraction	—	200 $\mu\mu g$	4.200 $\mu\mu g$	—
Lipid concentration, weight per volume	—	5%	5%	—

The big neurons are, in fact, the chief RNA- and protein-containing cells of the body. The reason for this specialization at first appears to be obscure, particularly if a comparison is made with other types of cells where the explanation is fairly obvious. Compare, for example, the pancreas and its cells. The cells of the pancreas produce digestive enzymes which are specialized proteins. The cell function follows the digestive demands. These cells contain RNA in high concentrations; in fact, pancreatic cells are the only cells that can compete with nerve cells in degree of RNA concentration. This high load of RNA is to be expected of pancreatic cells in view of their intense protein production.

In considering the energy utilization of the brain, one may say that the cell in general obtains energy for its functional processes by burning carbohydrates, lipids, and amino acids. In this process hydrogen and electrons are removed from the substrate and passed on in a series of steps, until finally the hydrogen, as well as the electrons, is accepted by the oxygen, so that water is formed. Energy is obtained in this process and is temporarily stored in adenosine triphosphate (ATP) ready for use. A similar process is also employed by the brain cells. It was long believed that the brain burned only glucose. However, we now know through the work of Geiger, among others, that the brain can readily utilize other substances, presumably amino acids and lipids. Many enzymes are active when the substrate is transformed, energy released, and hydrogen finally passed along the respiratory chain, passing stepwise from one acceptor to another. They are all situated in special small structures, the mitochondria. The nerve cell body and its dendritic processes possess a greater capacity for glucose metabolism than the other brain structures. The site of the greatest enzyme activity seems to be the dendritic processes [13]. Subsequently some results will be presented which are obtained by a technique in which a single nerve cell is sucked into a small so-called microdiver with a volume of 1/100 of a drop of water. Oxygen is consumed in the case of respiratory enzymes. From the oxygen consumption per hour and per cell, the activity of an enzyme can be computed. Cytochrome oxidase is active at the final step of the respiratory chain, and its activity reflects in a general way the rate at which energy on aerobic routes is utilized in the nerve cell.

The first set of experiments demonstrates the events accompanying increased brain activity in sensory neurons, which, even under ordinary conditions, have high activity. These are the big vestibular cells situated in the basal parts of the brain and belonging to the VIIIth nerve.

The retinal cells account for two-thirds of the 3 million neural quanta entering the central system every millisecond [14], but of equal importance for our organism are the specific stimuli entering the whole time through the equilibrium organ—that is, the VIIIth nerve, more specifically, the vestibular part. The force of gravity prevails continuously everywhere on this planet and is of prime importance in permitting the nervous system to perform all aspects of its function. As

Stanley-Jones [1] has pointed out, the sensory receptors of the vestibular apparatus in the inner ear responding to the force of gravity are non-adaptive and are the most important energy source for increased neuronal activity.

In these experiments animals were subjected to adequate stimulation of the VIIIth nerve; rotatory stimulation through 120 degrees horizontally and 30 degrees vertically was carried out for 25 minutes per day up to 6 days. The big vestibular nerve cells, the so-called Deiters' cells, and the glia cells immediately surrounding them were analyzed; the nerve cells and the glia cells have the same volume and weight, and could therefore be compared.

The diagrams in Figure 5 show that concurrently with the increased activity there is a significant production in the nerve cells of RNA, proteins, and the respiratory enzymes, cytochrome oxidase and succin oxi-

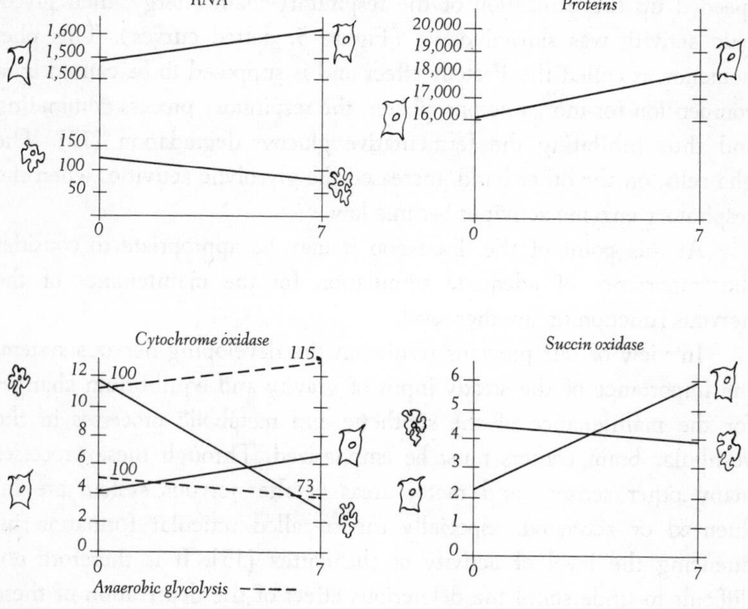

Figure 5 Vestibular stimulation 25 minutes per day for 7 days; RNA and proteins expressed as micromicrograms per cell, enzyme activity expressed as $\mu l\ O_2 \cdot 10^{-4}$ per hour per cell

dase. The data obtained in our laboratory provide evidence that there is not only an increased enzyme activity but actually a production of more enzyme proteins at an increased rate.

On the other hand, the glia surrounding the nerve cells react in the opposite way, being characterized by a decrease in RNA and a lowering of enzyme activities. Thus, when there is a high level of activity and production in the neuron, there is a low activity in the glia. Since the enzyme changes in the nerve cells signify an increased energy utilization during the production of proteins and RNA, the decrease in the aerobic respiratory enzyme activities in the glia indicates a specialization in the two types of cells.

It therefore seemed pertinent to ascertain whether the glia cells could switch over to anaerobic utilization of glucose when they slowed down the enzyme activities showing aerobic energy utilization [18]. It developed that, at increased neural activity, when the nerve cells speeded up the utilization of the respiratory-chain energy, their glycolytic activity was slowed down (Figure 5, dotted curves). This phenomenon is called the Pasteur effect and is supposed to be caused by a competition for inorganic phosphates, the respiratory process dominating and thus inhibiting the fermentative glucose degradation [17]. The glia cells, on the other hand, increased the glycolytic activities when the respiratory enzyme activities became low.

At this point of the discussion it may be appropriate to consider the importance of adequate stimulation for the maintenance of the nervous function on another level.

In view of our previous results on the developing nervous system, the importance of the steady input of gravity and equilibrium changes for the maintenance of the synthetic and metabolic processes in the vestibular brain centers must be emphasized. Through these processes many other sensory and motor areas of the nervous system are influenced or activated, especially the so-called reticular formation influencing the level of activity of the cortex [15]. It is therefore not difficult to understand the deleterious effect of the deprivation of these and other stimuli on the function of the nervous system.

In experiments by Hebb and his associates [16] to test the effect of sensory deprivation on man, the subject is immersed in a tank of warm water; he wears a special suit and a diving helmet. The usual supply of visual and auditory stimulation is also cut off. He experiences nothing, feels relaxed, and usually goes to sleep. When he wakes up his thoughts flow in repetitive circles then become chaotic; he loses his orientation, and hallucinations occur.

Our findings indicated that there is a biochemical relation between nerve cells and glia cells. In the next experiments, therefore, the animals were subjected to a stress situation, an atmosphere corresponding to 22,000 feet altitude, that is, to a decreased oxygen tension (the atmosphere at this height corresponds to 8 per cent oxygen). Our results demonstrated (Figure 6) that the nerve cells were sensitive to the lack of oxygen and answered with an increased respiratory enzyme activity of 300 per cent, and also with a 25 per cent increase of the anaerobic glycolysis; in order to maintain the necessary level of energy to carry on their function, the cells had to speed up the activity of the respiratory chain. Remarkably, the glia cells were unaffected by this decreased oxygen tension and remained at the control values with respect to cytochrome oxidase and anaerobic glycolytic capacity [18].

Having demonstrated this clear relation, we decided to study the behavior of a pertinent enzyme system in the two types of cells from a kinetic standpoint [19]. We proved that when the brain activity was raised to a progressively higher level the nerve cell and its glia react in different ways. The enzyme reaction rate in the nerve cell increased and became highly temperature-dependent, and its energy of activation increased. In the glia, on the other hand, no such changes occurred. Without discussing possible mechanisms behind this phenomenon, it is sufficient to note that the energy-requiring cell which demands priority for its processes is the nerve cell. In the continuous activity,

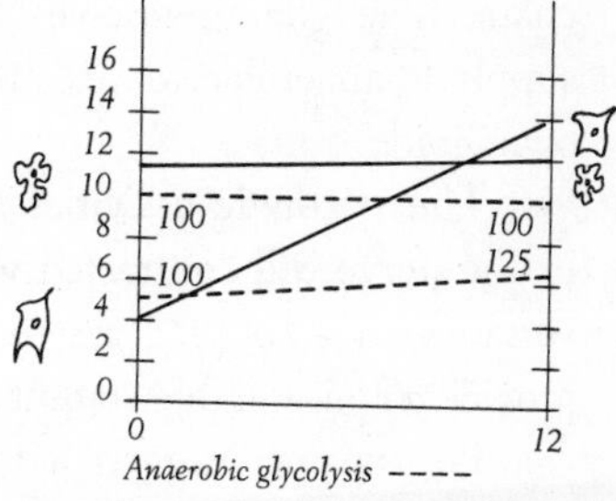

Figure 6 Effect of anoxia for 12 hours on the cytochrome oxidase activity of the Deiters' nerve cells and their glial cells; enzyme activity expressed as $\mu l\ O^2 \cdot 10^{-4}$ per hour per cell

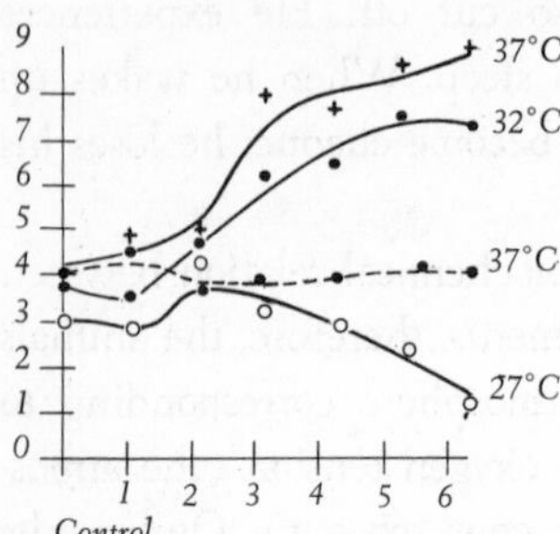

Figure 7 Effect of vestibular stimulation for 25 minutes per day for 7 days on the succin oxidase activity of Deiters' nerve cells at 37, 32, and 27°C.; enzyme activity expressed as $\mu l\ O_2 \cdot 10^{-4}$ per hour per cell; dashed line represents glia cells

the neuron and its oligodendroglia seem to constitute a metabolic symbiosis. From an energy standpoint, they form a coupled system.

The finding of a metabolic relationship between neuron and glia has received corroboration from electrophysiological studies. Svaetichin and collaborators [20–22] have found an inverse relationship of the action potentials recorded from neurons and from glia in the retina of fish.

Summarizing, it may be asserted that the glia and its nerve cell seem to constitute a functional unit. The neuron has a great capacity to produce RNA and proteins with increased nervous functions, which consume a high level of energy. The neuron is by far the biggest container and producer of RNA among the cells of the body. It is a kind of enormous gland-cell, producing RNA and protein in response to the functional state. This production of protein can be assumed to be as characteristic of the neuron as is the impulse of production and conduction. The data from the control material indicated that the glia could provide the nerve cell with energy-rich compounds. During increased brain activity the glia cells seem to give priority to the nerve cells for the supply of easily available energy coming through the respiratory chain. The glia themselves then resort for part of their own energy supply to anaerobic routes, and they may possibly also break down their own lipids.

The synthetic activities alternate between two states: low activity in the nerve cell contrasted with high activity in the glia cell, and vice versa. Such a coupled system would, from a kybernetic point of view, provide a considerable stability.

Let us now suggest a tentative over-all picture of the activity in the structural components of the brain, and possible ways in which the electrical phenomena could be related to some biochemical processes. These speculations are based on cytophysiological results. The general problem can be stated in the following way: we perceive the outer world and its stimuli with the sensory part of the central nervous system, producing a "change by use" in a memory mechanism which stores the accumulating experiences. The specific biological questions are:

1. What is the reason for the high protein production in the neuron and its remarkable content of RNA? It is to be remembered that the nerve cell is the chief RNA-containing cell in the cell body.

2. How is the glia linked with these processes, interposed as it is between the blood stream and the neurons?

Let us begin with the role of the RNA in the neuron. A most apparent property of the neuron is its electrical phenomena recorded at activity. The electrical currents propagating the nerve impulses are carried by sodium and potassium ions. During an action potential a new distribution of the ions across the nerve membrane occurs; the original distribution is rapidly restored by an energy-requiring pumping mechanism. A large proportion of biosynthetic reactions are driven through coupling to nucleotide phosphate. It may well be, first, that RNA acts as a reserve, providing the cell with the nucleotides taking part in the energy-yielding processes necessary to generate the nerve impulses. Second, it may be that the RNA and proteins produced within the neuron could serve as a substrate for a learning and recalling mechanism; that is, they could serve memory [25]. The capacity to recall the past to consciousness can certainly be expected to reside in a primary mechanism of general biological validity. A firm link to the genetic mechanism is important, and in this respect especially, the RNA molecule, with its many possibilities, would fulfill many requirements.

So far, only quantitative chemical differences have been found in DNA from different species [23], but the over-all composition and structure of the molecule seem not to differ [24,47]. Nevertheless, in its functional expression the DNA is specific. That means that the genetic capacity of the species is restricted by the DNA. Consequently the RNA, through which the DNA seems to mediate its long-term governing effect on the cell, also is a limiting genetic factor. The function of chromosomes and genes can as well be phrased in terms of "change by use" serving a memory mechanism. Therefore, individual memory and the inherited properties of the species could be assumed to have a similar biochemical mechanism.

The modulated frequency generated in a neuron by a specific stimulation is supposed to affect the RNA molecule and to induce a new sequence of nucleotide residues along the backbone of the molecule. This new distribution of components will then remain; the RNA has been specified [25]. This leads also to a specification of the protein being formed through the mediation of this RNA.

By a combination of this specific protein with the complementary molecule, the transmitter substance at the points of contact with the next neuron, at the synapsis, is activated. This allows the coded information to pass on to this next neuron in the chain. The reason for the response of this next neuron is that the protein which had once been specified through a modulated frequency now responds to the same type of electrical pattern whenever it is repeated. The specific RNA and protein are constantly produced in the neuron. From a statistical point of view, the molecules can be estimated to furnish the necessary permutation possibilities to store the memory experience of a lifetime. A recent finding from F. O. Schmitt's laboratory is suggestive in this connection [26]. It was found that the long fibrils in the axon are made up of a helical winding of small globular molecules. Schmitt is of the view that the filaments grow at the end of the neuronal tip by the addition of new globular molecules. Such a growth requires a very high degree of specificity of the amino acids sequence.

This memory mechanism does not require a strict localization of memory centers within the brain. The same neuron may participate as a link in many neuronal nets. Neuronal paths may grow by successive specification of the RNA molecules and the proteins formed; these paths will be complicated in form but will function on a basically simple principle.

A mechanism connecting the electrical phenomena of the neuron and glia with biochemical processes could be thought to operate in the following manner as a two-cell collaboration.

Assume an increase of neural stimulation. This leads to a modulation of the frequency produced by the neuron. The energy requirement of the neuron is increased. It is postulated that the energy needed is provided through the glia, which is one link in a negative feedback mechanism operating between the components—neuron, glia, and capillaries—in the following way.

The modulated frequency of the neuron serves a double purpose. It transfers a specific information to the next neuron. Besides, part of the *output* goes to the glia. The glia is characterized by potentials of about a thousandfold longer duration than those recorded from nerve cells [27]. When the neuronal frequency is modulated, a lock-in effect brings the slow frequency of the glia in synchrony, the difference being a multiple. This coupling of the frequencies of the neuron and glia forms the information system whereby the glia will furnish the neuron with substrates by regulating production of RNA and nucleotides and enzyme induction.

The following mechanism might operate. Our result of the kinetic study showed that the energy of activation of the nerve cells increased with the duration of the intermittent stimulation. When the flow of impulses increases, a change occurs in the ionic environment in the cell substance. This influences the fluctuating charges existing between the basic groups and their attached protons of the protein, as discussed by Kirkwood [28]. If the catalytic site of the enzyme-substrate complex is characterized by such an attractive force and there is a change in the dipole moment in the activation of the enzyme complex, then there will also be a change in the apparent energy of activation. This reasoning can be applied to the changes in temperature dependence and rate of enzyme reactions of nerve cells and glia. The interaction with the basic groups of the protein produces an increase in the energy of activation due to a decrease in dipole moment of the enzyme-substrate complex in its activation to the transition state. The increase in the energy of activation was what we recorded in our experiments.

The glia obtains the information about the increased energy demand of the neuron through the phase lock-in mechanism and can speed up the substrate supply to the neuron. Pinocytosis would be a probable mechanism in this process. There is ample evidence of structural arrangements at high resolution at the glia-neuron borderline which presumably are an expression of pinocytosis [29]. Furthermore, pinocytosis has been observed in glia and nerve cell cultures [30–33]. Pinocytosis has been shown to be induced by electric stimulation [34]. Therefore, it would be a suitable mechanism for the transfer of substrates into the neuron and could be triggered by the phase lock-in.

The substrate concentration increases in the nerve cell and can compete with the repressor at an enzyme-forming site [35], so inducing an enhanced enzyme formation, forming the *input.*

The functional relation between the glia and the neuron could thus be phrased in kybernetic terms as a negative feedback mechanism, whereby the glia act as energy donors and regulators to the neurons. The output comprises the modulated frequency in the neuron, which influences the electrical activity of the glia by a phase lock-in effect. This modified electrical activity regulates the input—the transfer of substrate to the neuron, and the enzyme induction and RNA and nucleotide synthesis serving the generation of nerve impulses—in addition to the RNA and protein production serving memory.

In every case analyzed we found that an increase of the brain activity introduced by emotion-producing stimuli—for example, sounds or tones, and even motor activities—was correlated with a production of RNA and protein [25], and a change in the enzyme activities in the neurons and glia was correlated with opposite changes in these cells [4,5,19]. In larger pieces of brain tissue, Geiger [36], Richter [37] Ungar et al. [38], and Palladin [39] have found evidence of increased protein and RNA metabolism in connection with electrical stimulation of the central nervous system. Richter found similar, though not so pronounced, changes after stress situations in rats.

In considering the problem of control of the mind, one finds that these data give rise to the following question: Would it be possible to change the fundamental of the emotion and the subjective experience of emotion-producing stimuli by inducing molecular changes in the biologically active substances of the brain? The RNA, in particular, is the main target for such a speculation, since a molecular change of the RNA may lead to a change in the protein being formed. One may phrase the question in different words to modify the emphasis: Do the experimental data presented here provide means to modify the mental state by specifically induced chemical changes? Results pointing in that direction have been obtained; this work was carried out using a substance called tricyano-aminopropene. Administered in small doses, it is a nontoxic substance which produces a slight rise in temperature

	Nerve cell	
	Cytochrome oxidase	*Succin oxidase*
Control	4.2	2.2
2 days	13.9	—
5 days	10.7	4.7
6 days	30.6	—

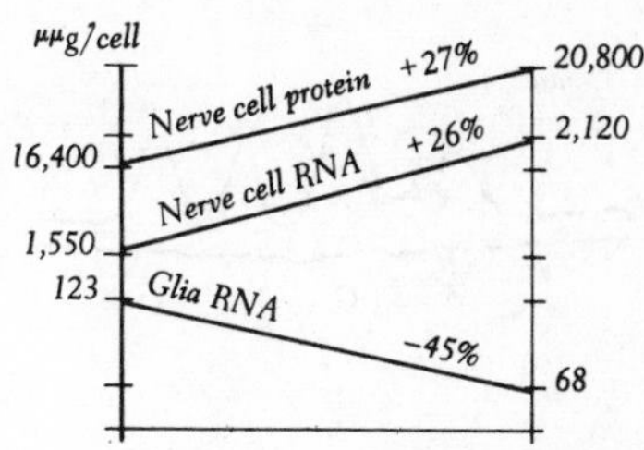

Figure 8 Effect of tricyano-aminopropene on the total amount of RNA, proteins, and on the respiratory enzyme activities per Deiters' nerve cell and per glial cell sample; rabbits injected with 20 milligram per kilogram and killed 1 hour later; enzyme activities expressed as μl $O_2 \cdot 10^{-4}$ per hour per cell; number of analyses 320

Table 4 Effect of tricyano-aminopropene on the composition of the RNA of Deiters' nerve cells and their glial cells: rabbits injected with 20 milogram/kilogram and killed 1 hour later; purine and pyrimidine bases as molar proportions in per cent of the sum; number of analyses 233

	Nerve cell			*Glia*		
	Controls	*Treated*	P	*Controls*	*Injected*	P
Adenine	19.7	20.5	—	20.8	20.1	—
Guanine	33.5	34.6	—	28.8	21.9	0.01**
Cytosine	28.8	26.7	0.001***	31.8	38.6	0.01**
Uracil	18.0	18.2	—	18.6	19.4	—

and has an antithyroid effect [40].* In a dose of 20 milograms per kilogram it produced in 1 hour remarkable changes in the neurons and glia. Grenell and the author [41] found that the quantity of RNA, proteins, and free lipids increased by more than 25 per cent in each nerve cell and that the RNA per sample decreased in the glia by 45 per cent. Following administration of this substance for 6 days, the respiratory enzyme activity increased progressively by more than 700 per cent. We found in our laboratory a significant change in the composition of the RNA molecule produced in 1 hour in this way, as shown in Table 4: the

* The author wishes to thank The Upjohn Company, Kalamazoo, Michigan, for kindly providing samples of tricyano-aminopropene for these experiments.

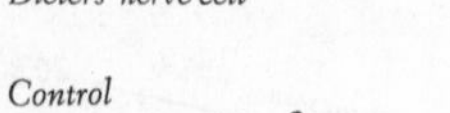

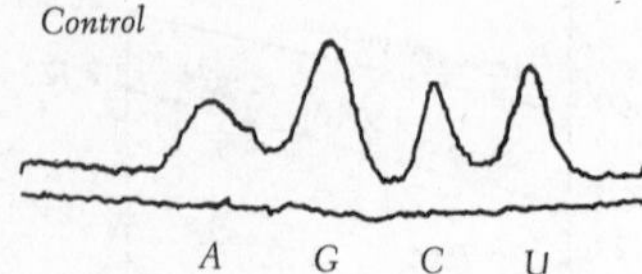

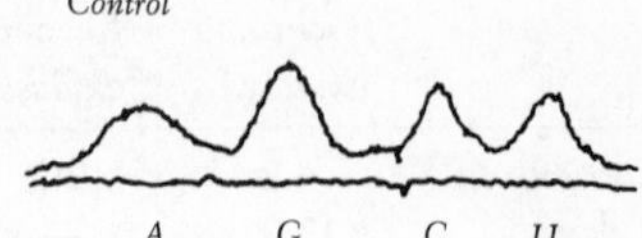

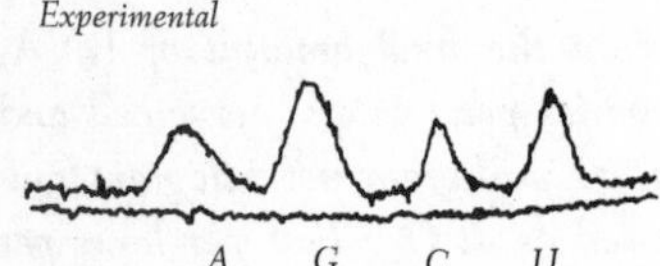

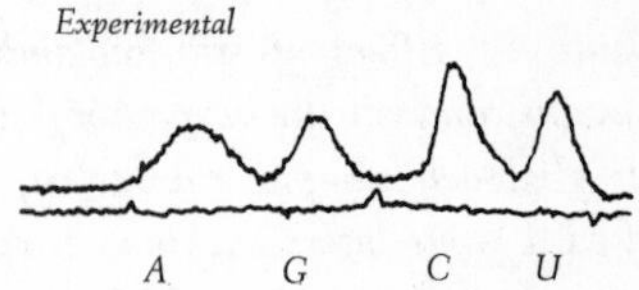

Figure 9

cytosine decreased in the nerve cells, but it increased—proportionally more so—in the glia, where the guanine decreased [48]. Figure 9 gives examples of photometric tracings of the microscopic threads on which the electrophoretic separations were performed.

The molar changes are of such magnitude that they may reflect a rapid increase of a particular RNA fraction within the cells, or they may show that tricyano-aminopropene acts through inhibiting a cellular control mechanism on the RNA synthesis. By the microelectrophoretic technique we have studied other cases in which increased RNA production occurs in the nerve cells as a result of physiological stimuli during regeneration [42] or as an effect of psychopharmaca such as tofranil [43], but we have not found such an effect.† Geiger [45] found that following electrical stimulation a rapid change occurred in the nucleotides, which he was able to extract from parts of the brain cortex; this was accompanied by an increase in the cytidine and adenine content of the nucleic acid. These changes, however, were reversible within a few minutes.

† Since this meeting was held the author has found a change in the RNA composition of nerve cells and glia after the administration of tranylcypromine [44], which is an inhibitor of mono-amino oxidase. The change in the RNA base composition of the nerve cells occurred, however, in a direction opposite to that found after tricyano-aminopropene in the nerve cells but similar to the glia changes: the guanine decreased and the cytosine increased significantly.

The application of a substance changing the rate of production and composition of RNA and provoking enzyme changes in the functional units of the central nervous system has both negative and positive aspects. There is now evidence that the administration of tricyano-aminopropene is followed by an increased suggestibility in man [46]. This being the case, a defined change of such a functionally important substance as the RNA in the brain could be used for conditioning. The author is not referring specifically to tricyano-aminopropene, but to any substance inducing changes of biologically important molecules in the neurons and the glia and affecting the mental state in a negative direction. It is not difficult to imagine the possible uses to which a government in a police-controlled state could put this substance. For a time they would subject the population to hard conditions. Suddenly the hardship would be removed, and at the same time, the substance would be added to the tap water and the mass-communications media turned on. This method would be much cheaper, and would create more intriguing possibilities, than to let Ivanov treat Rhubasjov individually for a long time, as Koestler described in his book. On the other hand, a countermeasure against the effect of a substance such as tricyano-aminopropene is not difficult to imagine either.

On the positive side are the possibilities opened by these findings to the study of mental illness. For example, this work will be especially useful if a metabolic defect is located in the glia, causing the neurons to be struck indirectly. If this situation turned out to be indeed the case, there is a possibility that the error could be corrected by stimulation of the production of certain molecules of RNA or proteins in the neurons or glia.

References

1. Stanley-Jones, D., and Stanley-Jones, K., *The Kybernetics of Natural Systems,* London, Pergamon Press, 1960, pp. 47, 85.
2. Brattgård, S. O., *Acta Radiol.,* Suppl. 96, 1952.
3. Lorentz, K., in *The Harvey Lectures,* Series LIV, New York, Academic Press, 1960, p. 60.
4. Hydén, H., *Nature,* 1959, 184:433.
5. Hydén, H., and Pigon, A., *J. Neurochem.,* 1960, 6:57.
6. Brattgård, S. O., and Hydén, H., *Int. Rev. Cytol.,* 1954, 3:455.

7. Hydén, H., and Larsson, S., *J. Neurochem.*, 1956, 1:134.
8. Hydén, H., and Larsson, S., in *Proceedings of the Second International Symposium on X-ray Microscopy and X-ray Microanalysis (Stockholm)*, Amsterdam, Elsevier Publishing Company, 1960, p. 53.
9. Hallén, O., and Hydén, H., in *X-ray Microscopy and Microradiography*, New York, Academic Press, 1957, p. 249.
10. Edström, J. E., *Biochem. Biophys. Acta*, 1953, 12:361.
11. Edström, J. E., *Microchem. J.*, 1958, 2:71.
12. Edström, J. E., *J. Biophys. Biochem. Cytol.*, 1960, 8:39.
13. Lowry, O. H., Roberts, N. R., Wu, M. L., Hixon, W. S., and Crawford, E. J., *J. Biol. Chem.*, 1954, 207:19.
14. Gesell, A., Ilg., F. L., and Bullis, G. E., *Vision: Its Development in Infant and Child,* New York, Hamilton H., 1949, p. 4.
15. Kempinsky, W. H., and Ward, A. A., Jr., *J. Neurophysiol.*, 1950, 13:295.
16. Hebb, D. O., *Sensory Deprivation,* Cambridge, Mass., Harvard University Press, 1961.
17. Lynen, F., Hartmann, G., Netter, K. F., and Schnegraf, A., in *Ciba Foundation Symposium on the Regulation of Cell Metabolism,* London, J. and A. Churchill, Ltd., 1959, p. 256.
18. Hamberger, A., and Hydén, H. (to be published).
19. Hydén, H., and Lange, P., *Proceedings of the Fourth International Neurochemical Symposium,* Varenna, 1960 (in press).
20. Mitarai, G., Svaetichin, G., Vallecalle, E., Villegas, J., and Laufer, M., (in press).
21. Vallecalle, E., Svaetichin, G., Mitarai, G., and Laufer, M. (in press).
22. Svaetichin, G., Vallecalle, E., Mitarai, G., Laufer, M., and Villegas, J. (in press).
23. Allfrey, V. G., Mirsky, A. E., and Stern, H., *Advanc. Enzymol.*, 1955, 16:411.
24. Doty, P., in *The Harvey Lectures,* Series LV, New York, Academic Press, 1960, p. 103.
25. Hydén, H., in J. Brachet and A. E. Mirsky, (eds.), *The Cell,* vol. IV, New York, Academic Press, 1960, chap. V.
26. Davidson, P. F., and Taylor, E. W., *J. Gen. Physiol.*, 1960, 43:801.
27. Tasaki, I., and Chang, J. J., *Science*, 1958, 128:1209.
28. Kirkwood, J. G., *Faraday Soc. Disc.*, 1955, 20:78.
29. Hess, A. J., *J. Biophys. Biochem. Cytol.*, 1958, 4:731
30. Pomerat, C. M., Hild, W., and Nakai, *J. Anat. Rec.* 1957, 128:601.
31. De Robertis, E. D. P., and Bennett, H. S., *Fed. Proc.*, 1954, 13:35.

32. Pomerat, C. M., and Costero, J., *Amer. J. Anat.*, 1956, 99:211.
33. Hughes, A., *J. Anat.*, 1953, 87:150.
34. Holter, H., *Int. Rev. Cytol.*, 1959, 7:481.
35. Szilard, L., *Proc. Nat. Acad. Sci.*, 1960, 46:277.
36. Geiger, A., in D. Richter (ed.), *Metabolism of the Nervous System*, New York, Pergamon Press, 1957, p. 245.
37. Dawson, R. M. C., and Richter, D., *Proc. Roy. Soc. B.*, 1950, 137:252.
38. Ungar, G., Ascheim, E., Psychoyos, S., and Romano, D. V., *J. Gen. Physiol.*, 1956, 40:635.
39. Palladin, A. V., in H. Waeloch (ed.), *Biochemistry of the Developing Nervous System*, New York, Academic Press, 1955, p. 177.
40. Eberts, F. S. (to be published).
41. Grenell, R. G., and Hydén, H. (to be published).
42. Edström, J. E., in D. Richter, (ed.), *Metabolism of the Nervous System*, London, Pergamon Press, 1957.
43. Hydén, H., and Løvtrup, S. (to be published).
44. Hydén, H. (to be published).
45. Geiger, A., Yamasaki, S., and Lyons, R., *Amer. J. Physiol.*, 1956, 184:239.
46. Gomirato, G. (in press).
47. Steiner, R. F., and Beers, R. F., *Polynucleotides*. Amsterdam, Elsevier Press, 1961.
48. Egyhazi, E., and Hydén, H., *J. Biophys. Biochem. Cytol.* (in press).

Donald O. Hebb

THE ROLE OF EXPERIENCE

In my title is an implicit contrast between heredity and environment, so I had better begin by clearing up one or two points to avoid later misunderstanding. For one thing, it is the role of the sensory or perceptual environment that we shall be considering, as distinct from that nutrient environment that is necessary for the growth of bone, nerve fiber, or sense organ and for their later functioning. It is obvious that the growth of the mind and its later stability depend upon conditions which make for physical health, just as they depend on the genetic endowment with which the organism begins its career, but it is now clear that mental function also depends essentially on sensory stimulation, upon the experience of the organism by way of smelling, hearing, feeling, tasting, and seeing. It is the implications of this fact that we are now to consider, with respect both to the stability of the individual mind and to its relation to society.

One other clarifying point: All one need do, sometimes, is use the word "environment" (or equally, "heredity") to achieve a state of confusion that puts an end to all understanding. I imply no opposition between heredity and environment, or any possibility of dividing up man's endowment to credit heredity with this part, environment with that. This is an old confusion that still persists, despite the clarifying analysis by Haldane from the point of view of genetics and by Beach from the point of view of psychology of the false antithesis of what is instinctive to what is intelligent or what is learned. One can distinguish conceptually between factors contributing to the end product, as I have done above, without supposing that they act separately or produce distinguishable end products or segments of the product. My question is: In mental growth, what is the part played by the factor of sensory stimulation, in its *collaboration* with (1) the genetic factor and (2) the nutrient and supportive factor of the physical and chemical environment? And further, what part does sensory stimulation play in maintaining mental function once growth is complete?

From the point of view of some sentient and intelligent being living in interplanetary space, independent of the physical and chemical needs of man, the air-breathing inhabitants of this planet must appear as the occupants of a goldfish bowl, who now, for the first time, seem to be on the verge of getting out of the bowl but, like goldfish, have to arrange to take a segment of their physical environment along with them. Man does not live on the surface of this planet, really, but at the bottom of a sea of air under very considerable pressure. The goldfish, to leave, would have to build themselves a little goldfish bowl full of water and arrange to have it propelled to wherever they wanted to go. Man, similarly has not merely the problem of freeing himself from earth's gravity, but must take along with him a much greater mass, to hold together for his use a segment of his supportive physical environment. The great masses involved, a matter of tons to maintain an air breather's environment for even one man for even a short voyage outside the sea of air, have been the chief limiting factor that prevents escape.

But it is now recognized also that this is only part of the problem. The sensory environment of earth, it seems, must also be simulated to some degree if man in space is to continue to be a man as we know him, man the sensitive observer, man the efficient agent, man the thinker. *Mind,* that is to say, is a function of the psychological or sensory environment, just as bone and muscle—and brain cells—are of the nutrient environment.

Perhaps I might say here that there is no necessary dualism in distinguishing mind from the cells that make up the brain. I use the term to refer to an organization of neural activity, a higher level of brain function. (On the other hand, we may note also that this is a working assumption whose final validation—or negation—remains for the future.) My proposition is that this organization or level of function is achieved during growth only as a function of complex sensory stimulation, and further, that once established it is maintained only in the presence of such stimulation.

I concede at once that the evidence for the proposition is incomplete, and we are far from being able to specify in any detail what the essential characteristics of the sensory environment are for the development or maintenance of mental function; but the evidence we do have points in one direction only, and at least is quite sufficient to invalidate classical—but tacit—assumptions concerning the nature of mind. Further, even if there were no question of man's being exposed to the new environments of Mars and the moon, the evidence points clearly to new conceptions of the relation of man to his social environment on this planet, with immediately practical implications.

The classical view to which I refer would not be easy to define, perhaps because it is not one view but many, or perhaps because if one once were obliged to make it explicit one would see its defects and renounce it. But I think it fair to say that we tend to talk of mind as something quite distinct from sensory processes, and to think of these latter as sources of information only, for the mind to use or not as it pleases. One assumes that the whole function of the sensory environment is to supply the adult with guidance for his thought or action. Whether my mind is receiving such information or not, *I* would still be *I*, the same person, whether or not in communication with my environment. As for the infant's development, it was orthodox even for the classical behaviorist, for all his environmentalism, to accept the notion that intellectual capacity is almost or wholly innate, determined by heredity—in other words, more or less independent of sensory events during growth. Orthodoxy, in its own peculiar way, then turned toward the opposite extreme with respect to the traits making up personality or temperament, and all was thought of as being learned.

But, as I have already proposed, neither of these orthodoxies can be accepted. Let me turn now to some of the experimental evidence that gives, I think, a very different picture of the relation of man to his environment first, with respect to the dependence of the adult mind upon its sensory experience and, second, with respect to the way in which sensory stimulation interacts with heredity (and the nutrient environment) to control the course and extent of mental development.

Let us take a young, vigorous, healthy male, a college student, and deprive him simply of the perceptions that are part of ordinary life, which we take so for granted. Make him comfortable, feed him on request, but cut off that bombardment of sensory information to which, normally, we are all exposed all the time except when asleep. We turn him in on himself, leave him to his thoughts. For some hours, this presents him with no great difficulty. He is, as we say, somewhat bored, perhaps, but the boredom is quite tolerable. He can see nothing, lying in darkness on a comfortable bed or floating in lukewarm water wearing goggles that prevent pattern vision, can hear nothing but a steady hum (again a loss of sensory patterns and meaning), and cannot examine his tactual environment because of shielding over his hands that permits enough movement to maintain physical comfort but does not permit tactual perception. He is then, quite literally, in touch with his physical environment but perceptually isolated. If he is not in darkness, but is wearing goggles that admit light without permitting pattern vision—the condition in which our own experiments were done—then we may say that the amount of sensory stimulation from his environment is not decreased; what he has lost is solely the normal variety of patterns of stimulation.

For some hours, then, this has little effect. But after a time a malaise appears, concerning the very center of the subject's being. The subject becomes restless and somewhat unhappy, but more significant is the report that he can no longer follow a connected train of thought. Some of our subjects entered the experiment thinking to review their studies or plan their research in the atmosphere of peace and meditation to be found inside the experimental cubicle. They were badly disappointed. Not only was serious thinking interfered with, but there was a repeated complaint that it was impossible to do any connected thinking of any kind.

Tests of intelligence showed changes occurring by about the second day, and after the subjects had come out of isolation there were marked disturbances of ordinary motivation and work habits lasting 24 to 36 or 48 hours. They were, of course, free to leave the experiment at will, so many left early; but some, finding the pay attractive, stayed until their mental processes were extensively disordered (endurance lasted only a few hours at one extreme and up to 6 days at the other).

A good many had elaborate visual hallucinations, but these did not seem to involve the subject's own personal identity. More significant in the present context is the occurrence, in about 8 per cent of the subjects, of sudden sharp emotional breaks, taking different forms (e.g., something like a temper tantrum, or an attack of claustrophobia), which put a sudden end to the experiment as far as these subjects were concerned; or in another group, alternatively, disturbances of the self-concept, in which the subject might feel that he had two bodies, that his head had parted company from his neck, or that he had become an immaterial mind wandering about space wholly detached from his body.

The mechanics of the mental disturbance are not our concern here, but I may say in passing that they now seem, pretty certainly, to involve primitive brainstem mechanisms of vigilance and consciousness, the existence of which was first inferred by Penfield in 1936 and which have been the subject of intensive investigation during the past 10 years, following the experimental demonstration of activation from the reticular formation by Moruzzi and Magoun.

The effects that have been described are not peculiar to the specific experimental conditions by which they may be elicited in the laboratory, but occur to some degree in the more or less normal circumstances of existing occupations. These "normal" circumstances, however, are always ones in which the sensory environment, or its variability, has changed in the direction of monotony. The Arctic explorer, particularly during the long polar night, the long-distance truck driver following that white line down the highway hour after hour, the solitary sailor with nothing to look at but his unchanging vessel and the monotonously changing succession of waves, and the solitary high-altitude pilot—all these report one or more of the forms of mental aberration described by the undergraduate subjected to the extreme monotony of experimental perceptual isolation.

For the space-travel problem, it is significant that among the most extreme abberations are the ones reported by the high-altitude airplane pilot. The "break-off phenomenon" described by Graybiel and others is fundamentally a disturbance of the self, in which the pilot may suffer from an acute sense of being cut off from existence, of losing his personal identity and perhaps becoming at one with the aircraft or even with empty space itself. Or he may feel separated from his body and feel himself to be a detached mind surveying his aircraft from a point in space, the aircraft now toy-sized and his body a puppet sitting at the controls. There are indications that this state of affairs would become intolerable if prolonged, or if not, might be tolerable only by one whose mental functioning was in one way or another significantly deranged and whose judgment could no longer be depended on. For the pilot in interplanetary space, evidently, the detachment and monotony will be much greater, and far more prolonged; he will not be able, as the test pilot is, to return closer to earth and reverse the development of an intolerable stress.

It is sometimes suggested, when this problem is discussed, that we may be able to rear human beings in comparative isolation, so that they are accustomed to monotony and will not suffer disruption in space. This brings me to my second point: The suggestion is not feasible psychologically, even if it were acceptable socially; for intelligence does not develop in a monotonous, or perceptually isolated, condition. A number of experiments in recent years have shown that exposure to something like a normal environment during growth—normal for the species—is essential for the development of normal potentialities. The rat reared in isolation is defective in problem solving and insightful learning (with the relatively mild degree of isolation that is feasible if life is to be maintained, rote learning may be unaffected). The dog reared similarly is physically vigorous and healthy, but again is grossly impaired intellectually, and his motivation and social behavior are very aberrant indeed. Experiments of this kind have not been done with monkey or ape, because primates are hard to take care of and take so long to grow up. However, it has been possible to rear chimpanzees with lack of pattern vision, or lack of normal somesthetic experience (i.e., experience of bodily movements, skin stimulation, etc.), and the results point in the same direction as the rat and dog experiments. In the sector of sensory experience where restriction is applied the animal shows lasting deficits of perception, and what evidence we have implies that some degree of deficit is permanent. In sum, the mammal reared with restricted access to his normal sensory environment lacks intelligence in proportion to the degree of restriction and shows disturbances of motivation (or of "personality") to match.

You may object that all this applies to animals, not to man. It is true that such systematic evidence as there is comes from animal work, since an experiment of this kind could not possibly be done with human subjects. But it is not true that the conclusions cannot be extended to man, with proper caution. In the first place, what human evidence we have, unsystematic though it may be, tells exactly the same kind of story. The congenitally blind patient, operated on for cataract after he is eight or ten or twenty years of age, shows defects of perception which essentially are the same as those of the chimpanzee reared without pattern vision, when we allow for the differences due to verbal learning in man, the longer period of restriction, and so on. There are also a number of analyses of IQ-test performance in subjects reared in a partial restriction from the environment all of which point to the conclusion that these conditions produce permanent defects of intelligence in man as in lower animals.

In the second place, man is a mammal; his brain is constructed on exactly the same master plan as that of the rabbit, the cat, or the monkey. He has a higher intelligence than the monkey, just as the monkey has a higher intelligence than the cat or rabbit, which means that caution must be applied in generalizing from any of these species to any other, but when we find a common characteristic among mammalian species, and particularly a characteristic that shows an increase as one goes from lower to higher species, one is certainly justified in tentatively applying it to man, to see whether it fits—to see, that is, whether the trend is still apparent or whether emergent evolution at the human level has, for some reason, produced a reversal of the trend. And if at this point, finally, we find that the application of the principle derived from such a comparative study clarifies the human problem, leads us to see man in a new and clearer perspective, then the objection that "animal data prove nothing about man" can be set aside as irrelevant. Cat data prove nothing about dogs, and vice versa; but an increased knowledge of cats may lead us to see new principles, new order and system, in the behavior of dogs. It is always dangerous to generalize from animal to man, but it is also dangerous not to try always to see man in the perspective of evolutionary development, when one is searching for principles of human behavior, as a corrective for the myopia inherent in regarding him as *sui generis,* quite unrelated to anything that is earlier or lower in the phylogenetic scale.

I emphasize this because in a moment or two I want to make some use of that perspective in looking at human motives with regard to their relation to the struction of human society. Here, however, the point is that the animal data say that intelligence, perception, and the ability to adjust adequately to the environment develop in the higher animal only with adequate exposure to a normal degree of variety; the lower the level of intelligence or complexity of cerebral function, the less true this is.

With respect to the "control of the mind," then, a complete control (not to say suppression) would be achieved by bringing children up in a radically restricted environment. The difficulty, of course, is that the adult produced by such a method would be of no use to anyone; he would be a vegetable and not man as we know him. It seems (but here our animal data have little to tell us) that by selecting aspects of the environment one could shape development in this direction or that; it is possible, perhaps, that the child could be brought up to endure a kind of monotony, in some one sector of normal experience only, that you or I could not tolerate, and thus produce a class of space-ship pilots to do our interplanetary explorations for us. But with this would go the risk of producing unanticipated distortions of the personality—the risk that such a pilot would have behavior so aberrant that he could not be permitted the freedom of society.

The problem of space travel is not directly relevant to our present topic, but I have used it as an approach that may help us to look at the problem of mind from a less habitual point of view, more detached and less narrowly anthropocentric. From the position we have now reached, let us look again at the question of man's motivation, the way in which it relates to the structure of civilized society, and the kind and extent of control exercised by society over the individual mind.

An outstanding feature of the isolation experiment was the demonstration that intellectual work—mental activity initiated from without—is wholly essential to the human being. Now, in one way this is nothing new, except for showing how strong such a need can be; but mostly we have concealed the fact from ourselves, in the first place by giving a special name, "play," to work that is done for its own sake, thus not classing it as work, and in the second place by assuming, when the question comes up of the man who likes *useful* work, who likes his job and does not want to retire, that this is an acquired motive, the result of long-established habit. Because of the complexities of human experience it is difficult to rule out such *ad hoc* explanations finally, but here the comparative data are conclusive. Harlow and others have demonstrated learning and problem solving for its own sake in the infrahuman mammal, where habit is not the explanation and no extrinsic factors such as the search for prestige or power can be invoked. Further, though exact quantitative comparisons in different species would be difficult, it seems clear that this is a tendency that is stronger in the higher animal, culminating in man, where it is very prominent indeed—especially when one realizes how large the intellectual component is in the "relaxation" of reading a novel, seeing a movie, or following the career of the San Francisco Giants, let alone such competitive games as golf and bridge.

One strategic consideration in the control of the mind, then, is man's insatiable need for intellectual activity, environmentally initiated but self-paced. It is, of course, equally obvious that there is a great deal of intellectual activity that he is opposed to: he objects to work when it is imposed from without, when it is not of his own choosing, and especially when it is in any way monotonous. This ambivalence brings us to another point at which motives deviate from the classical picture of the nature of man: his ambivalence with respect to the frightening and the horrifying.

There are fascinating phenomena in all this, and I must not get too involved in detail. We all know, of course, that man avoids pain and thus, being intelligent, avoids situations in which pain is probable, that is, fear-producing situations. And yet he may also go to a great deal of trouble to get into exactly such situations, ranging from mountain climbing to riding roller coasters. Again, consider the avoidance and emotional disturbance that death and the mutilated human body are capable of producing, on the one hand, and on the other, the fascination that stories and pictures of such things have for the newspaper or novel reader, and the speed with which the vultures gather on the scene of a disaster.

The comparative data show that the emotional ambivalence is both real and deep-seated. The fear and horror are not the product of special learning or of some abstract conception of death, but are a reaction in some way to the strange, which both attracts and repels. Also, the susceptibility increases with intelligence. To take but one example, the clay model of a head is a literally terrifying object to an adult chimpanzee, yet one he cannot take his eyes away from; for the half-grown (six-year-old) chimpanzee, the object is fascinating and exciting, but fear is not evident; and for an infant (twelve to eighteen months), it has no interest at all. The susceptibility appears directly related to the complexity of the machinery of thought, thus increasing with ontogenesis (development of intelligence in the individual) and phylogenesis (as we go from lower to higher species). Although the kind of situation which causes such reactions changes with increased intelligence, so that man is not frightened, for example, by a model of a head, the number and variety of causes of emotional disturbance in man appears to be significantly greater than in chimpanzee, and in the chimpanzee is certainly much greater than in the dog. Man, then, is the most emotionally erratic animal as well as the most intelligent.

Initially this may seem an obviously false proposition, but Thompson and I were, I think, able to show that the apparent immunity of civilized man from irrational fears and angers is mostly due to his success in setting up an environment in which the precipitating causes are infrequent. That is, urbanity depends on an urbane environment. This does not mean only that there is control of the physical environment by the economically successful society; equally important is the control of behavior embodied in the rules of custom, courtesy, morals, and religion, achieved principally by various formal or informal educational devices during growth and supplemented at maturity by ostracism or the law court. We live, day by day, in a sheltered physical world, but also most of the time in a sheltered psychological world consisting of the ordered behavior of our fellows. What we call "civilization" is a kind of behavioral cocoon which fosters the illusion that civilized man is *by nature* calm, dispassionate, and logical. This is illusion only, but on it rest most of our discussions of how to deal with the great social problems.

What I am saying implies that civilization depends on an all-pervasive thought control established in infancy, which both maintains and is maintained by the social environment, consisting of the behavior of the members of society. The mind is not an absolute, with properties that are the same in radically different circumstances. What we are really talking about in this symposium is mind in an accustomed social environment, and more particularly a social environment that we consider to be the normal one. It is easy to forget this, and the means by which it is achieved. The thought control that we object to, the "tyranny over the mind of man" to which Jefferson swore "eternal hostility," is only the one that is imposed by some autocratic agency, and does not include the rigorous and doctrinaire control that society itself exercises, by common consent, in moral and political values. I do not suggest that this is undesirable. Quite the contrary, I argue that a sound society must have such a control, but let us at least see what we are doing. We do not bring up children with open minds and then, when they can reason, let them reason and make up their minds as they will concerning the acceptability of incest, the value of courtesy in social relations, or the desirability of democratic government. Instead we *tell* them what's what, and to the extent that we are successful as parents and teachers, we see that they take it and make it part of their mental processes, with no further need of policing.

The problem of thought control, or control of the mind, then, is not how to avoid it, considering it only as a malign influence exerted over the innocent by foreigners, Communists, and other evil fellows. We all exert it; only, on the whole, we are more efficient at it. From this point of view the course of a developing civilization is, on the one hand, an increasing uniformity of aims and values, and thus also of social behavior, or on the other, an increasing emotional tolerance of the stranger, the one who differs from me in looks, beliefs, or action—a tolerance, however, that still has narrow limits.

You will see that I am touching here on the problem of social prejudice, and you may feel that I am getting away from my own area of competence. I must point out, however, that the accepted approach to this problem—the notion that prejudice arises in the first place from economic pressure and has to be learned—is entirely unsound psychologically. Attempts to deal with it on this basis are without hope of success. We are dealing instead with the puzzling reaction of the mammal to the strange, about which, unfortunately, we still know too little. It is not the thing that is quite unfamiliar that evokes the reaction; apparently there must be a mixture of both familiar and unfamiliar elements, but no one has yet come up with either an adequate explanation or a satisfactory statement of the conditions in which it does and does not occur.

To come back to my main argument, then, I may summarize by saying that the last 15 years or so have given us a new perception of the problems involved in understanding human motivation and the complex relation of mind to its environment. Man is not inherently a lover of ease and not, perhaps unfortunately, a lover of peace—not all the time, at least. It is quite true that he has no instinct to make war, as the classical students have said, but neither has he any built-in insurance of not stumbling into the war that his emotional susceptibilities can easily get him into. Up to a point, he *enjoys* trouble and trouble making, and the problem of social organization may be to provide him with sufficient opportunity for getting into trouble individually, for the excitement-producing experience that he needs by his very nature, without having it result in social disorder and trouble for others. The control of thought and behavior that is necessary for society to establish and maintain, if it is to continue in existence, must be based on a genuine understanding of motivation and of emotional needs, not on Rousseau-like notions about the noble savage misled by bad teaching, or on the fundamental misconception that man is essentially a rational animal.

THE PHYSICAL BACKGROUND FOR MENTAL PROCESSES

This is an actual transcription of the formal but spontaneous panel discussion of the papers immediately preceding. Only minor editing has been done where continuity and clarity required it. The editors feel that the spontaneity of the actual discussion gives a particular value to the panel in this form.

Moderator: Karl H. Pribram
Panel Members: Donald O. Hebb, Holgar Hydén, Wilder Penfield

Dr. Pribram Professor Hebb, would you please reply to Dr. Penfield's questions concerning the relation of mind and brain somewhat in the way you did in the first chapter of your book on psychology? This gives, I think, a very good picture of how psychologists handle this problem in a philosophic as well as an experimental scientific manner.

Prof. Hebb That was a very complicated question, as I think we all agree. It is my conviction that part of the difficulty here is an attempt to make science operate in a way that it normally does not—that is, to provide final answers. The scientific method, it seems to me, normally starts by biting off a manageable piece and leaves the rest for the next bite. There is one scientific method that is called the null hypothesis, in which you set up the proposition, not because you believe it, but perhaps because you don't believe it, and you expect eventually to show that it leads to an absurdity. I would say that, on this basis, one could adopt the hypothesis of complete monism. I don't care if you call it idealism or materialism, because I think what you say in either case is complete monism. But you can make monism the working assumption, and those whose beliefs are that things are dualistic would be accepting such a working assumption for the purpose of showing that it is nonsense. Those who believe the other way would be attempting to show that the working assumption is valid. It seems to me that we are not in any position at the present to be dogmatic about an issue such as dualism or monism, but to begin with, we can agree, surely, on a working assumption.

Dr. Pribram The next question is addressed to the relation between what Professor Hebb and Dr. Hydén have to offer—the problem of memeory. Could we discuss here the model that Dr. Hydén has presented to us, and how it relates to some of the models that Professor Hebb has given us about memory processes and phase sequences in the brain?

Dr. Hydén One point is that the memory, learning, and recall mechanisms last a lifetime; this is connected with the fact that nerve cells do not divide. A second point is that the structures of the neurons are complicated. With respect to the molecular level, the fact is that there are very few things, apart from the Korsakoff syndrome, which can be said about this strict localization with respect to definite properties in the nervous system. I remember Dr. Lashley's experiments on rats. He removed up to 80 per cent of their cortex and still they could run a maze experiment, so the conclusion was that the capacity to remember this was residing in the other structures, or that the cortex left over was sufficient. Now we come to the human conditions and the grave memory defects of the Korsakoff syndrome that have attracted quite a lot of interest recently. Are there any reasons to believe that memory mechanism for the whole nervous system should have more strict localization in the brain?

Dr. Penfield I think that what you have been showing us so brilliantly is the basis of memory mechanism wherever it is organized. In man certainly it is possible to recognize different organizations, different departments of memory, such as the memory of words. Certainly, it is an organization of its own, and yet no doubt it depends on recall and some of the elements that you have been demonstrating.

We are quite clear now that a bilateral lesion of the hippocampal gyrus on two sides of a man will produce a strange effect on memory. Certain things will be left. For example, if the man earns his living by cutting and making gloves, he continues to do it just as well as ever. That is a form of memory; the memory of skills is not involved. He is able still to remember for as long as he keeps his attention focused on a certain situation, but when he shifts to some other attention, it's gone. His recent recording has disappeared; something in the memory mechanism has been lost by the loss of the hippocampal gyrus and its part of a true mechanical arrangement. It may not be that the engram, which is somewhere, is there. It may not be there; it may be somewhere else—and I think the reason Lashley missed it was because he was making his removals in the wrong place. I don't say that he could have made them in the structure separately where the record is placed. I am speaking in the presence of two of Lashley's pupils and I do so with a good deal of hesitation.

Dr. Pribram I think the misinterpretation of Lashley is due to two things: first, misinterpretation of his own data and, second, misinterpretation by other people of what he said. First of all, he did not say that all parts of the brain were the same. He was quite aware of the fact that the front end of the brain and the back end of the brain had different functions.

Dr. Penfield Did he know that when he was a young man in Minnesota?

Dr. Pribram He knew it as early as 1934, when he replied to a note in the *Journal of Psychology* to Fred Mettler's attack on the problem. In 1934 a letter was published in which Lashley said approximately, "Yes, I did not mean, of course, that the motor cortex and the occipital lobe are equivalent." He did talk about equivalence of brain function within a limited area conserving one such mechanism, but there was a mistake that Lashley did make, which was pointed out by Hunter. When one runs a maze, for instance, the problem can be solved in a variety of ways, as Professor Hebb has pointed out. Environment is not only part of the processes by which we live but also part of the memory process, as many of you who carry lists in your pockets to know where you are going the next hour or two will know. Similarly, the rat, even when deprived of part of his cortex, may use a different mechanism to solve the same problem. It looks equivalent to us from the outside, but whether the equivalence is in the maze or in the brain matters a great deal to those of us interested in brain function. It does not matter so much otherwise, as long as you realize that the rat does not have just a hunk of cheese inside its head.

Prof. Hebb I wanted to know more about Dr. Hydén's memory mechanism. I was not clear whether he was saying that modification of RNA would provide for changed relations between neurons and that a changed memory might consist of relations between neurons, or whether he was stressing that the modification was essentially within a single cell.

Dr. Hydén I was suggesting that the changes were within the hyper-RNA of one particular neuron, which then gave rise to a protein, also specialized, and that whether or not the next neuron responds further to the stimulus would depend on whether or not it has also in its turn been specified with respect to RNA and protein production; if not, the next neuron will not respond to the stimulus.

Prof. Hebb In the course of learning no one has had any success, as far as I can see, in avoiding the conclusion that learning involves changes of probability of transmission at the synapses; it used to be called synaptic resistance, which is a lowering by transmission—a poor term. But the process of learning, it seems to me, has to involve some quantification of the problem of transmission, going one direction or another at the synapses. If I understand correctly, your proposal would be that this modification could be the mechanism of the modification of the synapses?

Dr. Hydén Yes, that is right.

Dr. Pribram Would you agree, Dr. Penfield, that although you want to dethrone the cerebral cortex, you don't want to throw it away?

Dr. Penfield Yes, I altogether agree that the mechanism I have been discussing is a means of using the cerebral cortex; but I think we have to recognize that with the change in one's consciousness from moment to moment there is a complete change—or there is a change—in the setup of the activity within the brain. I think we ought to be clear, if I can go back to memory for a moment, that we talk about so many different things when we talk about memory. In most instances memory—for instance, how to run a maze or how to sing a song—is a generalization from many different experiences. Anyone here who can sing a song very likely cannot remember any particular time when he heard that song, so that his memory of it is a generalization—we will leave the maze out for the moment. But this mechanism that is demonstrated by stimulation of the interpretive cortex poses something quite different. It would seem that visual and auditory experiences combine which are recorded exactly as they occur and remain equally available 20 years later. Now I am leading up to a question, Dr. Hydén. Do you feel what you are showing psychologically and chemically could explain the fact that somehow or other a neuron sequence, which is followed during a strip of time, leaves the cells altered permanently and that that sequence has no part in any other sequence?

Dr. Hydén I see what you mean—that the commutation occurring in a molecule at the particular time when it is impressed with a specific stimulus is retained over a long time?

Dr. Penfield And perhaps is resistant to all others?

Dr. Hydén And that it is resistant too? I would say of neuron regeneration that when you cut off a large part of the neuron, if the methods are sensitive enough you ought to be able to detect whether or not the sequences in the RNA are the same as before. What we have done is to determine the molar proportions of the bases making up the RNA being formed during regeneration. The piece cut off is, in fact, larger than the piece left; it regenerates, and in the case where we did this the RNA was very much increased during the first 2 months. We started with 500 micromicrograms and analyzed that with electrophoresis, and we obtained the order of molar proportions throughout. But that does not, of course, exclude a change, because the change can be of another type. After all, even 500 micromicrograms is a statistical expression of several fractions of RNA in one cell. But to take a firm stand, I should say that if RNA on the whole can serve as a substrate for a learn-and-recall mechanism, then there must be residual changes. We cannot alter it by any other stimulus coming in; from the point of view of permutations, this has to be stable.

From the Floor What is the place of the hypothalamus in your scheme in relation to the brainstem? Does it play any role at all?

Dr. Penfield The thalamus certainly, but the hypothalamus, I suppose, may well enter into it and play some role, indeed, in the activity of the higher brainstem in the sense of connections between the two sides. But for the most part, the hypothalamus, I should think, is a rather separate organ to be used and to be active at specific times. I do not know how to separate the hypothalamus from the thalamus exactly.

From the Floor Is a neuron in one of the sensory areas the same as a neuron over the motor area?

Dr. Penfield The connections of a neuron are what determine its function more than its shape and size. We have progressed a long way since the thinking of 20 and 30 years ago in regard to cytoarchitectonics.

From the Floor Does Dr. Hydén suggest the possibility that the biochemical nature of the nerve impulse differs with the differences between the stimuli that initiate that impulse?

Dr. Hydén Not quite. I didn't say that every stimulus left a special biochemical imprint.

Prof. Hebb Some of the sensory neurons have different frequencies for different sets of events. It has been shown that the same fibers respond differently to cold and warm. This would bear a direct relation to your hypothesis—or is one neuron capable of only one biochemical pattern?

Dr. Hydén If you look upon a modulated frequency as recorded information, and if the postsynaptic neuron is going to carry this on this code of information, then you have to assume that.

Dr. Pribram One must remember that many conversations can be carried simultaneously on telephone wires; the chemical composition and physical structure of these wires do not change, but the carrier frequency can carry various modulated frequencies and reproduce different voices. The notions that have gone back and forth here are thus not beyond the ken of modern engineering.

Aldous Huxley

HUMAN POTENTIALITIES

I would like to begin with a question, a very simple and seemingly absurd question: What are people for? In a totalitarian country, I suppose the answer would be that people are for cannon fodder in the extreme case or else for strengthening the state and consolidating the power of those who happen to control the government of the state. There are certain elements in our Western culture which would say that man exists for the purpose of consuming more and more irreplaceable materials at a greater and greater rate, going deeper and deeper into debt. Personally, I think neither of these descriptions of what man is for is correct.

As an act of faith, and I think it is an act of faith which is shared by most people who are concerned with human decency and liberty, I believe that man is here for the purpose of realizing as much as possible of his desirable potentialities within a stable but elastic society. This, as I say, is the fundamental concept which underlies all of our Western democratic view of life. It is not a proposition of reason; it is a proposition of feeling and of faith, and I shall start with this as axiomatic.

Let me ask another question: What would have happened to a child with an IQ, say, equal to that of Isaac Newton if he had been born in a family of Upper Paleolithic cave dwellers 15 to 20 thousand years ago? The biologists assure us that there has been extremely little biological change in human beings since that time; the native equipment of such a child was probably just as good as it is today, but what possibilities would he have had for realizing his potentialities? The answer is that he would have had incredibly small possibilities, that in the very nature of things he could never have become more than a food gatherer or a hunter, which is what his whole culture was based upon, and even if he had had the gigantic IQ of Isaac Newton he would have never gone beyond the very narrow horizon which the cave dwellers were capable of seeing.

It is quite extraordinary, when one comes to think of it, that here, with the same native equipment as belonged to the later Paleolithic man, we have been able to realize such an immense number of human potentialities. Instead of being confined to being a food gatherer or a hunter, a man in our modern Paleolithic culture has an immense number of choices to be any number of different things, and for this, of course, we have to be duly grateful.

Now let us briefly consider the relationship between individuals and the culture in which they live. One definition of culture would be, I think, a machine for making it possible for human beings to develop their potentials. Obviously, outside an organized culture it is virtually impossible for even the most gifted human being to develop and actualize what lies latent within him. However, this condition is paradoxical, because culture is not only a machine helping us to actualize potentialities, it is also a machine for preventing us from actualizing them—and it may, moreover, be a machine for helping us to actualize the most undesirable potentialities. We must never forget, after all, that while human beings are perfectly capable of being human and sometimes almost angelic, they are also perfectly capable of being like beasts and much worse than beasts. There have been cultures which have not only prevented human beings from actualizing their desirable factors but have positively encouraged them to actualize the most undesirable factors.

It is thus paradoxical that we are both the beneficiaries and victims of our culture. We can use an analogy and say that the grace of a dancer is a function of the skeleton; the muscles are kept in place by the skeleton, and it is thanks to the skeleton these graceful movements can be carried out, but the arthritis of the dancer's grandmother—this, too, is a function of the skeleton. It is the same with a culture—this fixed framework within which and out of which we can develop human potentialities, but which, because it is a fixed framework, may become somewhat rusty and completely paralyze us and prevent us from passing beyond its limits. We have to somehow work out a society sufficiently stable and rigid to support the human being and allow him to function out of its rigidity but at the same time sufficiently elastic to permit him to go beyond its bounds, for it is only by transcending the limits of the culture at any given moment that an advance can be made.

As we look back over history we see that these advances have, indeed, constantly been made, but they have often been made at the expense of the individuals who made them. After all, we have merely to observe what happened to Socrates and to Jesus to realize how extremely dangerous it is for somebody to try to transcend the limitations of his culture. Nevertheless, these advances have to be made, and so the duty, it seems to me, is to try to achieve a culture that combines the qualities of stability and elasticity to permit them with less sacrifice. Our business is to see that the culture shall not have pockets of what may be called collective badness to which people are expected to conform. Practically every culture has had these pockets, and I think we are perhaps in a better position now to understand this fact because of the enormous extent of our knowledge of previous cultures and contemporary cultures of different kinds. Unquestionably, the historians of the future—if we have a future—will look back on this age and will point, for example, to the culture of nationalism, which is, I suppose, the religion of the twentieth century; it is the religion for which men will fight and die. We shall look back upon this as probably one of the most appalling examples of a collective insanity to which people conform, but this, as I say, is the paradox of culture and society, and we have to work within this framework of the culture. Needless to say, it is only in a perfect culture that we should be able to get the highest possible development of the individual, but we're certainly not going to get a perfect culture within any measurable time and I propose not to be utopian and talk about no place, but to be topian and to talk about something that can happen in the kind of place in which we find ourselves at this time. What could be done within the limitations of the culture in which we exist today?

Let us consider the various factors controlling human existence. Man is a multiple amphibian living in many worlds at once: he lives in the world of the individual and in the world of society; he lives in the world of symbols and in the world of immediate experience; he lives in the world of given heredity and of acquired cultural values; and anything that happens to so complex a human being must necessarily have multiple causes and we must always think about human problems in terms of all these causes at once. We must attack upon all fronts simultaneously, otherwise there is no prospect of our succeeding at all in our efforts. The human oversimplification may be described as the original sin of the intellect. We all tend to oversimplify, because we do not like the effort of thinking in terms of multiple causation. Nevertheless, in trying to solve any human problem we have to think in these terms. As Nurse Cavell said a few moments before she was executed, "patriotism is not enough." It is not only patriotism that is not enough now; politics are not enough, law is not enough, science is not enough, religion is not enough, in fact, nothing short of everything is enough. This, I think, has to be stressed very strongly: that we have at all times to think in terms of this multiple causation in dealing with these problems which must be faced on all the levels at once.

In regard to the heredity factors we could, of course, talk in the utopian way about what ought to be done by selective breeding. Unquestionably, as Professor Herman Mueller frequently pointed out, a great deal could be done to improve the human stock, but at present we certainly don't know enough about human genetics to embark upon such a policy, and even if we did know enough, it is quite clear that the climate of public opinion is such that this policy could not be carried out at the present time, so, rather than discuss this matter, I shall merely point out given the kind of human stock we have now, there is an immense amount which could be done to actualize potentialities which are still latent. We have seen what has been done over the past 15,000 years, and I strongly suspect that a great deal more can be done, since everything is now accelerated to such a degree.

However, there are other hereditary factors to consider. I think one of the most important factors in any question of actualizing human potentialities is that of human differences. Human beings are sufficiently alike one another that all can be classified as members of one species, but they are also sufficiently unlike one another for each of them to be recognized as a unique individual. The differences are just as important as the similarities, and this is something, I think, we have to recognize and to make allowances for.

In a totalitarian society there is a real effort to iron people out into a kind of uniformity, but in our society, fortunately, we have inherited a system which does permit a good deal of latitude, and we should go further in this direction, I think, in admitting that every human being has a right to his own physique and temperament, has a right to develop along the lines which come natural to him, and that he should not be forced by some kind of cultural fashion to adopt forms of existence which do not suit him. The differences in human potentialities have been recognized, of course, in traditional religion. There are differential ideas in the various great religions of the world. For example, in Christianity we have the ideal Master and the ideal Mary, the ideal work and the ideal contemplation. In the Hindu tradition we have, I think, a more realistic division of the ideals into a tripolar system: there is the idea of Bhakti, devotion to the one ideal, of Karma Yoga, the pursuit of the ideal of disinterested work, and the ideal of Dhyama Yoga, contemplation and intellectual life, and these three concepts have been recognized as each having its own value, so that it is quite wrong to insist that people whose natural bent is in one direction shall be made to conform to the dictates of people of a different temperament. For example, Dr. Freud stated categorically, because he himself happened to be a rather aggressive, miserable man, that extroversion was the only way of health for man. However, anybody who happens to have been born with a different kind of temperament knows quite well that it is not for everybody's way of health; there are lots of people for whom aggressive, driving emotional extroversion is extremely distasteful and unpleasant. They are by nature introverted and should be permitted to cultivate their special gift. "It takes all sorts to make the world," and we have no right to impose a special brand of ideal or horizon determined by our own natural temperament upon other people.

We may even find that it will be useful in time to develop methods of differential education for people at the extreme limits of temperamental variabilities. We recognize already that it is useful to have differential education for people with an exceptionally high IQ or for people with an exceptionally low IQ, similarly perhaps we could get more out of our natural potential by bringing up young people in slightly different ways according to the sort of temperament and constitution with which they are born. I throw this out as a possibility.

Now let us pass on to what may be called the physiological aspect of the problem: What shall we do physiologically, on a bodily level, to help people to realize their potentialities? To start with, there is the question of nutrition. Dr. Ansel Keyes has pointed out that in this country 40 per cent of all calories that are taken in are in the form of fat; consequently the coronary rate is 10 times what it is in Japan, and some very large percentage of the population is overweight. I think it is quite clear that if this is the case we are not doing all we can to elicit the latent potentialities of human beings; we are blocking some of the realization of these potentials by feeding ourselves the wrong way. This is something, I think, which certainly is going to come to the fore as more and more people fall dead from heart attacks. Without any question, this matter of nutrition is going to become of major importance in the prosperous countries of the West.

But then, closely related to the problem of nutrition and its capacity to help us or to harm us is this question, which has been touched upon already, of pharmacological methods of changing the mind. It is said that the Russians are hard at work developing a pharmacological means of improving intelligence—that is, of making people more capable of sustained attention, of concentrated work, probably of getting on without sleep. If all these factors could be achieved by pharmacological means without seriously upsetting the body as a whole, they would undoubtedly improve the quality of intelligence, and obviously one of the main desirable potentials for which we are working is the potential of greater intelligence.

I should have said this before: quite clearly the two great things for which we aim are the improvement of intelligence and the deepening and the extension of the feeling of friendliness and love, and the diminishing of the realization of those deep-seated potentialities for violence and aggression which lie within people. We have two positive aims and one negative aim, and in regard to intelligence it does seem that something might be done by pharmacological means to improve the intelligence of people as a whole. What was mentioned by Mr. Brown a while ago as a possibility, a political possibility, arises here. It is quite clear that if such a method were developed it could be used either to consolidate democratic institutions by distribution of this intelligence-improving chemical to everybody, or it could be used to increase the gauze between the elite and the masses by being distributed to only a small minority. This is a typical example of how the technological advances could be applied on a political level, either for good or for evil.

Let me now come to the educational problems, and these, I think, are the most interesting. Education, for the most part, exists on the verbal level. Certain liberal arts in the Middle Ages were entirely verbal, there were only two of the arts which involved anything nonverbal: one was the art of astronomy—and even the art of astronomy during the Middle Ages was extremely verbal, everything illustrated something in a book—and the other was the art of music, and in the Middle Ages the art of music was treated more as a science than an art. The remainder of the seven liberal arts were wholly verbal, and to this day, although there has been considerable modification, most of our education is essentially on the verbal level.

One of the things we might do on this level—which we do not do at the present time, and which would help us, I think, both to be more intelligent and to avoid some of the more disastrous misbehaviors to which human beings are subject—would be to teach children the limitations in the nature of language. This teaching can begin very early and should go on right through adult life. It is quite clear—recall for example, the days of Hitler—that an abuse of language when used systematically in conjunction with the modern methods of broadcasting communications, can be immensely powerful in creating and eliciting most undesirable potentialities in men, and as Hitler had a formula for propaganda, he said specifically, "you must confine yourself to very, very simple slogans, very few and simple slogans; you must never admit the other side could possibly be right; you must never admit there are any gradations; things are either black or white, either very good or very evil; and you must repeat incessantly." By means of these simple formulas he was able, as we know, to influence an entire nation and to carry it with him for a number of years.

My own feeling is that we should make use of the remarkable advances in linguistic analysis which have been made during the twentieth century. These advances, I think, are among the most important intellectual efforts of the twentieth century, and I see no reason why simple applications of them should not be taught from a very early age so that people would be in a position to distinguish between propaganda aimed at creating conditioned reflexes and propaganda aimed at offering the materials on which a rational choice could be made. There is a profound difference between the two types of propaganda.

Unfortunately there are considerable difficulties in the way of introducing this linguistic analysis into education. There is a rather pathetic incident in this context which deserves to be recalled: In 1937 the Boston philanthropist Mr. Filene set up an institute which he called the Institute of Propaganda Analysis. This was at the time when the Nazi propaganda was at its height, and the institute did very good work in analyzing the extraordinary diabolic nonsense which was coming over the Nazi radio, and they published a number of interesting booklets. However, by 1941 when this country was at war and the whole West was at war, all countries were employing what was gracefully called "psychological warfare," and the process of analyzing propaganda seemed hardly tactful; consequently the institute was dissolved in 1941. This illustrates very clearly the inherent dangers of such a process. It is quite clear that any serious analysis of language taught to great numbers of children is in itself profoundly subversive. It subverts advertising, it subverts all kinds of political and military notions, it is extremely dangerous. There were many objections, even before the rise of psychological warfare, that this thing would make young people cynical, etc., and it was regarded as a kind of un-American activity. Possibly it is. It is an un-everything activity. It is opposed to any kind of organized misuse of language on which so much of our social uniformities are based. Nevertheless, I do feel that somehow or other it is very important to make young people aware of the nature and the limitations of language.

Needless to say, a great deal more could be said on the subject, and there is one more point before I move away from it. I was reading 3 months ago Professor Breuner's little book *The Process of Education,* in which he summed up a week-long conference on educational methods held at Harvard in 1959, and what interested me most in this book was that virtually every chapter ended with the same phrase, "but we must do a great deal more research." The total impression one got from reading this book was that human beings had been educating the young for the last 3,000 or 4,000 years without knowing what they were doing, or at least without any degree of accuracy, and obviously there remains a great deal to be learned about what should be imparted, how it should be imparted, and at what stages of the child's development. I think there is no doubt at all that a great deal more could be done even within this conventional field of education on the verbal level.

Now it seems to me that we have to think of education also on the nonverbal level: we have to think of the possibility of training directly the mind-body that has to do the learning and the living. We don't do very much of this at present. We concentrate chiefly on the verbal level and don't do very much for the strange multiple amphibian organism which we possess. There is a very remarkable phrase which Spinoza uses, which seems all the more remarkable when one thinks of the extraordinary abstractness of his writings: he says "Teach the body to do many things; this will help you to perfect the mind and to come to the intellectual level of thought." I think it is a phrase of immense importance. If we substitute for the word "body" the word "organism," and for the word "mind" and the word "mind-body," this could be made the motto of an entirely new branch of education, the deliberate training of the mind-body, which then has to make use of its concepts and its words.

It is all the more important, I think, that such training now be done deliberately, inasmuch as advancing technology has removed a great number of occasions on which in the past human beings were invited or indeed compelled to use hand and mind in the most exquisite coordination. The word "masterpiece" is derived from the work which an apprentice did at the end of his apprenticeship; it was his thesis, which, when passed on by his masters and his masters' colleagues, permitted him to become a master in turn. The true essence of earlier techniques was the use of extremely simple tools to make very, very complicated things, simply by extraordinary skill of hand, the coordination of eye, mind, and hand to a degree of virtuosity which is sometimes incredible. One has only to look at some of the very, very primitive stone and thong and wood instruments and tools made by primitive savages to realize the enormous skill involved in producing such objects. Today we have exactly the contrary. We have extremely complicated tools to make not only complicated things but also very simple things. We have now an immense number of foolproof machines and corresponding foolproof organizations, but a foolproof machine or a foolproof organization is proof to more than foolishness, it is also spontaneityproof, it is also virtuosoproof, it is also inspirationproof.

In a society in which elaborate and delicate collaboration of mind, eye, and hand is not required at all and is, in effect, undesirable, I think it is very important to think of the deliberate training of the mind-body. In the past we could leave it to a great extent to the accidents of developing technology, but now developing technology has in many spheres abolished the necessity of elaborate and beautiful co-ordination, and it is all the more necessary, as Spinoza advises, to teach the body to do many things.

Let us consider a few of the many things that can be done with the mind-body. The most basic of our faculties, to use an old term, is that of perception. Our thoughts, our feelings, our will—all are based upon perception, and perception may be either good and discriminating or else poor and inadequate. We don't do very much to train perception. We do a lot, I think, in the sphere of music to train the auditory senses, but we do very little in regard to the other senses. There is a great deal to be said for systematic training of perception and other kinds of awareness, which I would call the nonverbal humanities. We give training in the verbal humanities, and we think this will somehow offset specialization in the scientific field, but what we are actually doing is merely trying to offset one specialization in terms of symbols with another specialization in terms of symbols. I am all for courses in humanities, but I don't think there are enough. I think we require now to add these courses in the nonverbal humanities, beginning with the training of perception.

I cannot go into the details here, but much experimental work has been done in this field. For example, Prof. Samuel Renshaw of the University of Ohio has done a great deal in training visual perception, taste, and even memory—and he is very successful in this field, using ingenious methods of various kinds. It has been shown that when you give children on the elementary level training in perception you do improve their intelligence; you improve their interest in what they are doing, you improve their reading, you improve their arithmetic, and because they pay more attention you improve their behavior in school. It has also been shown by Prof. Hoyt Sherman, one of Renshaw's colleagues at the University of Ohio, that these methods for increasing speed and discrimination of visual perceiving are of great value in art training. There is already plenty of evidence to show that if we were to devote ourselves systematically to this kind of teaching of perception, we should do a great deal to improve the quality of intelligence.

In this connection there is a book that I recommend to anybody interested in this field of work: *Gestalt Therapy,* by Pearls, Effelein, and Goodman, published about 8 or 9 years ago. It contains a great mass of material precisely on this problem of developing perception, developing awareness of what is going on inside and outside. This is clearly therapeutic for the simple reason that in this context we can define neurosis as not living here and now, as living somewhere in the past or somewhere far away over Hades or in the future. Training in perception is a training of being aware of this flower here, of this glass here—and this in itself is therapeutic. It is not merely a question of therapy, however; I think it is a question of invention and of the art of living in general.

The procedures described in *Gestalt Therapy* are by no means completely original. In our own century one of our most successful European psychotherapists, Dr. Roger Vitos, made use of just this kind of teaching of awareness, and he got results as good as, if not better than, those attained by most other methods. In addition, we find a similar approach in certain ancient oriental texts. I was greatly struck the other day to find a Sanskrit text, perhaps 1,000 or 2,000 years old, in the form of a dialogue between Shiva and his spouse Bharvati. Bharvati asks him, "What is the secret of your divine mode of consciousness?" and Shiva answers by giving her a list of 112 exercises in awareness which are extraordinarily searching and elaborate. They cover every field of human experience, teaching awareness of everything from praying to sneezing to eating to making love to swimming to everything. It is curious that these old procedures have been completely neglected, that one can find again and again individuals or whole cultures that had developed very important techniques which were then totally neglected thereafter—but which yet retain enormous value.

In both gestalt therapy and in these Sanskrit texts there are many imaginative exercises which might be used with children. Their own wild and extremely powerful imaginations could, I think, be of immense help to them in getting rid of all kinds of obsessional fears and troubles and in enabling them to deal with their life problems more intelligently. I have seen the imagination games, as they are called, being used very successfully by mothers of young children. (There is a curious little book, whose title is *Imagination Game,* by a man called DeMille.) I have corresponded recently with people in Australia who have been doing the same thing in the schools and in therapy, making use of this immense power of imagination for the improvement of the quality of the child's life, and for those who are interested in the imagination in relation to art, I recommend a very remarkable book by Sir Herbert Reed, *Art as an Education,* a most striking book which contains a great many valuable hints about the ways in which imagination can be used as a means of actualizing our potentialities.

In passing from this field of improving the intelligence and the awareness, from these techniques for realizing and for implementing the old command "Know thyself," let me quickly point out that it is curious and a distressing fact, particularly in our civilization, that we are apt to propound very high ideals and to issue deep moral injunctions without ever offering the means to implement the ideals or obey the injunctions. We have been saying "Know thyself" for an enormously long time, but we never have put forth, as did the Sanskrit people, 112 exercises as methods for knowing thyself. So often we find in our particular civilization this curious assumption that exhortations and commands will of themselves help you to obey those exhortations and implement your good intentions. In fact, however, they don't, and you have to propose at the same time means by which to fulfill them.

Now we come from the realm of knowledge and awareness to the other immensely important realm: How can we increase the amount of love in the world? How can we elicit from individuals their potentialities for friendliness and for love, and how can we, if possible, do something constructive about their potentialities for violence and aggression?

Here again we find another strange factor. Whereas all the great religions have insisted upon the importance of love—Christian charity or Buddhist universal compassion—very little has been done in the way of suggesting means whereby love can be actualized on a wider scale and in a deeper way. It is a strangely ironical fact that, as far as I know, the only people who have gone out deliberately to create in their children a prejudice in favor of friendliness are an extremely small and primitive tribe described by Margaret Mead in New Guinea, the Arapesh. These people have used the best possible Pavlovian method for creating prejudice in favor of universal love. The mother as she nurses her child strokes the child so the child is enjoying both the pleasure of eating and the pleasure of being stroked and being in contact with the mother, and while this is happening the mother will rub the child against other members of the family or against anybody who happens to be around, or even against the domestic animals which roam about the huts, and murmur, "Good, good." The child, of course, does not understand the word at that time, but it certainly understands the tone of voice; and as soon as it learns to speak it knows what the meaning of the word "good" is and therefore associates this extremely pleasurable experience of being fed and of being caressed with being brought into intimate contact with other human beings and with animals. According to Margaret Mead, this method is immensely effective. These people are exceedingly friendly, and it is, as I say, a curiously ironic thing that it has remained for this primitive people in the remote area of New Guinea to have invented an effective way of creating a prejudice in favor of friendliness.

There are, I am sure, many other things which can be done to foster friendliness in young people, and there is, of course, the problem of negative prejudice. Professor Gordon Allport, who has written at great length on the subject, is not particularly optimistic about it, he says a great deal can be done with prejudice in individual psychotherapy, but obviously individual psychotherapy cannot be applied to millions of people, and the other methods used are not strikingly effective. It may be that we have to start at some deep-seated level such as that dealt with by the Arapesh before we can hope to overcome this terrible thing.

There obviously are deep-seated drives toward aggression in many human beings, and there is the distressing fact that these aggressive feelings pay higher psychological dividends, so to speak, than gentle and friendly feelings. They provide a greater kick. William James summed this up very succinctly when he said, "Damned braces, bless relaxes." People like being braced, they like damning. In consequence, one of the gravest problems which confronts us is this: How do we find an outlet for something which evidently many people find natural and pleasurable and which shall not do a great deal of harm in the world, but which if violently repressed does a great deal of harm to the individual? On the physiological level I suppose the problem is linked with the fact that we carry around with us a glandular system which was admirably well adapted to life in the Paleolithic times but is not very well adapted to life now. Thus we tend to produce more adrenalin than is good for us, and we either suppress ourselves and turn these destructive energies inwards or else we don't suppress ourselves and we start hitting people and upsetting the whole social structure. The problem is how to find ways in which our aggressive tendencies can be given an outlet in such a manner that they will damage neither ourselves nor other people.

This issue was discussed in one of its aspects by William James in his Essay "The Moral Equivalent of War." This interesting essay points out the desire for heroic action or the need to feel that one is working for a cause greater than himself and suggests that this desire can be channeled along peaceful lines, perhaps through some kind of conscription for creative social work. This is a very limited form of getting rid of aggressive tendencies, but I think it suggests the kind of line which might be pursued. We have somehow, as I say, to find ways by which these "damned braces" feelings can be let out without doing serious harm to ourselves and to others, and here again I think we can learn a great deal from what other cultures have done. We don't have to go far back to the primitives—although they have much to contribute in this field. If we go back even to the Greeks we find a number of very sensible things having been done. The Greeks were using their reason to cope with the irrational, and this is one of the great uses of reason, one sphere where reason requires to be applied in its most subtle way. We have to accept the fact that man has irrational and often destructive drives, and we have in a rational way worked out means by which these drives can be channeled so they will not do harm. One of the ways we attempt to cope with these drives is, of course, the completely ineffective one of preaching sermons and giving commands. This does not work too well. What the Greeks did was to work out methods by which these drives could be satisfied by violent action which was not harmful. The whole tradition in Greek religion of the Coribatic dances is an interesting one. The Coribatic dances were used both diagnostically and therapeutically: the doctors and the priests first observed how the patients responded to certain types of music and movement, and then prescribed certain types of dancing. There is no doubt that a great deal of what we would now call anxiety syndromes were worked off very successfully by means of these dances.

At an earlier date there were the Dionysian orgies, which again helped to work off a great many aggressive tendencies. I must confess that, judging from the Bacchi of Euripides, they went a little far—the ladies watched unfortunate men torn from limb to limb. But I do think the ladies probably could find some satisfaction with less painful effects on their husbands, and I think that along these lines lie valuable techniques for getting rid of violent and deeply buried and powerful antisocial tendencies in men; the methods for getting rid of them are there and can be used successfully. It is significant in this context that Dionysius was called Lucios, the Deliverer. He did deliver people from all kinds of disturbing emotional states, and he also made it possible for them to rid themselves of frustrations and aggression in a relatively harmless way.

So much for this problem of love and hatred, but let me touch very briefly on one other aspect of it: How do we implement our good intentions? St. Paul said, "That which I would I do not, that which I would not I do." This, of course, happens to all of us. We are constantly doing what we would rather not do and constantly not doing what we would rather do. We make good resolutions, but we don't know how to implement them, and again the immemorial technique of preaching sermons and giving orders does not work very well. Even the technique of rewarding or punishing does not work very well. Perhaps there are more effective techniques. One of these, I would say, is the technique described in a book by Prof. Cornell Hutt on *Auto-conditioning,* which is simply a description of simple autosuggestion and very mild self-hypnosis. This method is extremely effective in many ways, and I see absolutely no reason why children should not be taught this very simple means of implementing their good intentions and perhaps also of turning off some of their minor pains. Many dentists who work with children find that a little suggestion will turn off pain like a charm. I have an oriental friend who is a doctor by profession and who, while studying in the Middle East for his medical degree, also studied with the Dervishes. He is able to do such extraordinary things as lying on beds of nails and sticking enormous skewers through his arms and pectoral muscles. He has a phrase I am very fond of: "Pain is merely an opinion." He chooses not to have this opinion. I would be very glad if I could choose not to have the opinion of pain at certain moments, but there is plenty of evidence to show it is relatively easy for many children not to have the opinion of pain. This is also something which could be taught and which, I think, would be very valuable in improving the quality of life and making possible the realization of desirable potentialities.

In conclusion, let me say that there is an immense amount of material, material of other cultures and other times, material on empirical work done by widely scattered and often forgotten individuals—work which achieved considerable fame and for strange reasons is now quite neglected. There are also many things which have been discovered by people whom we tend to regard as charlatans or phonies. Still it is very necessary to look into their work. After all, truth lives at the bottom of a well; the well may be extremely muddy, but very often truth is there, and we should not be too squeamish about at least going down to see. Empirical evidence has been found in many nonacademic places, and it might possibly behoove one of the great foundations to spend a few million dollars creating a team to look into all these various scattered techniques for realizing desirable human potentialities—look into them, test them, see whether they work, see whether they work as well as they're supposed to work, determine the underlying principle in the various techniques, and finally formulate means by which these techniques and these principles could be applied in general education on every level, from kindergarten to graduate school. My own feeling is that if this were done we would find within 5 or 10 years an enormous amount of valuable material, which, if applied to our educational system, would do a great deal to improve the system and a great deal for the actualization of intelligence and friendliness and creativity among human beings.

PART TWO

THE INFLUENCE OF DRUGS ON THE INDIVIDUAL

Chairman: Robert M. Featherstone

The symposium moved from a general discussion of the mind to the more specific question of the use of drugs to alter the operation of the mind, taking as a point of reference the extent to which drugs are capable of modifying the chemical structure, the physical action, or the total behavior pattern of the individual. Discussion ranged over the characteristics of available drugs and their effect on the nervous system, the significant differences in individual response to particular drugs, and the level of precision that might be achieved in the use of drugs. Particular attention was given to the technical questions associated with "thought control" and the popular belief that the use of drugs might facilitate tyrannical control of great masses of human beings by a small elite.

In the panel discussion that followed presentation of the papers, considerable attention was given to the need for careful structuring of future research in psychopharmacology and to the relation between previous discussions of brain activity and brain models and the findings of psychopharmacology.

Seymour S. Kety

CHEMICAL BOUNDARIES OF PSYCHOPHARMACOLOGY

I see my function in introducing the very important field of psychopharmacology as an attempt to relate the physiological, biochemical, and experiential determinants of behavior to possible mechanisms of drug action. In order to do this, I think it is well for us to bear in mind a very important principle of pharmacology, which to the best of my knowledge has never been breached. That principle is simply that no drug ever introduces a new function into an organism; it merely accentuates or inhibits or otherwise modifies a function which already exists. We cannot expect drugs to introduce anything new into the mind or into behavior, but merely to accentuate or to suppress functions in behavior which are already present.

It will help in searching for possible bases for drug action on the brain and on the mind if we have some sort of theoretical model of how the brain works. I have drawn the beginnings of such a model in Figure 1. Since it is a model, of course, one isn't bothered by the necessity of relating it to actual fact, although I must say that this model does satisfy me, at least, in incorporating in it some of the current concepts of neurophysiology and neurochemistry. It is rather a rudimentary one, but in the next thousand years or so we expect to fill in many of the details.

I should like to discuss this model in terms of current concepts in

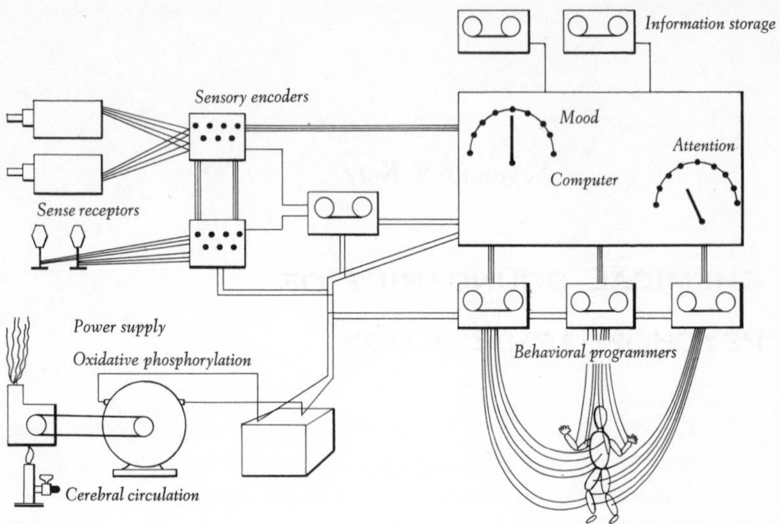

Figure 1

the study of the brain. We have here some symbols of sensory inputs. A television camera is an example of a mechanical model of one such sensory transducer. These sense inputs feed into the nervous system a tremendous amount of data, an amount of data so large that it would very quickly overwhelm even the most complex nervous system and exhaust any possible mechanism for the storage of such information. I think it is safe to say that every moment of our waking lives we are bombarded by at least 10 million different kinds of sensory bits of information, and over the course of a lifetime this number becomes fantastically large. There must be some way of economizing as far as the brain is concerned, and therefore the brain and the sense organs themselves have built into them processes of data reduction in which this vast amount of information is digested, condensed, and coded before it is otherwise handled. These mechanisms for data reduction are at the sense organs themselves, and they are at various places within the brain. The process of data reduction is modulated, in turn, by factors such as attention, motivation, mood, past experience. What gets past the data reducers to be stored or used by the rest of the brain depends to a very large extent upon mood, attention, and past experience. A child exposed to the proof of the Pythagorean theorem does not understand it and does not remember it until, when he is older and has had more appropriate experience, he is able to encode it in some meaningful concept.

If an individual blind from birth has his vision restored—as it sometimes is by surgery—he does not remember the first thing that he sets his newly functioning eyes on; in fact, in all probability, he does not even see those things. He neither sees them nor remembers them until he has learned, on the basis of living with these new experiences, into what form they can be encoded.

In any case, this reduced information is then fed into the brain, and I have indicated a rather simplified version of memory, a tape recorder, where this information may be stored. It may also be fed directly or at a later time into another system, the computer. The computer portion of the brain takes this present information that is pouring in, already coded, and evaluates it against past experience, which it has a remarkable ability to retrieve. On the basis of this present and past information, it is able to make decisions with regard to action—decisions whether to act, whether not to act, and how to act. This action is achieved by means of various behavioral programs, themselves stored on the basis of inborn (instinctive) or acquired information.

I have emphasized that these are behavioral *programs,* rather than individual behaviors; we are coming to realize that just as sense information is digested, coded, and electrically transmitted within the brain, so behavior is also coded and handled in the same way. The brain would be very hard pressed if it constantly had to attend to the movement of every muscle that went into each aspect of behavior. Instead, the nervous system has within it certain programs of activity—arising in the morning, dressing, shaving, driving down to the office, having lunch, getting away from a situation, getting toward a situation. These things are all little programs built into the nervous system, so that the computer, having made decisions, merely sets in action a program, and the program itself semiautomatically carries on from that point forward.

This complicated gadget, like all other computers, requires power, and so we have built into the nervous system a power supply which supplies all these components with energy. I should like to mention certain distinctions between this model and the actual nervous system that we know.

In the first place, this is a model only for the behavior that the nervous system is able to effect; it is not a model for feeling. One can think of various complexities to introduce into this model in order to account for even the most complex forms of behavior—decision making, judgment, and so forth. What I have not been able to introduce into this model, and what for me, at least, seems quite impossible to introduce, is feeling and consciousness. I don't know where that occurs in this system, and I don't know of a physical-chemical model for feeling, so we start off immediately with a subscription, perhaps, to the dualistic philosophy which Dr. Penfield described so beautifully previously and admit immediately that physics and chemistry and biology and pharmacology, although they can develop constructs for behavior, are not likely to explain feeling.

There are other differences between this model, or any model we can conceive of today, and what actually takes place in the nervous system. This model is a predominantly electronic one, based upon our experience with man-made computers. Interestingly enough, the brain is as much a chemical machine as it is a physical or electronic one. We don't quite understand how the brain, by means of chemical processes, can do the same kinds of things that a television camera or an IBM computer is able to do with electronic tubes and condensers and resistances. This, of course, is going to be one of the great problems of neurophysiology: to explain how it is that properly organized chemical processes can effect these remarkable phenomena.

Furthermore, in most electronic systems the power supply is very neatly isolated at the bottom of the cabinet and sends out the energy to the various components. In the case of the brain the power supply is intimately associated with every one of the components. Each neuron apparently has its own power supply, each neuron is capable of transforming its own energy requirements from foodstuffs along certain chemical pathways, and because the brain is more a chemical instrument than it is an electronic one or a physical one, its actions can be influenced by other chemical substances, which we call drugs. It would be a little silly for us to think of pouring some LSD or some Miltown over a television receiver and expecting it to do very much to the image, and yet that is exactly what we expect to do with regard to the human brain. Of course, we can do it, simply because of the tremendous importance that chemical processes have in the brain as opposed to their relative lack of importance in man-made computers.

Now the next question I should like to consider is where in the chemistry of the brain drugs can act and where, in fact, they do act in so far as we know at the present time. I should like to start with the most rugged and fundamental of the chemical processes, namely, the chemical processes involved in power supply, the chemical processes involved in the simple generation of energy within the brain for its utilization in more complex patterns.

Table 1 presents some data obtained by my colleagues and me some years ago on the blood flow and, more important, the oxygen consumption of the conscious human brain. They were obtained in healthy young men, and we see that the brain under normal circumstances utilizes oxygen at the rate of 3.3 milliliters of oxygen per 100 grams per minute, which in the case of a brain of average weight corresponds to 46 milliliters of oxygen per minute for the brain as a whole. This, you will recognize, is a very large fraction of the total oxygen consumption of the body at basal conditions; in fact, it represents about 20 or 25 per cent of the total body basal metabolism. The glucose consumption by the brain under these same circumstances has also been measured, and this turns out to be 5.4 milligrams, or 76 milligrams of glucose per minute for the whole brain, which corresponds to 4 grams of glucose, or 1 teaspoonful of glucose per hour, as the foodstuff which provides the energy for the brain.

Table 1 Cerebral circulation and metabolism, normal values, healthy young men

	Per 100 grams per minute	*For whole brain per minute*
Blood flow	54 ml	750 ml
Vascular resistance	1.6 units	0.115 units
Oxygen consumption	3.3 ml	46 ml
Glucose consumption	5.4 mg	76 mg
Respiratory quotient	0.99	0.99

The respiratory quotient of the brain is very close to 1, and if we express these quantities in moles rather than in milliliters or milligrams, we see what has been known for some time now, that for every mole of glucose which disappears into the brain, 6 moles of oxygen are also utilized. This is exactly the amount which is required to burn the glucose fairly completely to water and carbon dioxide, with a release of a certain amount of energy.

From this it has been possible for the first time to calculate the total energy requirements for the conscious human brain, and this turns out to be, remarkably enough, 20 watts. Here we see another striking difference between the human brain and any computer we can think of. These computers of today utilize thousands of watts in order to perform their rather restricted functions.

It is also important to point out that glucose is still the primary foodstuff of the brain. The brain is quite unique in being able to utilize only glucose for normal energy under normal circumstances, and much more than 95 per cent of the energy utilized by the brain is derived from glucose. Of course, it is possible under special conditions to have neural tissue for brief periods of time utilizing other foodstuffs such as amino acids and fatty acids directly, and in the course of utilization of glucose, of course, the carbon atoms of glucose exchange with various other components of the brain, but the fact still remains that for human consciousness glucose appears to be essential. We have little evidence of any other substance being able to replace glucose for the production of energy.

In Table 2 we see a listing of states in which the power supply of the brain is interfered with by some generalized physical, or more important, chemical or pharmacological process. In these various conditions one can see to what extent the over-all energy utilization by the brain is reduced. In senile psychosis it has fallen to 80 per cent of the normal value; in insulin hypoglycemia, where the glucose from the blood falls appreciably, there is a reduction of 20 per cent in the energy utilization of the brain; in insulin coma, where the blood sugar has fallen even lower and very little glucose is available to the brain, the energy consumption of the brain falls to nearly 50 per cent of its normal values. In alcoholic coma and in surgical anesthesia we see pharmacological agents which depress the power supply to the brain and diminish the over-all utilization of oxygen. But, as is obvious from the computer diagram, the power supply is only one important limiting factor in behavior and in consciousness, and there are many things which happen to behavior or the human mind that have very little to do with its power supply.

Table 3 is a listing of a number of conditions in which there are serious disturbances in thinking or changes of efficiency of mental processes, but little changes in the over-all energy requirement. Normal sleep, for example, is found to be associated with exactly the same over-all energy utilization as is the waking state. There appears to be a change in the distribution of the energy in sleep, so that different circuits are brought into play, rather than any over-all change in total energy. We see, thus, that sleep is quite different from anesthesia.

In schizophrenia there is exactly the same oxygen consumption in the brain as there is in normal conditions. In fact, we are able to conclude from these observations that it takes just as much oxygen to think

Table 2 Cerebral oxygen consumption and mental state

Condition	*Per cent of normal*
Senile psychosis	82
Diabetic acidosis	82
Insulin hypoglycemia	79
Artificial hypothermia	67
Surgical anesthesia	64
Insulin coma	58
Diabetic coma	52
Alcoholic coma	49

Table 3 Cerebral oxygen consumption and mental state

Condition	*Per cent of normal*
Normal sleep	97
Schizophrenia	100
LSD psychosis	101
Mental arithmetic	102
Anxiety	118
Epinephrine infusion	122

an irrational thought as it does to think a rational one. Also, drugs such as LSD produce a toxic psychosis that resembles schizophrenia in certain phases, and this is also associated with no change in the over-all power supply.

Mental arithmetic is associated with no change in over-all oxygen utilization, and this is perfectly understandable. Whether a computer is operating on a complicated arithmetic problem or whether it is just idling, we find that it uses just as much energy in one case as in the other; a television receiver does not use more energy or less energy depending upon how important the program is to which it is tuned.

There are two states somewhat associated, anxiety and epinephrine infusion, in which there appears to be a significant elevation in the total energy utilized by the brain. Except for the state of anxiety and for convulsions, we are not aware of conditions in which there is an increase in over-all energy utilization. I know of no instance in which forcibly increasing the oxygen utilized by the brain will increase the quality or the quantity of thinking. I therefore don't think it is likely that one can improve mental function by drugs which act upon the over-all power supply any more than one can improve the quality of the jokes on television by supplying more current.

Thus far I have been talking about the over-all energy consumption of the brain, but actually we know that the brain is not a homogeneous mass of jelly; rather it is a highly organized complex of organs—in fact, to our knowledge the most highly organized structure in the universe. Since the power supply of the brain is not fixed in one place but is distributed throughout the brain, we would expect that this power supply would vary notably throughout the brain.

Figure 2 is an autoradiogram of the brain of a cat that had been exposed to radioactive gas during life and in which the densities obtained correspond to the blood flow in that region during life. We have considerable reason to believe that blood flow in the brain is very sensitively regulated by oxygen consumption, so that in a way this is a map of the oxygen consumption of the various parts of the brain in an unanesthetized cat. There are remarkable differences there. We can see the very high metabolism of the cerebral cortex; in fact, if we look carefully, we can even see that certain parts of the cerebral cortex are even more actively outlined. These correspond to the visual centers, and this was

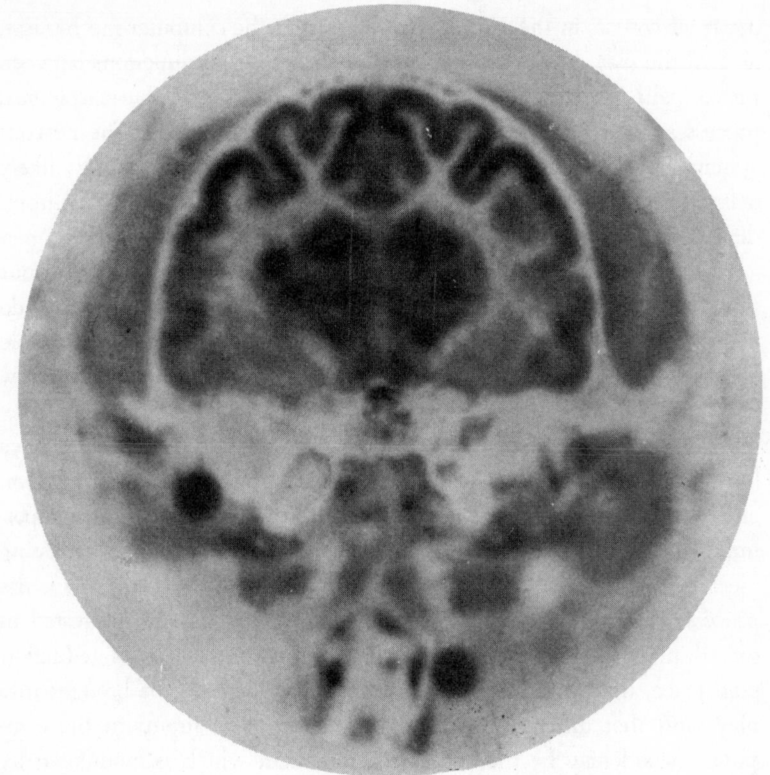

Figure 2

taken from a cat whose eyes were open during the inhalation. If the cat is blinded these visual centers no longer appear as intensely, and if the animal is exposed to flashing light during the process, there is an even greater intensification of the blood flow and, presumably, the energy supply to that particular region.

Even at the regional level, however, the power supply to the brain or to any component in the brain is merely a limiting factor, rarely a determining factor, in behavior. We are interested now in getting to some of the other aspects of the brain to see how biochemical processes can modulate some of the more subtle aspects of behavior. Synaptic transmission is a chemical process which involves the transmission of information from one part of the nervous system to another. Synapses occur, of course, in the sensory system, within the computer mechanism, and all the way down the line, and these synapses, or junctions between nerve cells, can be modulated by chemical and pharmacological processes. It is quite possible that the various synapses in the nervous system show a selective response to various drugs, and it is highly likely many of the differential actions of drugs are dependent upon their differential action on different synapses.

At the present stage of our knowledge we know much more about how drugs act at peripheral synapses in the nervous system than we do about how they act in the central nervous system. In fact, the whole science of central synaptology has developed only within the past few years, and we look forward during the next 20 or 50 or 100 years to remarkable strides in that aspect of the situation. Our mechanisms have built into them a process which has not yet appeared in this diagram, and that is a process of mood. It would be very sensible to have superimposed upon this very rugged instrument a gentle, subtle, long-lasting mechanism for modulating whole aspects of its behavior, and this is the process which I call mood. It is important when we are interested in something, or afraid or happy, that different types of data reduction take place, that different storage mechanisms, perhaps, be brought into play, and that different values be put upon these inputs in the computer. Mood may be the process in the brain which is modulated by chemical reactions and where, in fact, at the present time we have certain suggestive insights.

From the point of view of neurophysiology it appears that mood may be established by a part of the brain called the limbic system, which derives from the old smell brain, or rhinencephalon of lower animals. In the limbic system there are distributed in a very highly selected manner certain agents, the biogenic amines, which have only recently been discovered. The two earliest to be discovered, and those upon which the most work has been done are serotonin and norepinephrin. It has recently been learned that these compounds change in concentration in response to the action of certain drugs which modify behavior. With reserpine, for instance, which is a behavioral depressant, serotonin and norepinephrin fall very markedly in the brain. In the case of other compounds such as the monoamine oxidase inhibitors, iproniazid, and newer ones, which block the enzyme that destroys these amines, the concentrations of serotonin and norepinephrin rise in the brain. These groups of drugs are associated with certain characteristic patterns of behavior—reserpine with depressant, the monoamine oxidase inhibitors with activation or excitement or euphoria—and many speculations have developed which attempt to relate the concentrations of these biogenic amines to these particular moods.

Suffice it to say that at the present state of our knowledge it is hard to accept any one of these hypotheses as explaining the whole picture. Since reserpine causes a fall both in norepinephrin and serotonin, and iproniazid will cause a rise in both of these, it is difficult to ascribe the action of these drugs to one or another of these amines. As a matter of fact, if one pulls together all the information that is available, there seems to be a certain predominant convergence of information which suggests that perhaps the fall in serotonin is more closely correlated with the depressant action of reserpine and the rise in norepinephrin more closely associated with the excitement-producing aspects of monoamine oxidase inhibitors. There are many exceptions to these general rules, however, and I think it is fair to say that at the present time we do not know the basis upon which the amines act in the brain, nor do we know their role in behavior, although we have reason to believe that they probably play an important role. For that matter we have no information that the amines that have thus far been discovered, serotonin, norepinephrin, tryptamine, GABA, are the only or even the most important amines. There are probably dozens of other amines in the brain, many of which may be found to correlate much better with behavior and mood than the ones that have thus far been isolated and studied.

Now let us call sexual feeling a form of mood—and in a way it is, since by feeling feminine or masculine, we may determine to a very large extent sensory-data reduction, computation, and behavior—and cite the recent experiments done by Michael and Harris at the Maudsley Institute in London, in which chemical substances have definitely produced or elicited sexual behavior. Castrated female cats, which do not normally exhibit feminine behavior, were stimulated with minute amounts of female sex hormones introduced into appropriate parts of the brain, and they showed typical patterns of female sexual behavior. This does not happen when these substances are introduced in those amounts into any other parts of the brain or any other parts of the body. We are also aware of other work in Sweden in which the injections of salt solutions into certain parts of the hypothalamus will produce a typical thirst response in animals, followed by their drinking large quantities of water.

Finally we come to the process of information storage in the brain, which is undoubtedly a chemical process in our brains, as opposed to the rather simplified version of a physical storage in the tape recorder. Dr. Hydén has already given us a very imaginative hypothesis of how information storage may be effected in the brain on the basis of protein synthesis. I certainly think it is fair to say that protein synthesis represents today the most widely accepted chemical process by which information can be stored in the brain. The protein molecule is the only one of which we are aware at the present time which contains within it sufficient flexibility and diversity to permit the tremendously complex codes that have somehow to be stored.

There are drugs which will interfere with protein synthesis in the brain, and there are some recent experiments that are as yet unpublished in which the administration of such drugs to animals can be shown to retard the learning of new information without upsetting the behavior of the animal or his ability to retrieve old information. This, of course, supports but does not prove the hypothesis that protein storage or protein synthesis is related to the memory process.

I should like to sum up now by pointing out that the drug effects that we have been talking about, in common with most drug effects, are fairly gross modulators of behavior. They are not likely to establish new behavior. The reason is that human behavior is so largely determined by the information itself which is stored and present in the sensory input. I know of no way in which a drug can modify the stored information in any meaningful way. Of course, it can erase it, it can suppress it, it can, perhaps, help to accentuate certain parts of it, but it is not likely that a drug will be discovered that will affect the stored information in a discriminatory and meaningful manner. Even in the sexual-behavior experiment that I mentioned before, the chemical substance, the female sex hormone on the brain, triggers an instinctual and learned behavioral pattern. You won't get male behavior in a castrated female cat by stimulating the brain with male sex hormone, because the brain in that animal just has not learned how to behave like a male. The most you can hope to get is female behavior in a female cat.

No drug is likely to substitute for better schools in the injection of knowledge or attitudes into the brains of our children. Drugs may obtund the mind, and where the mind is disturbed by disease or disorder, may help to stabilize it by suppressing abnormal activity. It may even some day be possible to improve the mind by improving the efficiency of some of the chemical processes in the brain—but we must not be too sanguine about these possibilities. I know of very few drugs which are capable of improving normal functions, even in other aspects of the body.

We know a great deal more about the action of muscle and the action of the heart than we do about the action of the brain. We have been studying the pharmacology of these organs for a longer period of time, but it is interesting to note that there isn't yet a drug which will improve the function of the normal heart or a drug which can safely and effectively be given to an athlete with any guarantee that it will improve his record. In other words, in these relatively simple aspects of bodily action drugs appear capable of remedying defects by suppressing abnormal activity or by accentuating normal activity, but they don't yet appear to be capable of improving normal activity. I suppose that is reasonable, because nature has been at this business for a few hundred thousand years longer than pharmacologists have and has had much more opportunity to discover the possibilities.

Far more potent than drugs in effecting behavior is the information which is acquired through experience and education and is stored in the brain. In that area, even today, lie the potentialities for good and evil. That is why I look forward so much to hearing what the rest of the symposium is going to tell us. It seems to me that in the areas of the social sciences and the political sciences we have much more effective mechanisms for controlling the mind than we have in pharmacology. If we ever permit a state of affairs to develop in which a drug can be fed to large populations for the purpose of controlling their minds, I submit that control of the mind will already have been achieved, and the drug itself need be no more than a placebo.

James G. Miller

THE INDIVIDUAL RESPONSE TO DRUGS

Thomas Jefferson was one of many who have been concerned with controls upon the mind [1]. On his memorial in Washington appear his words: "I have sworn upon the altar of God eternal hostility against every form of tyranny over the mind of man." However, the forms of tyranny which controlled men's minds in Jefferson's day were greatly different from some of the controls possible now. Jefferson knew about slavery and the degradation of women, about ostracism, torture, and the Inquisition, and he was fully aware of the prompt and ultimate control of the mind which could be accomplished with the headsman's axe. But even though he realized that the pen was mightier than the sword, he could not have demonstrated, as did Stuart Chase [2], the tyranny of words in the semantic morass of ordinary speech. Nor could he have pointed out, as did Whorf [3], the controls on our speech behavior that are exerted by the very structure of the languages we speak. In the time of Franklin, with his kite and key, it would have been more fantastic than any Jules Verne science fiction to imagine a possible tyranny to the brain by electroshock and implanted electrodes, or the self-betrayal of the "lie detector," or the subtle but potent impact of a multitude of different psychoactive drugs. What Noah and his sons discovered about alcohol and what Marco Polo told the Western world about opiates were as much as Jefferson knew about psychopharmacology.

Jefferson and the other founders of our country were not confused about the nature of man. To them it was clear that man had certain inalienable rights, though the Constitution and Bill of Rights did not cope with the modern question of whether some of the onslaughts possible with new technologies constitute infringements upon these inalienable rights. Just as English common law makes a castle of every man's home, so the Anglo-Saxon legal tradition has guaranteed each man an unassailable sanctity of solitude within his own subjective experience. This is the "peace" that others dare not disturb. This experience, or "the mind," is, in Whitehead's terms [4], the subjective pole which is the internal view of the external, objective pole. The physical world, including the brain, the endocrine glands, and the rest of the body, belong to the objective pole. Their structure and function can be examined and experimented upon. Because the brain, the seat of man's mind, exists in the external world, it is subject to impacts from outside, and as our control of various types of physical and chemical manipulation has advanced, the potency of these impacts has increased.

Man is an open system with inputs, throughputs, and outputs of energy, specific forms of matter including various chemical compounds, and information in the sense of modern mathematical information theory [5]. In such fluxes man behaves in order to maintain in equilibrium a number of variables in different subsystems of his total organism. Recognizing this, we can place in categories the various inputs which affect his behavior.

There are transmissions of information. Some of these come to the organism through the genes, information which it now appears is stored in some chemical or physical configuration of the DNA substance. Here are the inherited templates which pattern an individual's development. Here are blueprints from which the brain is built, with its maze of tracts and centers. These templates also are important in determining function, such as some of the stable patterns of species-related behavior which we call instinct. Jung's conception of the inheritance of certain ideas, the archetypes of a race unconscious [6], does not at the moment seem so incredible as it did a decade ago. As the contemporaries of Jefferson conceived of man, his original genetic input seemed immutable. Today, however, it is becoming clear that if the genetic information is stored in chemical structures or physical arrangements of chemical molecules, then chemical or physical forces can change these patterns. What bizarre results can come from such alteration is not yet known, but the teratoma, the blighted ovum, the anencephalic monster, and other congenital defects start us thinking.

Then there is the information which flows into the nervous system after birth, what we call learned experience. Where is the memory of it stored? Does the RNA material have a role in this storage? Is it, as some now wonder, coded like a message on a magnetic tape in the neurofibrils of nerve cells? Biochemistry and biophysics are nearer to being able to answer such questions than they were a few years ago, but they do not yet have solutions. However, since memory is stored somewhere, either in reverberative circuits or in some more permanent trace, it can potentially be altered by chemical or physical means.

Viewing a human being, then, as a bounded open system in space and time, we recognize that through such a system energy, matter, genetic information, and experiential information must flow continuously. An irreducible minimum of functions is necessary for life to go on, and all higher animals have specialized subsystems, different in different species, which carry out these activities. Information flows through the many channels of the complex communication system of the organism to coordinate its subsystems and enable it to adapt to its environment. Research has demonstrated that there must be a minimal rate of continuous flow through the system of information from outside for it to be in adjustment. The environment fluctuates, and great changes in inputs from it can be stressful, producing pathological behavior either when there is information-input underload (or sensory deprivation) or when there is information-input overload [7]. Both can alter the functional characteristics of the nervous system.

Likewise, in a single channel or set of channels, an energic or material chemical input—a drug—can distort the message in a nonrandom fashion, or diminish its precision by decreasing the signal-to-noise ratio with random "chemical" noise. By altering the physical characteristics of neural communication channels, by either energy inputs such as flows of electricity through electrodes or matter inputs such as various chemical compounds, we can affect brain function and related behavior.

As we come to learn more and more about the metabolism of this information-processing network called the brain, a vast complex of interrelated equilibria maintained by many reactions of substrates with enzymes, we come to see at how many points it would be possible for drugs to enter into such reactions, either blocking them, altering their rates, or distorting them in some other manner. There is a multitude of ways to throw molecular monkey wrenches into the works. As neuropsycopharmacology deepens its understanding of all this, it is quite possible that specific categories of behavior can be influenced predictably by administration of measured amounts of appropriate compounds which change functional characteristics at particular locations in the neural network. The present power of such pharmacological techniques for fundamental research on behavior as well as its potential power, when our knowledge is much more advanced than at present, for controlling human action and experience should not be lightly dismissed. Batteries of objective tests and subjective rating scales are continually being developed to demonstrate the multiplex possible drug effects on our thoughts, feelings, and actions.

For a long time the world has assumed that individuals differ greatly in their responses to drugs. However, De Quincey, in *Confessions of an English Opium Eater* [8], reported that he could drink more than a pint of laudanum—a 10 per cent tincture of opium—daily. That would be roughly equivalent to 5 grams of morphine a day, or as he said, the common hospital dose for 320 adult patients. Some people can consume ten cocktails at a party and drive themselves home, while others pass dreamily out after taking two. While most people are sedated by nembutal, a few are excited. Minute amounts of house dust or ragweed pollen which would not bother most people can stimulate the neural sneezing centers of a few to intense spasms. What causes these individual differences in behavior?

To begin with, there are a number of constitutional factors, for example, sex. Various investigations have shown that males and females respond differently to drugs. For instance, Marquis, Kelly, Miller, Gerard, and Rapoport [9] found that 800 milligram doses of meprobamate increased vasomotor activity and sweating in females but not in males. In the total population there seemed to be no significant drug effects on sweating, but when it was split according to sex a clear-cut difference appeared.

There are also important age differences. The response of infants to barbiturates, for instance, is quite different from that of adults, even when the dosages are properly adjusted to their body weights.

Furthermore, this factor of body weight is important. Other things being equal, a man of 300 pounds can absorb a much larger drug dosage into his voluminous fat deposits and other parts of his body than can a man of 90 pounds.

Drugs also affect occasional individuals atypically because of allergies. A tranquilizer which has had no unfavorable effect except occasional drowsiness on 10,000 patients can cause the 10,001st to break out in purpuric blotches all over his body, or can seriously and permanently damage the function of his liver. Underlying such side effects are alterations in the patient's background of sensitivity and previous sensitizing experiences.

Then there are idiosyncratic effects such as the well-known actions of nembutal and seconal on some patients who take a capsule hoping for quiet sleep and are instead jarred to jittery wakefulness for the whole night. Such responses may be related to interaction between the particular metabolic state of the nervous system at the moment and the given drug level, but the mechanism is not fully understood.

Besides these constitutional explanations for deviations between one man and another in reaction to drugs, other causes develop during life. One is the well-known phenomenon of tolerance from continued and increasing use of a given compound over time. One man can smoke a dozen cigars a day, but a nonsmoker can be nauseated by a few puffs on a single cigarette. A. E. Housman found drug tolerance worth a poem [10]:

> There was a king reigned in the East:
> There, when kings will sit to feast,
> They get their fill before they think
> With poisoned meat and poisoned drink.
> He gathered all that springs to birth
> From the many-venomed earth;
> First a little, thence to more,
> He sampled all her killing store;
> And easy, smiling, seasoned sound,
> Sate the king when healths went round.

They put arsenic in his meat
And stared aghast to watch him eat;
They poured strychnine in his cup
And shook to see him drink it up:
They shook, they stared as white's their shirt:
Them it was their poison hurt.
—I tell the tale that I heard told.
Mithridates, he died old.

Like the ponies who graze near arsenic mills, Mithridates had developed a tolerance to arsenic, strychnine, and other lethal delicacies.

Another reason for differing drug reactions lies in pathologies which arise as life goes on. Fifty units of insulin do not react on a normal individual as they do on a diabetic. They can cause the lightheadedness and confusion of insulin shock in normal persons but have no effect on the subjective experience of a patient who suffers from inadequate insulin production and takes insulin simply to keep his physiological balance in the proper range. If you are well you will not notice any change after taking an aspirin, but if you are sick it can dull your headache. Similarly, we have found in a number of researches that certain tranquilizers have no effect on normal subjects, while the same dosage frequently relieves anxiety in neurotic patients.

The character of psychiatric pathology can also alter drug response from patient to patient. Himwich has said [11]:

> One patient will receive most benefit from a certain tranquilizing agent, and a second from another. . . . Some drugs like azacyclonol, can bring about better social adjustment, so that the atmosphere in the ward becomes friendlier, especially among patients who are only moderately disturbed. The choice of a tranquilizing drug must be decided empirically; the best one for a given patient can be found only by the process of elimination.
>
> The most dramatic improvements are observed in the first acute attacks or in the chronic patient who has developed an acute exacerbation of his disorder. At our hospital, however, tranquilizing drugs have also been found to benefit markedly patients with schizophrenia of long duration. . . . But the improvements were mainly seen in patients with obvious active schizophrenic processes—those who had hallucinations and delusions or who were hyperactive, agitated, and tense. Blocked, retarded, and apathetic schizophrenics are more difficult to help. . . .

Similarly, senile patients who are irritable, quarrelsome, and apprehensive show greater improvement than patients who exihibit negativism, apathy, and withdrawal. . . . Similarly, depressions not accompanied by anxiety and tension are less apt to be ameliorated by a psychopharmacologic agent.

As research evidence accumulates, we are getting more and more indications that differences in personality explain many variations in reactions to drugs, particularly those which are psychoactive. Summarizing these findings, Uhr says [12]:

Kornetsky and Humphries [13] related scores on four Minnesota Multiphasic Personality Inventory subscales with the performance of subjects. . . . The psychasthenia and the depression scale each predicted changed in subjective reports of the effect of 200 mgs. of chlorpromazine. . . . Karnetsky and Humphries [14] found further indications of differences between subjects in general drug responsivity.

Kelly, Miller, Marquis, Gerard, and Uhr [15] using 68 objectively measured personality variables . . . first determined their interrelations by means of a factor analysis, and then correlated 20 selected variables with drug effects on 40 of the behavioral measures used. They did not find many more significant correlations than might be expected by chance alone, and therefore they concluded that individual significant relations could not be asserted, but might fruitfully serve as hypotheses for further validation studies. Klerman, DiMascio, Rinkel, and Greenblatt [16] determined that sedative drug action was ego-threatening to athletic, extrapunitive subjects but anxiety reducing to passive, intrapunitive, anxious subjects.

Ellsworth and Clark [17] found that variability in palmar sweat significantly predicted subsequent improvement in behavioral scores of patients administered reserpine, chlorpromazine, or both. Heller, Walton, and Black [18] found that division of subjects into two personality types—Eysenck's hysterics and dysthymics (anxious)—enabled them to predict which subjects would decrease in tension (as measured by items chosen from the Minnesota Multiphasic Personality Inventory) as a result of meprobamate. They found no effects from meprobamate on their entire group of subjects, and no effects within groups on the Taylor Manifest Anxiety Scale or on a headache scale.

A surprisingly large percentage of the studies that have tried to correlate the personality of the patient with his response to drug therapy has yielded positive results. Differences between subjects might well turn out to be crucial in the future untangling of apparently opposing results from different laboratories where, inevitably, different populations are treated and examined.

Other researchers have found that dividing subject populations in terms of their personality characteristics clarified drug effects. Schneider [19] discovered in one study that when he separated his subjects into two groups distinguished by their level of functioning on a control day—increased versus decreased central sympathetic reactors, those who condition easily versus those who do not, and fast reactors versus slow—the size of change in performance after drugs were administered was clearly related to the predrug level of functioning. Shagass and Kerenyi [20] determined that the sedation threshold to amobarbital, that is the intravenous dosage at which speech is slurred and the frontal brain-wave amplitude is definitely increased, was positively correlated with introversion as measured by the Guilford S and R scales as well as with ratings of hysterical-obsessional trend.

From clinical observations Kubie [21] has noted relationships between what he calls "the central emotional position of the personality" and reactions to a psychoactive drug such as alcohol. He states:

> The same drug affects different men in quite different ways, or may alter any one man in different directions on different occasions—the differences with which all are familiar between the man who fights when he is drunk and who hates and distrusts everyone and becomes an isolationist, and the man who laughs and loves and becomes gregarious; the man who weeps into his beer in a crying jag; the man who becomes erotic and the man who becomes impotent, the man who becomes heterosexual and the man who becomes homosexual, or the man who, still under alcohol, shifts from one of these phases to another. In a similar way other drugs can release or make manifest latent central affective positions.

When the superego, sometimes defined as that part of the personality which is soluble in alcohol, relaxes its inhibitory action under drugs, differences between one man and another come obviously to the fore. Often, inhibited persons who cannot under ordinary circumstances express their feelings use a drug such as alcohol or sodium pentothal in small doses as an excuse for much more flagrant acting out than is justified by their chemical intake.

The information stored by experience in the memories of patients has much to do with the specific symptoms produced by psychoactive drugs. While a psychotomimetic such as LSD-25 can cause a toxic psychosis in every man, the fantasies elicited differ with each person, because his previous experience is unique. This is also why patients give different responses to the same set of Rorschach ink-blot cards. As a consequence, as Gottschalk and his associates have shown [22], introspection and free association can be used as tools of fine sensitivity to assess drug effects. This is true, however, only if the observer is trained in such self-observation. The interviewer asks the subject to discuss any interesting or dramatic life experiences and then records the reply by tape recorder, studying the typed transcript. A detailed analysis of samples of such speech provides reasonably precise indices of the relative intensity of a complex psychologic state or of the degree of a person's social alienation and personal disorganization. Also, the rate at which words are spoken in such free association differs significantly under administration of a drug such as the energizer pipradol and administration of a placebo.

Dreams are another sort of subjective experience whose content is determined by stored memories. Whitman, Pierce, and Maas [23] compared dreams under no medication with those under meprobamate. There were marked individual differences among the dreams of different subjects, but they were found by both themselves and the experimenters to have a greater sense of movement and a greater feeling of dependency under meprobamate than when no drug was given.

One of the best-known personality differences among individuals is the distinction between those persons whose reaction is changed by placebos and those who are not so influenced. There is no question that there is such a phenomenon. A noted study on it by Beecher [24] reported that placebos have an average effectiveness of 32 per cent. They also have toxic and subjective side effects. Kurland, in a small sampling of psychiatric studies [25], discovered that placebo reactivity varies between 4 and 52 per cent. He found no research using placebos in which some degree of activity was not recorded. Lasagna, von Felsinger, and Beecher [26] discovered that atypical responses to placebo and drug therapy appeared most frequently in persons whose personality structures were inadequate in dealing with everyday stresses, and who were impulsive, hostile, anxious, and fearful of losing control of themselves. Trouton [27] found placebo reactors to be older, conscientious churchgoers with a greater acceptance of pain and suffering than consistent nonreactors, and Rorschach tests indicated that reactors were less mature and more dependent on outside stimuli than nonreactors. He thought that introverts tend to acquire placebo reactions more easily and lose them less readily than extraverts. Fischer and Dlin [28] studied seventy-four patients with psychosomatic complaints who were classified as psychotic, severe neurotic, or mild neurotic. Negative placebo reactors exceeded positive reactors in the psychotic group, they were approximately equal in number in the severe neurotic group, and positive reactors were more numerous in the mild neurotic group.

So it is apparent that personality and diagnostic differences have deep significance in explaining why various persons respond in divergent ways to placebos.

From all this evidence, we can conclude that both constitutional factors and influences acquired throughout life, including sensitivities, tolerances, and personality differences, underlie the variety of ways drugs act on each one of us. These influences are not under our voluntary control. It is not a question of will. A neurotic patient took one tablet of chlorpromazine and one bottle of beer and then drove his car recklessly through a safety island. Did he will to break the law, and should he be found guilty of reckless driving? His defense was that the drug and the alcohol had interacted in an unexpected fashion. To this interaction the scientist would add a consideration of constitutional and experiential determinants of his personality. Science and the law have not yet made their peace on how to deal with such cases, and as we shall see, this is dramatically true of our current regulations for conduct of our military if they are made prisoners of war.

More fundamental than the varieties of ways drugs affect each of us is the fact that in one deep sense there is *no* difference among us in our responses to them. In the motion picture *I Want to Live,* the condemned woman was in the gas chamber when one of her keepers, trying to be humane, advised her what to do after the pellets dropped into the acid. "Take a deep breath," he said, "it's easier that way." The prisoner looked at him and said cynically, "How do you know?" The keeper had concluded from frequent observation that in such things all people are alike. British ships in the sixteenth century were always out from shore the same number of days without fresh fruits or vegetables when their sailors began to get scurvy. The deficiency of ascorbic acid showed in everyone aboard, captain and crew. Five minutes without oxygen and you are unconscious. Five minutes beneath the ocean and you have drowned. The brain is a delicate organ protected by a skull, by the fluid in which it floats, and by duplicate arteries which supply it with oxygen. But it has no adjustment mechanism against cynanide or anoxia, against the impacts of the tranquilizers, the energizers, or the psychotomimetics.

What does all this mean for those who would use drugs to extract intelligence, elicit confessions, or change opinions of others? Prisoners of war are potential reservoirs of stored information which, if communicated to an enemy, might benefit him. Criminal suspects may have a store of information the police want. Can psychoactive drugs aid in obtaining this information? Gottschalk [29], who has carefully surveyed what is known about this question, states:

> Studies and reports dealing with the validity of material extracted from reluctant informants, whether criminal suspects or experimental subjects, indicate that there is no "truth serum" which can force every informant to report all the information he has. Experimental and clinical evidence indicates that not only may the inveterate criminal psychopath lie or distort under the influence of a drug, but also that the relatively normal and well-adjusted individual may, with some drugs, successfully disguise factual data. Less well-adjusted individuals plagued by guilt and depression, or suggestible individuals who are compliant and easily awed, are more likely to reveal withheld information; but they may, at times, unconsciously distort this information and present fantasies as facts. The anesthetic action of the drug, as in narcosis with barbiturates, can interfere with cerebral functioning and promote the presentation of fantasy material as fact, or otherwise alter the form of verbalizations so that they are relatively unintelligible. It would be very difficult under these circumstances for an interrogator to distinguish when the verbal content was turning from fact to fantasy, when the informant was simulating deep narcosis but actually falsifying, which of contrary stories told under narcosis was true, and when a lack of crucial information coming from a subject under a drug meant the informant had none to offer.
>
> Barbiturates have been found helpful in detecting whether an individual is feigning ignorance of the English language. . . .
>
> Without adequately controlling his study, one author claims that methamphetamine produces such a strong urge to talk that the criminal

who feigns amnesia or withholds vital information cannot control himself and gives himself away. . . .

The psychotomimetic and hallucinogenic drugs . . . would tend to produce a state of anxiety or terror in most subjects and to promote perceptual distortions and psychotic disorientation. Their use could constitute a definite threat to most medically unsophisticated subjects, i.e., threat of making the subject crazy. When the subject is not under the influence of such drugs, vital information might be extracted, as a price for ceasing further medication. An enlightened informant would not have to feel threatened, however, for the effect of these hallucinogenic agents is transient in normal individuals. . . .

There is a possibility that tranquilizers might be of use in selected informants who are highly agitated and disturbed, and who might give information they prefer to withhold in return for the tranquility they experience with such a sedative. Under the influence of such a drug, the less emotionally upset informant might find that he can better master his anxieties and keep his resolve to remain silent. These are speculations and require testing and experimentation.

Gottschalk lists other possible uses for drugs in such situations and then concludes:

Combined with the many other stresses in captivity that an individual may be obliged to undergo, drugs can add to the factors aimed at weakening the resistance of the potential informant. But, for many reasons, the use of drugs by the interrogator is not sure to produce valid results. The effects of drugs depend to a large extent on the personality makeup and physical status of the informant and the kind of rapport that the interrogator is able to establish with him. . . . Even under the most favorable circumstances the information obtained could be contaminated by fantasy, distortion, and untruth, especially when hallucinogenic or sedative drugs are employed.

President Eisenhower officially decreed by executive order on August 17, 1955 [30], that, if captured, one of our prisoners of war should give from his information store only his name, rank, serial number, and date of birth. It was decided that this is the accepted alternative to (1) remaining mute, (2) freely expressing anything except military information that could aid the enemy or disloyal or treasonable remarks, or (3) saying anything he wishes and having his government make it generally known that no statement of its prisoners of war under enemy control can be relied upon because it is made under stress.

At the end of the Korean War, American public opinion was shocked to learn that a few of our prisoners seemed to have capitulated to the Communist ideology. After a tradition of Nathan Hales who wished for more than one life to give for their country and of a Navy which never has had a mutiny, we were ashamed at such developments. The services could not agree among themselves how to handle such problems. Major General William P. Dean admitted that he had considered suicide while in prison, and that he had written and signed two documents which could be used by the enemy for propaganda purposes. He said he would rather die than be captured by the North Koreans again—yet he received from the President the Congressional Medal of Honor. Colonel Schwable of the Marines, on the other hand, was court martialed for signing a single confession.

After all this came the current presidential executive order directing each prisoner to "counter and withstand all enemy efforts against him." The American military man was expected to have the fortitude and will power to withstand any subversive attempt. How does this jibe with trends in psychopharmacology?

Olds [31] has shown that rats will avidly and repeatedly, over many minutes or hours, press a bar which injects into their brains minute amounts of various neurally active substances. They do this in preference to eating or drinking or sexual gratification, so the satisfaction derived must be great. We do not know certainly that human beings would react the same way animals do. But suppose they would. What would a captured American GI do under similar circumstances?

Numbers of pharmaceutical firms are continually searching for new drugs to add to our present varied armamentarium of compounds, each with a different effect, each capable of selectively and often reversably stimulating or knocking out a special subsystem. The methods of torturing, of eliciting information, of producing predictable behavior, are becoming ever more subtle and effective. Probably this trend will continue.

Our present code of conduct for the military forces is not prepared for potential technical developments in brainwashing, any more than is the general concept of the average citizen. Fortunately, we are still, and may well remain for years, in the TNT age of brainwashing rather than a future possible atomic age.

An officer would not order a soldier to remain at attention under ether anesthesia. It is the simplest common sense that, no matter how patriotic he may be, he cannot do so. The situation may not be much different with future chemical methods of brainwashing. The magnitude of their influence on actions may be so great as to dwarf any individual difference, any moderate superiority of resistance which a dedicated, disciplined soldier might have over one who goes AWOL. For such a day, if it should come, our present regulations do not effectively protect the information in a prisoner's brain either from being destroyed by drugs or from being undammed and escaping from him.

It is intriguing to note that psychoactive drugs might even in some future day be used as counterweapons against a physiologic technique of control by others. For instance, Kristofferson and Cormack [32] have found, in support of evidence obtained by a number of other investigators, that meprobamate can raise the baseline of the lie detector's galvanic skin response, and that therefore emotional responses are harder to detect by this method. Those were laboratory studies, but they seem perhaps to confirm the judgment of some New England villagers. In December, 1957, a Newbury, Vermont, farmer [33] who was thoroughly despised by his neighbors for his general "orneriness" beat his hired man. A few days later the farmer disappeared, and after weeks his corpse was found trussed with a rope, floating in the Connecticut River. Many assumed that this was a "white lynching," his last act of brutality toward his hired man having led his neighbors to gang together to kill him. Investigators moved into the area, administering lie-detector tests to many in the neighborhood. Then, according to radio reports, they discovered that some of those questioned had prepared themselves by taking a tranquilizer in order to defeat the lie detector. A relatively recent discovery of a physiological control on the mind was conceivably being neutralized by an even newer invention, the drug that can even manipulate a man's galvanic skin responses.

The following ethical principal can be applied to all forms of control of the mind, whether it be by drugs, by subliminal perception, by electrodes, by the hidden persuaders of advertising, or by old-time religion: Every adult person concerned, while clothed and in his right mind, should be informed and voluntarily give his consent before having these forces applied to him. His ultimate sanctuary of freedom should be his right to decide whether or not to submit to them. No one should be compelled to do so except by the ordinary democratic processes of the state. Even the state should be hesitant in using such techniques, because the legislation of too many such influences on the mind constitutes the ultimate totalitarianism.

Yet, paradoxically because of the nimbus of mystery which surrounds these control techniques, there has often been a too gingerly shunning of them. In the real world attempts to convince people by conversation and other information flows short of physical duress are nothing new. The nub of the current problem is that these techniques are becoming much more competent and precise, on the one hand, and the difference between pure information flow and physical stress by drugs or electricity is becoming blurred. The banning of subliminal stimulation by all the television networks, both in the United States and in England, is an example of too hasty disavowal. To begin with, subliminal stimulation probably would not work well on television, but *with prior warning* to the viewer, what harm could it do? Perhaps it is almost a contradiction in terms to use it with advance notice, and no one would ever want to. But in relation to efforts to control the mind, there is nothing more inherently wrong than the principle behind the use of woman's ageless form of chemical influence, perfume—which every woman knows is more effective if it is subliminal.

Can drugs affect the mind and mold behavior? The answer is an obvious, but qualified, yes. Marco Polo knew that opium could influence actions when he learned that Alo-eddin, the Old Man of the Mountain [34] in the land of Alaù about 1260, seduced his young warriors into a paradise on earth with it. No one can deny that drugs may dramatically influence our actions. As yet the effects are only rough, relatively unharnessed, and limited, but the last decade has seen a more accelerated surge forward in this than any previous period. We have many more anesthetics now than we did in the time of William Morton and Crawford Long, codiscoverers of the anesthetic use of ether in the 1840s. We have many more soporifics than did the Aristocat of the Breakfast Table. We have purified the caffeine and synthesized the dextroamphetamine which can keep you awake and alert. We have drugs that diminish neurotic symptoms and drugs that counteract psychotic symptoms, as well as those that temporarily cause them. We are beginning effectively to combat even the deepest depressions.

After much more such advance drugs could conceivably enslave man, but they can also increase his freedom. Choice is the essence of freedom. A man who lived in a pioneer village in the last century had few constraints, but he did not have many alternatives among which to choose. Today a person who lives in Washington or San Francisco or Chicago or Boston may select among symphony, ballet, lectures, motion pictures, television, or simply staying home in bed every night of the week. Freedom expands as feasible alternatives of choice increase.

Drug research *could* lead to a new tyranny beyond Jefferson's imagination, to control of man's acts by chemical strings. But it need not make him a puppet. Indeed, as a road to release from illness and as a means someday perhaps to extend his abilities, it may increase the number of his alternatives of choice, and so his individuality and freedom.

References

1. Jefferson, Thomas, *Letter to Dr. Benjamin Rush,* Sept. 23, 1800.
2. Chase, Stuart, *Tyranny of Words,* New York, Harcourt, Brace, Inc., 1959.
3. Whorf, B. L., in John B. Carroll (ed), *Language, Thought and Reality: Selected Writings,* New York, John Wiley & Sons, Inc., 1956.
4. Whitehead, A. N., *Adventures of Ideas,* New York, The Macmillan Company, 1933.
5. Miller, J. G., Toward a General Theory for the Behavioral Sciences, *Amer. Psychologist,* 1955, 10:513–531.
6. Jung, C. G., *The Development of Personality,* New York, Pantheon Books, Inc., 1954, pp. 116–117.
7. Miller, J. G., Information Input Overload and Psychopathology, *Amer. J. Psychiat.,* 1959, 116:695–704.
8. DeQuincey, T., *Confessions of an English Opium Eater,* London, Oxford University Press, 1955, p. 212.
9. Marquis, D. G., Kelly, E. L., Miller, J. G., Gerard, R. W., and Rapoport, A., Experimental Studies of Behavioral Effects of Meprobamate on Normal Subjects, *Ann. N.Y. Acad. Sci.,* 1957, 67:701–712.

10. Housman, A. E., *A Shropshire Lad,* New York, Henry Holt and Company, Inc., 1922, p. 94.
11. Himwich, H. E., Biochemical and Neurophysiological Action of Psychoative Drugs, in L. Uhr and J. G. Miller (eds.), *Drugs and Behavior,* New York, John Wiley & Sons, Inc., 1960, pp. 46-47.
12. Uhr, L., Objectively Measured Behavioral Effects of Psychoactive Drugs, in L. Uhr and J. G. Miller (eds), *Drugs and Behavior,* New York, John Wiley & Sons, Inc., 1960, pp. 624–625.
13. Kornetsky, C., and Humphries, O., Relationship between Effects of a Number of Centrally Acting Drugs in Man, *Arch. Neurol. Psychiat.,* 1957, 77:325–327.
14. Kornetsky, C., and Humphries, O., Psychological Effects of Centrally Acting Drugs in Man: Effects of Chlorpromazine and Secobarbital on Visual and Motor Behavior, *J. Ment. Sci.,* 1958, 104:1093–1099.
15. Kelly, E. L., Miller, J. G., Marquis, D. G., Gerard, R. W., and Uhr, L., Personality Differences and Continued Meprobamate and Procloperazine Administration, *Arch. Neurol. Psychiat.,* 1958, 80:247–252.
16. Klerman, G. L., DiMascio, A., Rinkel, M. and Greenblatt, M., The Influence of Personality Factors on the Effects of Phrenotropic Agents: An Experimental Procedure to Integrate Physiologic and Psychologic Action, paper read at meeting of Soc. Biolog. Psychiat., San Francisco, 1958.
17. Ellsworth, R. B., and Clark, L. D., Prediction of the Response of Chronic Schizophrenics to Drug Therapy: A Preliminary Report on the Relationship between Palmar Sweat and the Behavioral Effects of Tranquilizing Drugs, *J. Clin. Psychol.,* 1957, 13: 59–61.
18. Heller, G. C., Walton, D., and Black, D. A., Meprobamate in the Treatment of Tension States, *J. Ment. Sci.,* 1957, 103:581–588.
19. Schneider, R. A., The Influence of Predrug Level of Functioning on the Effects of Sedatives, Tranquilizers, and Stimulants on Central Autonomic Function and Reaction Time, in L. Uhr and J. G. Miller, (eds.), *Drugs and Behavior,* New York, John Wiley & Sons, Inc., 1960, pp. 420–426.
20. Shagass, C., and Kerenyi, A. B., Neurophysiologic Studies of Personality, *J. Ment. Dis.,* 1958, 126:141–147.
21. Kubie, L. S., A Psychoanalytic Approach to the Pharmacology of Psychological Processes, in L. Uhr, and J. G. Miller (eds.), *Drugs and Behavior,* New York, John Wiley & Sons, Inc., 1960, p. 214.
22. Gottschalk, L. A., Kapp, F. T., Ross, W. D., Kaplan, S. M., Silver,

H., Macleod, J. A., Kahn, J. B., Jr., Van Maanen, E. F., and Acheson, G. H., Explorations in Testing Drugs Affecting Physical and Mental Activity, *J. Amer. Med. Ass.*, 1956, 161:1054–1058.

23. Whitman, R. M., Pierce, C. M., and Maas, J., Drugs and Dreams, in L. Uhr and J. G. Miller (eds.), *Drugs and Behavior,* New York, John Wiley & Sons, Inc., pp. 591–595.
24. Beecher, H. K., The Powerful Placebo, *J. Amer. Med. Ass.*, 1955, 159: 1602–1606.
25. Kurland, A. A., The Drug Placebo: Its Psychodynamic and Conditional Reflex Reaction, *Behav. Sci.*, 1957, 2:101–110.
26. Lasagna, L., von Felsinger, J. N., and Beecher, H. K., Drug-induced Mood Changes in Man, *J. Amer. Med. Ass.*, 1955, 157:1113–1119.
27. Trouton, D. S., Placebos and Their Psychological Effects, *J. Ment. Sci.*, 1957, 103:344–354.
28. Fischer, H. K., and Dlin, B. M., The Dynamics of Placebo Therapy: A Clinical Study, *Amer. J. Med. Sci.*, 1956, 232:504–512.
29. Gottschalk, L. A., The Use of Drugs in Information-seeking Interviews, in L. Uhr and J. G. Miller (eds.), *Drugs and Behavior,* New York John Wiley & Sons, Inc., pp. 515–518.
30. *The New York Times*, Aug. 18, 1955.
31. Olds, J., Self-injection in the Rat Brain, in P. B. Bradley, P. Deniker, and C. Radouco-Thomas (eds.), *Neuro-psychopharmacology: Proceedings of the First International Congress of Neuro-pharmacology in Rome, 1958,* Amsterdam, Elsevier Publishing Company, 1959, pp. 20–32.
32. Kristofferson, A. B., and Cormack, R. H., Meprobamate and Electrical Conductivity of the Skin, mimeographed paper, 1959.
33. *Life* Magazine, Nov. 2, 1959, 47:31–34.
34. Polo, M., *The Travels of Marco Polo the Venetian* (trans. by W. Marsden), Garden City, N.Y., Doubleday and Company, Inc., 1948, pp. 48–51.

Jonathan O. Cole

DRUGS AND CONTROL OF THE MIND

Since I have been asked to give a paper on the relationship of psychopharmacology to human behavior in a conference which focuses its attention on the control of the mind, I must conclude that those organizing this conference believed explicitly, or implicitly, that drugs could be used to control the mind. An alternative hypothesis, of course, would be that the group organizing this meeting believed that drugs could be used to enhance the freedom of the mind. I will examine the evidence relating to both hypotheses.

I also believe I detect in this conference an implicit assumption that control of the mind is bad and freedom of the mind is good. B. F. Skinner, the father of the operant approach to the study of behavior, has seriously questioned this assumption [7], believing that behavior can be controlled effectively, or is about to be able to be controlled effectively, and that it is the duty of our society to actively attempt to control human behavior in such a way as to achieve effects which we consider desirable before some other group becomes more proficient at controlling behavior and directing it into paths which we consider undesirable. He assumes, of course, that human behavior can be controlled in an effective and precise manner, and that someone, somewhere, in this country or in the Western world, is capable of making value judgments concerning the kinds of behavior which are good and should be positively elicited and the kinds of behavior which are bad and should be suppressed. This, of course, complicates the whole matter. We must consider whether drugs can be used to facilitate the control of "good" behavior and the abolishment of "bad" behavior, as well as the possibility that drugs may be used by enemies of our society to suppress desirable behavior and to elicit undesirable behavior. Can drugs do any of these things?

To answer this complex set of questions it would be necessary to define what kinds of behavior are bad and what kinds are good. This I feel uncomfortable doing, except in clinical situations, and will therefore retreat to the simpler question concerning the possibility of using drugs to control any behavior, noting in passing the effects of drugs on extremes of behavior which many people would unanimously consider to be clearly undesirable or clearly desirable. Skinner, of course, prefers to restrict himself to overt behavior. For the purpose of this conference, however, one must also consider less readily observable subjective phenomena, such as mood, creativity, imagination, etc.

Assuming one wished either to control or to free the mind, or to influence behavior, what classes of drugs are available for this purpose? Existing psychopharmacological agents fall rather nicely into five groups. First, one has the major tranquilizers [3], which include chlorpromazine and a variety of other phenothiazine derivatives, reserpine and a few related Rauwolfia alkaloids, and a few newer compounds such as haloperidol, which are chemically unrelated to the other two groups but appear to share certain properties with them. These drugs are relatively effective in the control of the symptoms of schizophrenia and other psychotic states.

The second group consists of the minor tranquilizers and sedatives [3], a group including such compounds as meprobamate (Equanil, Miltown) and methaminodiazepoxide (Librium), which may be effective in relieving neurotic anxiety at dosage levels that do not produce undesirable degrees of sedation, and sedatives such as the barbiturates and the bromides, whose clinically undesirable sedative properties may be more prominent than their anxiety-relieving properties.

The third discernible group is that of the stimulant drugs, including amphetamine [4]. These drugs have a euphoriant action in some individuals. They also increase wakefulness, decrease fatigue-induced performance decrement under some conditions, and in addition sometimes causing jitteryness, tachycardia, and other relatively undesirable signs of central nervous system stimulation.

The fourth group is that of the antidepressive drugs [4], including iproniazid (Marsilid) and other monoamine oxidase inhibitors and imipramine (Tofranil). These drugs have some demonstrated effectiveness in the relief of depressive syndromes. In contrast to the stimulants, they are slow to act, requiring approximately 2 weeks for desirable clinical effects to manifest themselves. The monoamine oxidase inhibitors appear to share with the stimulants some euphoriant effect in some individuals and some capacity to speed reaction time, increase verbal productivity, and otherwise stimulate the organism. Imipramine does not seem to possess these particular properties.

The fifth group is that of the psychotomimetic drugs, including older compounds such as mescaline and LSD-25 and newer and more diverse compounds such as Sernyl and Ditran and psilocybin.

It may be that other classes or types of drugs with different, more discrete, more specific, or more varied effects will be found in the near future. Since all existing new types of drugs have been identified as having unique properties in man only on the basis of their observed effects in human subjects, rather than as a result of well-planned extrapolations from their effect in animals to their effects in man, it is extremely difficult to predict what kinds of drugs the future will bring. I suggest with some reluctance that it is unlikely, at present, that any chemical compounds with specific identifiable and predictable effects in human subjects can be developed on the basis of animal experimentation alone. In short, even if I felt that I could identify in man the psychological or behavioral function which I or anyone else wished to control, or for that matter to free, I would not be willing to predict that a rational and energetic attempt to create a drug which would have these specific effects would be particularly likely to be fruitful. This is not to say that investigation in man of compounds with new and different behavioral or neuropharmacological effects in animals may not lead to the discovery of drugs with new and surprising clinical properties, but I doubt that at this stage in our knowledge the discovery of such compounds can be systematically engineered. It is possible, of course, that having identified a drug with some specific desirable properties in animals one can by examining related compounds find one which possesses a particular property in greater degree while lacking some other undesirable or confounding properties. However, given the present state of drug development, it seems more appropriate to concern oneself with the effects of drugs we now have than to speculate further about the possible effects of possible drugs which might conceivably be developed to control specific mental functions or behaviors.

The physician, particularly the psychiatrist, is currently using the first four of the above five groups of drugs for the control of the mind. Most of the available evidence concerning the ability of drugs to control the mind or to control behavior comes from exactly this clinical use. The physician usually does not worry too much about the social goodness or badness of controlling behavior, since many patients come to him asking that their behavior, feelings, or thoughts be controlled. Other patients, of course, are brought to him by relatives or by society because their behavior is such that others feel it needs control. The need for such control is, in fact, not uncommonly legally certified by a court, and the patient is committed to a hospital for treatment until such time as the aberrant behavior has been brought under control. Physicians now have an extensive experience in using these drugs to control behavior, and I think most physicians would agree that the reliability with which existing drugs control specific behaviors leaves much to be desired.

Overwhelming doses of a barbiturate or an anesthetic will, of course, put anybody to sleep, and adequate doses of a drug like Metrazol will produce convulsions in anyone. Even with such clear-cut endpoints, there is considerable individual variability in the doses required to produce these profound effects.

Moreover, our clinically most effective drugs, the phenothiazines and the antidepressives, appear to produce quite different effects in psychiatrically ill individuals from those they produce in normal subjects. Thus, a dose of chlorpromazine which renders a disturbed schizophrenic relatively calm and reduces the prominence of his delusions and hallucinations and improves the clarity of his thinking processes would leave a normal individual fatigued, lethargic, numb, and miserable. The evidence concerning the effects of the more potent antidepressives in normal subjects is very scanty, but again it seems likely that their effects are much less dramatic and much less desirable than they are in seriously depressed individuals.

The phenothiazines and Rauwolfia alkaloids could, of course, be used for the control of behavior in normal subjects by giving doses large enough to produce, in effect, a chemical straight jacket in which the individual had his muscles so stiffened by the Parkinsonianlike effects of the drugs and his energies so reduced by their anergic properties as to render him ineffective for most purposes. But I would judge that the use of drugs to induce the temporary states of physical incapacity is of less interest to this group than their use in producing less dramatic and more socially meaningful alterations in thinking and behavior.

The milder tranquilizers and sedatives can cause, in some individuals, a decrease in anxiety when anxiety is present to a discernible degree, and the amphetamines may prevent the occurrence of a fatigue-induced decrement in performance at monotonous tasks such as airplane flying or radar-screen watching, in addition to producing mild euphoria and some increase in talkativeness in some subjects. The sedatives and mild tranquilizers are likely to produce temporary decrements in psychomotor performance, and some evidence has recently been presented by Beecher [2] to the effect that a barbiturate in athletes caused an impairment of athletic performance while causing the subjects to judge themselves to be doing much better than they usually did. Although it is suspected that the stimulants may also cause some alteration in judgment, this has not been clearly demonstrated.

All of the psychotomimetic agents can effectively impair behavior, if only through their autonomic side effects. Sernyl [6] can produce a complete anesthesia in adequate dosage, while Ditran [5] seems to be the one most capable of producing a severe and intense delirium with marked disorganization of thought, auditory and visual hallucinations, and complete loss of contact with reality.

The trouble with all existing psychopharmacologic agents as tools to be used in the control of the mind is that, even from the standpoint of the practicing psychiatrist, they are not completely satisfactory. Although both the phenothiazines and the antidepressive drugs may produce startling improvements, and even what appear to be complete remissions in some patients, these patients are usually in the minority. There is generally a larger proportion of patients in whom some change in the desired direction is produced, and such patients are usually classified as moderately improved, or slightly improved. There is always a residual group of patients, often in the neighborhood of 20 to 30 per cent who are unchanged or worse. Worse, in this sense, means movement in the opposite direction from that desired. To date, clinicians have been notably unsuccessful in predicting which patients will respond in which ways. For this reason, even if one were only attempting to control the minds of a homogeneous group of psychiatric patients with a drug with which one had had considerable experience, the desired effect would not be produced in all patients, and one would not be able to plan specifically that any particular effect would be produced in a particular patient.

With the milder stimulants and sedatives one runs into great difficulty in predicting their effects on normal subjects or patients. Some patients become more active, stimulated, and euphoric when given sedatives; some normal subjects find the effects of amphetamine unpleasant and undesirable and experience no euphoria whatever. In hyperactive, hyperkinetic children, amphetamine often has a tranquilizing, slowing effect, and I have known adult depressed patients to take Benzedrine to go to sleep at night.

Particularly in normal and neurotic subjects, there is considerable evidence that the individual's expectations, the cues provided by the milieu, and the attitudes of the therapist may significantly alter the effectiveness of the drug. In a pilot study recently made at Denison University in collaboration with the Psychopharmacology Service Center on the response of normal college students to d-amphetamine, on some psychological measures there was a tendency for subjects who believed they were getting d-amphetamine and actually received d-amphetamine to have typical amphetaminelike reactions in both mood and psychomotor performance, while subjects who received Dexedrine and believed they were receiving a barbiturate showed a tendency toward barbituratelike reactions, at least in some aspects of psychological functioning. This study is in the process of being replicated to see whether these preliminary trends will be strengthened. Although further work may show that specific combinations of social influences and pharmacological effects may be very powerful methods for producing specific types of results, I know of no strong evidence that this is in fact the case.

There has been considerable discussion in recent years of the capacity of psychotomimetic agents, particularly LSD-25, mescaline, and psilocybin, to produce what may be described, in the context of this conference, as a "freeing" of the mind. Visual and auditory experiences may be made more vivid, and dramatic flights of fantasy, pleasurable or terrifying, may accompany the administration of these drugs. Artistic productions by persons in drugged states have elicited interest. These altered states of consciousness have also been reported to have been followed by profound and lasting changes in personality functioning and psychiatric symptomatology [1].

Two questions arise: First, do these psychotomimetic drugs "free" the mind in any useful manner during the period of their pharmacological activity? Second, do they have a useful effect in altering psychological functioning after the drug's acute effects have passed?

The first question is hard for me to answer. It is possible that artistic productions, poetry, or story plots conceived or executed under a psychotomimetic agent may, in some individuals, be superior to those produced in a drug-free or predrug state. I doubt this, being dubious that any interference with brain functioning is likely to produce an improvement in performance in a normal subject, but I suggest that the matter is susceptible to scientific test. A series of artistic productions by a series of artists produced predrug, during drug, and postdrug could be judged by other artists who were unaware of the conditions under which each production was executed. If the work produced during the influence of a drug such as LSD-25 were to be judged consistently superior, this would be powerfully convincing evidence indeed.

It should be noted, however, that the setting, including the expectations of the person administering the drug and the person receiving it, play a very powerful role here. There even is what I believe to be an artificial "geographical" effect on the response to the drug LSD-25 [1]. Workers in the East Coast, such as Malitz and Klee, do not appear to obtain from their subjects much in the way of bizarre fantasy material. Occasional subjects may become paranoid, and most experience visual illusions and autonomic side effects, but none of the subjects have reported self-revelations or other dramatic personal experiences. Hartman and Chandler and other workers in the Los Angeles area, on the other hand, seem to be able to induce most subjects to experience cosmic events such as union with the sun or death and rebirth with comparative ease. Other investigators such as Jackson and Savage report similar, though less dramatic, results. Since it seems unlikely that the subjects on the West Coast are organically different from those on the East Coast, it is more reasonable to assume that something in the test situation produces the striking difference in response. Does LSD-25 really increase a subject's suggestability? Is the West Coast phenomenon entirely physician-induced or due to cultural differences in expectations of patients, or do investigators in the East somehow manage to create a situation in which flights of fantasy and dramatic emotional experiences are effectively, and perhaps unconsiously, suppressed?

As possible additional evidence in favor of LSD-25 as a tool for eliciting a response desired by the administrator, one may note Abramson's utilization of it as a method for getting patients to work on their resistances in an approved psychoanalytic manner with an almost complete absence of more exotic or fantastic productions.

I view recent work on LSD-25 and psychotherapy with very mixed feelings. The drug may really be enabling patients to obtain startling new insights into their problems and may be able to cause them to strikingly alter their behavior, but I am at a loss as to how much of this to attribute to a drug-induced "freeing" of the mind and how much to attribute to a therapist-induced mystical experience similar to religious conversion. Either effect conceivably could be therapeutically valuable, but the whole area is now so highly charged with emotion and so lacking in adequately controlled research as to make firm conclusions impossible. I am also concerned with the possibility of prolonged psychotic episodes being precipitated by psychotomimetic agents and the possibility of suicidal attempts or other aberrant behavior occurring during the drugged state.

There remains the unpleasant possibility that psychotomimetic agents or other drugs may make individuals overly responsive to the demands of another person and therefore may be usable as a means of altering loyalties or changing moral attitudes or political beliefs. Certainly these drugs could be used to incapacitate individuals temporarily, but can they be used to establish long-term control over minds? The published scientific literature is not at all informative. Both experimental and clinical reports deal chiefly with volunteer subjects or amenable patients, and I know of no experimental attempts to specifically alter beliefs, attitudes, or perceptions during or after the psychotomimetic drug experience. Chronic schizophrenic subjects certainly appear to be very resistant to reporting any subjective effects of LSD-25, but whether this resistance is secondary to any inner will to avoid responding is impossible to say.

Other drugs, intravenous barbiturates or amphetamine derivatives, can certainly alter verbal behavior, increase talkativeness and emotional expression, and occasionally enable patients to recall repressed experiences or talk about subjects which they had previously consciously avoided mentioning. The extent to which such procedures are useful outside the combat-neurosis type of situation is difficult to assess. The fact that three such otherwise diverse drugs as sodium amytal, desoxyephedrine, and LSD-25 are all used to facilitate psychotherapy by increasing emotional expression and activating unconscious material is, in itself, evidence of the confusion in this area of psychiatric practice.

In summary, I advance the proposition that drugs are not, in and of themselves, useful tools for the control of the mind, nor are they particularly well suited to free the mind if one is primarily concerned with the subjective experiences, attitudes, or beliefs of relatively normal human subjects. Some drugs such as LSD-25 and psilocybin can enable subjects to experience bizarre and perhaps rewarding experiences, but usually only if the subjects are interested in having such experiences or if such experiences are expected by those administering the drug. Barbiturates or stimulants (or alcohol for that matter) may increase emotional displays or promote talkativeness, but again the drugs are probably only facilitating the expression of emotions or thoughts already present in the subject.

Drugs such as the phenothiazine tranquilizers or the antidepressives are often effective in altering psychiatric symptoms in some, but not all, patients presenting appropriate symptoms. These clinical effects, however limited, are the phenomena closest to specific drug effects on behavior and psychological functioning, but these effects are confined to psychiatrically ill individuals and do not have any obvious applications to the control of thought or behavior in normal individuals.

Large enough doses of almost any of these five groups of psychopharmacological agents can disorganize or suppress human behavior by generally incapacitating the subjects receiving them, but there is no real reason to believe that these acute effects would have any long-term effect on the minds of the subjects.

There remains the possibility that some drug or drugs combined with some structured situation, e.g., some type of brainwashing program, might make the latter more effective or might reduce the time or effort required to produce a desired effect.

Although published research even vaguely relevant to this last problem is almost totally lacking, I see no reason to believe any drug would be more effective than social and psychological pressures or physical discomforts in producing changes in an individual.

The great interindividual variability in response to psychopharmacological agents in normal subjects and in patients makes it unlikely that any single drug would be a reliable aid in any planned program of mass thought control, although I accept the possibility that individual attempts at thought control may have something in common with psychotherapy, and skilled practitioners of such a black art may find drugs tailored to the practitioner and the subject of some use.

Furthermore, I consider it unlikely that current methods can be used to develop a new drug with any specific and reliable effect on either the freedom or the control of human mental processes, although I confidentially expect that new types of drugs with different effects on brain functioning and behavior will be uncovered by present drug-development methods.

In short, present psychopharmacological agents, though often chemically useful, have relatively nonspecific and quite variable effects on human behavior. How much of this variability is attributable to existing physical and psychological differences among human beings and how much variability is produced by the setting and by the behavior of the person administering the drugs is impossible to estimate. The difficulties in developing and evaluating drugs for the control of clinical psychiatric states are many; the difficulties in developing and/or evaluating drugs for the control of mental functioning or for the freeing of mental functioning in normal human beings appear to be well-nigh insurmountable.

References

1. Abramson, H. A. (ed.), The Use of LSD in Psychotherapy, *Transactions of a Conference on d-Lysergic Acid Diethylamide (LSD-25), Princeton, N.J., April, 1959,* New York, Josiah Macy, Jr., Foundation, 1960.
2. Beecher, H. K., and Smith, G. M., Amphetamine, Secobarbital, and Athletic Performance. III. Quantitative Effects on Judgment, *J. Amer. Med. Ass.,* 172:1629–1632, 1960.
3. Cole, J. O., Klerman, G. L., and Jones, R. T., Drug Therapy, in E. J. Spiegel (ed.), *Progress in Neurology and Psychiatry,* vol. XV, New York, Grune & Stratton, Inc., 1960, pp. 540-576.
4. Cole, J. O., Jones, R. T., and Klerman, G. L., Drug Therapy, in E. J. Spiegel (ed.), *Progress in Neurology and Psychiatry,* vol. XVI, New York, Grune & Stratton, Inc. 1961.
5. Gershon, S., and Olariu, J., JB 329: A New Psychotomimetic, Its Antagonism by Tetrahydroaminacrin and Its Comparison with LSD, Mescaline and Sernyl, *J. Neuropsychiat,* 1960, 1:283–292.
6. Luby, E. D., Cohen, B. D., Rosenbaum, G., Gottleib, J. S., and Kelley, R., Study of a New Schizophrenomimetic Drug—Sernyl, *A.M.A. Arch. Neurol. Psychiat.,* 1959, 81:363–369.
7. Skinner, B. F., Freedom and the Control of Men, *Amer. Scholar,* 25: 47–65.

HORIZONS OF PSYCHOPHARMACOLOGY

This is an actual transcription of the formal but spontaneous panel discussion of the papers immediately preceding. Only minor editing has been done where continuity and clarity required it. The editors feel that the spontaneity of the actual discussion gives a particular value to the panel in this form.

Moderator: David Krech
Panel Members: Jonathan O. Cole, Seymour S. Kety, James G. Miller

Dr. Krech As I was listening to the people who have been speaking to you, I learned three laws of psychopharmacology, each of which really represents a summary of each speaker. These are my first three laws of psychopharmacology: The first law, which really represents what Dr. Kety had to say, is that there are no generalizations concerning the biochemical control of the complex mind that can now be made. The second law of psychopharmacology, which represents, I think, Dr. Miller's contribution, is that there are many exceptions to the generalizations set down by the first law. The third law of psychopharmacology, which represents Dr. Cole's contribution, is that the first and second laws hold only for extreme cases of pathology, except where they do not hold. I trust that this has aroused my three colleagues, since I summarized their positions inadequately, though truthfully. Now I want to address to them a specific question. This derives from something that Dr. Cole said at the very end, which I think Dr. Kety hinted at and would agree with, and so would, I am sure, Dr. Miller. The problem to which I refer is that our work in this field is in many senses of the word a sort of hysterical reaction. We have been randomly—and sometimes not so randomly—trying every new drug made available. We have not given enough attention to basic research to find out how the nervous system does work and what the role of the various chemical compounds in the brain may be. More than that, the people who have been working in this field have paid very little attention to behavior. It is very interesting that the experimentalists in this area try to be somewhat precise about biochemistry and neurology, but about behavior they make one of two assumptions: they either assume that behavior is so complex and subtle that there is no point in trying to attack it scientifically, or they assume that behavior is so simple that anyone can tell when a man is disturbed or is not disturbed, when a drug has a good or a bad effect, and when it liberates a man's mind or restricts his mind. Of course, I accept neither assumption. This random search of testing drugs on random bits of behavior, which may come to mind on random patients in random hospitals, will, I suspect, get us nowhere. Therefore, my question comes to this: Don't you think that before we begin to invest so much of our substance into psychopharmacology that we had better spend a great deal of time in something I would prefer to call psychobiochemistry—the basic research in the relation between biochemical processes in the nervous system and behavior, taking both of these seriously as serious scientists?

Dr. Cole May I object to that? I think that work on the biochemistry of the brain, the effect of drugs on the brain, and its interrelation with behavior is good, and needed. But I think the gap between the experimental and the clinical application of drugs is still sufficiently large that one cannot let drugs be administered to large numbers of patients for the next 10 years, hoping to come up with good, hard knowledge of what is going on in the brain and eventually to produce a rational psychopharmacology. There are preliminary evidences of some kind of a marriage between the two. I know of some preliminary data on the effects of monoamine oxidase inhibitors on depressed patients which appear to indicate halfway through the study that most patients who become less depressed also have effective inhibition of their monoamine oxidase enzymes in the blood, whereas those who are not improved also do not have effective inhibition of the action of this enzyme. So there are some bridges being built. But I think there is need for careful, descriptive, clinical work, using both description to generate hypotheses, and massive, computerlike techniques to analyze the data. This would enable one, for example, to predict on an empirical basis more accurately which patients would respond to which drugs and which would not, leaving the central nervous system a mess of pottage for the interim until it can be better explained to us by basic scientists.

Dr. Miller I am sure, Dr. Cole, that Dr. Krech did not intend to suggest that we stop treating patients until such time as we understand the biochemistry of behavior. But I would like to disagree with your dissent, because I feel that one of the areas of psychopharmacology which is being inadequately expressed and supported is exactly the one that he was talking about, and that the primary drive should be toward the development of more precise, quantitative, and objective measures of behavior. So I would emphasize the need that this be done in human beings as well as in animals, so that we can begin to get adequate correlations between biochemistry and behavior. I am particularly interested in seeing the mass application of psychology brought into the clinic as rapidly as possible, because I am convinced that there are a series of measures available now with a degree of dependency superior to the clinician's rating or impression in many cases that can be applied in clinical settings but are not being so applied. I view the role of the clinical *cum* experimental psychologist in the clinic as bringing some measure of the fundamental dimensions of behavior as an important —but quite independent—adjunct of the clinical impressions and evaluations. This is one of the most important needs we have at the present time. We should not stop treating the patient in the meantime, but we should get a little more of what I am advocating.

Dr. Kety I would like to disagree with just one word in Dr. Krech's proposition: the word "before." I believe you said that before we invested so much of our substance in study of the over-all clinical effects of these drugs on patients, we should investigate the basic biochemical, neurophysiological, and psychological parameters upon which these effects depended. If you would substitute "along with" for "before" I think I should agree. I object so strenuously to the word "before" because this implies that somehow we know where the answers are going to come from, and since we know that, obviously we should attack that area. As a matter of fact, rational drug therapy, although we hold to the idea so avidly, is much more the exception than the rule in the development of pharmacology. Quinidine was not discovered by a biochemist or a pharmacologist; it was not even discovered by a clinician. It was discovered by a patient; and digitalis was discovered by a midwife. That doesn't mean that we ought to support midwives and patients to the exclusion of biochemists, but we ought not be blind to the possibilities of understanding drug action or at least developing new drugs on the basis of the crudest kind of empiricism. If we had waited until we could develop insulin from an understanding of what it does in the body, we still would not have insulin, because biochemists still don't understand how it lowers the blood sugar and how it improves diabetes. It will take, in the case of the brain, much longer to understand the basic mechanism of these agents. I would agree, however, that even empirical observations can be sharpened up, that they can be made more economical on the basis of carefully controlled experiments—carefully controlled even in terms of the whole man rather than a synapse. I would also agree most heartily with your anxiety about the disproportion of attention which is being given today to the biochemical and physiological aspects, as opposed to the behavioral aspects, of the problem. The biochemists studying the action of the brain of some of these agents are extremely careful in their control of the enzymes, of their substrates, of the dosage, of the concentration of these agents, and then report upon behavior in terms of the crudest and most unsophisticated measures. I think certainly the kind of thing you are doing, Dr. Krech, is being done in many places where students of behavior are working who are as precise as they can be in their field as the biochemists are in theirs.

Dr. Miller I think we are dealing here with a problem we should not moralize about, because biochemistry is rapidly receiving increasing attention. We should not say it should stop; but rather, we should look on it as one of many examples in the history of science of an interest in the development of a field resulting from the availability of instruments which can give facts with precision. Take the field of computers. They involve nothing new mathematically, yet the very existence of those tools, which are simply more rapid, with a larger memory capacity and a few other characteristics than previous computational devices, has resulted in a vast efflorescence of activity around them, none of which is fundamental in the development of science. It is therefore the responsibility of those of us who are particularly interested in the development of rigorous behavioral measurements to get tools and instruments so that the expansion in our activities will occur. When we get those tools and instruments, I don't think there will be the slightest difficulty in getting the necessary support and interest for the work.

Dr. Krech I made a rather extreme statement before for two reasons. First, my personality structure is such that I like to make extreme statements; that is, I think, an accident of genetics. But there is another reason, a very cold, calculated reason, and to tell you simply what I mean I should like to quote a maxim of my mother-in-law. When my mother-in-law wants to tell people that they should at least reduce their tendency to inflict corporal punishment on children, she says in her lecture, "If you will take a firm oath when your first child is born never, never under any circumstances to whip, slap, or pinch your child, you will whip him, slap him, and pinch him just enough." I am applying the same principle in my assertion that it is most important that we first have departments of psychobiochemistry before any other departments of psychopharmacology, and so on. We may then have just enough, because today there are quite a number of departments of pharmacology in the United States; any medical school of consequence has one. There are a number of departments and groups of psychopharmacology. But I know of only one committee in one university which is really concerned with psychobiochemistry, and I am not even sure of that since they are in psychopharmacology. I know of no departments of psychobiochemistry. Therefore, it is most apparent that the first thing to do is to create them. Now let me ask another question. I have been listening to today's and yesterday's discussions as a psychologist, not only as an "acetylcholenologist." I have been struck by one thing. We are supposed to be discussing the control of the mind. Now the word "mind," at least to some people, brings up connotations of thought—what we psychologists used to call cognition. The word "mind" does not necessarily mean only pathology, it does not necessarily mean only anxiety, it does not necessarily mean only frustration and screaming and running through the streets naked; the word "mind" means thinking, believing, creating, and so on, and as I look over most of the work on the effects of drugs on behavior, I am struck with what one might almost call an anti-intellectualism among researchers. They are not interested in the effects of drugs on the mind from the cognitive or intellectual point of view; they are interested in the effect of drugs on the mind in the emotional, mood, or pathological sense. I think this may reflect the concern of these researchers with the ill, because they come from hospitals and from the medical profession. Again, if we had a department of psychobiochemistry, we would not have that state of affairs. But in a sense it also reflects—and here I say "*mea culpa*" again—the attitude that I think has been partially true of American psychology. American psychology has been really anti-intellectual; it has concerned itself more with personality and gross behavior, but relatively little with cognition, thinking, and problem solving. Don't you think that here we have a whole area of the mind which is being neglected?

Dr. Kety I would like to assent very strongly to that statement and try to speculate as to why that anti-intellectualism has occurred. I think that you psychologists or your antecedent psychologists were to a large extent responsible for this. There was a school of psychology, the behavioral school, which was rather doctrinaire in its approach and felt that since the only thing which could be studied scientifically was behavior that nothing existed but behavior, and therefore that the mind, mentalism, protection, and feelings were subjective phenomena not suitable for experimental measurements and which had best not be spoken about. Therefore one hears members of this particular persuasion talking about the most sensitive and subtle aspects of human creativity, but never discussing consciousness, never mentioning the mind—as if it were a dirty word—but talking about it as behavior, which it obviously is not. Actually, the mind means a variety of different things, and Dr. Krech encompassed different things in his definition of the mind. If we think of the mind as the complex computation that goes on, the process of thinking, of making judgments, of evaluating, that is one way of looking at the mind. On the other hand, one can look at the mind as the subjective aspect of these processes, as feeling, as consciousness, and as sensation. I think that a great deal of confusion in the history of philosophy and our thinking today represents an unwillingness to separate these things. The monist can explain the first aspects of mind, namely, computation, judgment, and so forth, on a mechanical basis; and if that is all he means by mind he can be perfectly happy in his monistic philosophy. But if he really recognizes the other aspects of the mind, the subjective, personal quality of consciousness and feeling, then I think he will have to admit that a monistic philosophy can hardly encompass that in a mechanistic interpretation. I want to voice a very strong assent to your feelings about this. I think we can and should talk about the mind and all its subtleties, all the phenomena and epiphenomena, and we should be willing to study the mind and its relations with matter. There is a psychopharmacology, there is an effect of a drug on the mind, and that is not divorced from scientific discourse; it is something which can be studied just as effectively, if perhaps with more difficulty, than the effect of a drug on a synapse.

Dr. Miller Once again I think I agree with you and would like to support your view that not enough has been done in this particular area, either in psychology or, even more important, in the field of psychiatry. The emphasis on pathology in psychiatry has been overwhelming, as it has been in psychology. But I think the reason historically perhaps is the lack of adequate instruments. Introspection does not turn out to be a very good instrument for studying thinking, reasoning, problem solving, and the so-called higher mental processes. I think we are coming a little bit now into the period of 1790, with the revolution and the age of reason coming on. If you can just hold on a few years there will be quite a change, because computer simulation of internal processes of the "mind" is rapidly coming to the fore. There have been various conferences and papers on this, but I have not noticed yet a single simulation of nonrational or affective processes. It is very difficult for the sort of person who plays with computers to deal with nonlogical processes, anyhow. Second, it is difficult to think how you would write a program into a computer that would simulate the theory of revision, for example, or some other notions of affect that we have at the moment. I think it could be, and probably will be, done. But it seems to me likely that, with computers now available, the next area of attention in the processes of the mind will be toward a tremendous emphasis on cognitive processes, not only learning but apperception and the other things that you mentioned. This is where we are likely to be going in the near future.

Dr. Kety Do you really believe that in the foreseeable future there could be a computer simulation of feeling?

Dr. Miller Yes, if you take feeling out of the subjective context of the term.

Dr. Krech A moment ago I defended myself against some comments which took exception to my position. Now I want to defend myself against the comments which agree with my position.

Dr. Miller To protect us from our friends.

Dr. Krech I am delighted that Dr. Kety thinks we should study consciousness. As a matter of fact, I knew that before he said so, because he had an extremely interesting and provocative article in *Science* in December, 1960. So I am glad that he agreed that we ought to pay attention to cognition and thinking and so on, but I do not agree with him that this necessarily commits us to a dualistic philosophy. I think psychologists take Professor Hebb's position, and I would accept the monistic hypothesis as a working hypothesis. Yet I would not feel restrained at all from working with feelings, thoughts, fantasies, creativity, and so on. So please associate Dr. Kety and me in our advocation of more work on thinking by both pharmacologists and psychologists. Please disassociate us in so far as this monistic-dualistic position is concerned.

Now, Dr. Miller, I take a dim view of the computer model as the model of the brain. I think that the best model of the brain we can have is a brain, and we know that a brain is not a computer. We know some things about the biochemistry, anatomy, and electrophysiology of a brain, and we know that those things are different from the things that go on inside a computer. So that when I ask for more work on thinking, feelings, and so forth, I am not asking for more computer studies; I am asking for more careful, clean, dedicated, tough-minded observation of normal people as they think and solve problems. Most of them don't go around being frustrated; they go around solving problems. So again I am delighted to be associated with Dr. Miller on the need for more research on thinking, and I knew he would agree with that, because he and his group have done some most interesting work on the problems of thinking. But I take a dim view of the newest fad in psychology.

Dr. Cole I think one of the other reasons you may not have had so much work on the effect of drugs on thinking and cognition is that the drugs are not very effective in this area. Their most startling apparent effects at least, are on symptomatology, or on sleepiness or alertness, or something of this sort. I may be wrong, but if drugs were more effective in altering decision making or intelligence, somebody would have picked this phenomenon up empirically in their studies.

Dr. Miller Of course, drugs affect these cognitive processes. But, like LSD-25 or enough alcohol, they have a destructive influence on cognitive processes. You can get a beautiful dosage curve on the effects, objectively measured, of alcohol on reasoning processes. But we have known that for a long time. We also know that alcohol impairs the efficiency of the information transmission, causing it to come out with the wrong answers in a very fine, delightful, and systematic way. But there isn't anything particularly new in that. What we have to do is to find some chemical which transmits a message with its molecule. The molecule then becomes incorporated in the RNA material, and when one checks later on the RNA one obtains a message different from what was there originally. We are not very close to that as yet.

From the Floor I would like to ask the panel whether they consider the mystical transcendental experience of psychotomimetic drugs—LSD, for example—a distortion allied to the hallucination or delusion of a sick patient, or whether it is a new intuitive form of knowledge of some kind. Is it a real experience, or is it a distortion of something that was previously present in the mind?

Dr. Kety The question that I shall try to answer is whether we believe that the psychotomimetic drugs induce new concepts or percepts into the brain or mind, or whether they produce merely distortions of previous information. The only answer I can give is that I cannot see a mechanism whereby a small molecule such as LSD or mescaline can introduce new information into the brain, since even from what we know thus far this information is stored in a most complex, systematic, and highly organized manner. Therefore, since one is entranced with that concept, one would have to answer that these drugs can only modify or distort previously acquired information; they cannot create something new.

From the Floor Would you comment on maturation and the ordering of information?

Dr. Kety Certainly the ordering of information is something which we acquire along with the information, and which is also genetically, biologically, and experientially determined. There are generalized and local biochemical and chronological growth factors which may modulate orderly, sequential coding, and which, when disordered, may be responsible for disordered sequential coding. I think also that experiential factors can distort the ordering of these phenomena, so that by one or another mechanism a malcoding may occur.

Dr. Krech To conclude, I have three summaries of our findings. First, we have renounced our anti-intellectualism, and, as research people, we are going to study cognition and the intellectual life of man. Second, we are going forth to establish a number of departments of psychobiochemistry. Third, the study of the role of acetylcholine deserves top priority.

PART THREE

THE MIND AND SOCIETY

Chairman: Glenn T. Seaborg

The first two phases of the symposium dealt primarily with the mind seen from within, with the manner in which the various sciences view the operation of the mind and the problems attending that point of view. In Part Three, the symposium turned from the consideration of mind as process to the discussion of mind as content, to the manner in which human thought is conditioned by and a conditioner of human society. Again, primary emphasis was placed on the possibility of control of human thought and the factors relevant to the establishment of such control. The question is examined historically, psychologically, theologically, and as a determinant of the creative process.

In the panel discussion that follows, attention is given to the possibility of drawing together the broad view of human behavior commonly associated with the humanities and the more narrow perspective of the experimental scientist. Much of the discussion is related to the social and cultural patterns that emerge as societies change from a penurious state in which the prime activity is subsistence-oriented to a state of affluence in which the driving force of human action is no longer survival.

H. Stuart Hughes

THE EXPERIENCE OF RECENT HISTORY

The techniques of thought control and of brainwashing, which seem to distinguish so sharply the experience of recent history from that of the past centuries, are not as novel as they are commonly supposed to be. Pressures of the same kind—if not of the same degree—have always been sustained by human beings, even in societies which regard themselves as nonauthoritarian. Nor are the pressures as thoroughgoing and as irresistible as the popular press would lead us to believe: even in the most extreme situations, some margin of autonomy remains. What has been novel about contemporary techniques for the control of the mind is the universality of their application and a heightening of the effort to wrest from their victims a conscious and heartfelt assent.

A brief look at the major authoritarian regimes of the past century and a half will suggest how this intensification of official pressure has come about. We historians usually date the inauguration of modern authoritarianism with the establishment of Bonaparte's rule in France in 1799. And we do this because the Napoleonic regime offers the first important example of a tight official control *reimposed* on a society which had already experienced intellectual freedom and the beginnings of democracy. Such a regime cannot find the same naïve assent among the people it rules as supports a traditional authority with a claim to age-old legitimacy. The new authority must *manufacture* assent through a mixture of police control and emotional manipulation.

From the vantage point of our experience of authoritarian techniques in the past four decades, Napoleon's methods of rule look amateurish indeed. At the beginning of the nineteenth century, France was still too close to a traditional society—its level of literacy was too low, the lines between its classes too sharp, and its communications system too rudimentary—to permit any large-scale mobilization of popular backing. It apparently never occurred to Napoleon to make a systematic appeal to the inarticulate masses, for whom, in any case, he had little but scorn. Under the Bonapartist system, most French peasant communities (and France was still an overwhelmingly agrarian country) were subjected to the power of the Emperor's government only in the form of tax collection and conscription. These are no more than the customary ways in which a routine-minded central authority makes itself felt in the back country under its nominal control. The novelty in the Napoleonic period lay only in the vast extent of conscription and the consequent uprooting of entire age groups among the population for military service in distant lands.

In the armies of Bonaparte, for the first time in European history, the common people had the sense of "actively participating in the transformation of the world" [1]. Under Napoleon's rule, military service, which had traditionally ranked as a scourge inflicted from on high, became genuinely popular. It widened horizons, it awakened national pride, it provided the chief avenue for upward social mobility. Military glory and suffering, even defeat itself, were the mainstays of the Bonapartist appeal, both during the Emperor's reign and after his fall. In the generation of peace between Waterloo and the advent of Napoleon III, the veterans of the Grand Army remained the opinion leaders among the peasantry: a nose or an ear frozen off in the bitter retreat from Moscow was the surest mark of distinction and the source of greatest pride. Here at the very start of the modern authoritarian experience we are faced with one of its central paradoxes—its ability to make people love what has hurt them most.

Aside from his almost accidental mobilization of enthusiam through military service, Napoleon did little to win the active endorsement of his subjects. His methods—like censorship of the press—were not much different from the police supervision which was usual in traditionalist monarchies; in Bonapartist France its pressure was almost equally sporadic and ineffective. The only Napoleonic attitude which has a really modern ring was the Emperor's hostility to intellectuals: he discouraged speculative thought and tried to channel talent into science and technology instead; his epoch was barren in *belles-lettres* but one of progress in applied science.

The attitude of the intellectuals has been the crucial problem for modern authoritarianism; the rising curve of pressure on them has been the clearest single indicator of refinement in thought-control techniques. In Napoleon's day it was a comparatively simple matter to bring intellectuals to terms; the mere threat of losing official favor was usually enough. The only writer who gave the Emperor real trouble was the redoubtable Madame de Staël, and her influence was restricted to a special literary and ideological circle. It was a sign of the change of times—and with it, a rise in the status and financial independence of intellectuals—that the great Napoleon's nephew, Napoleon III, found it impossible to cow his country's literary men; their supreme arbiter of status, the French Academy, remained a citadel of opposition throughout his reign. Indeed, the eventual conversion of the Second Empire into a quasi-parliamentary monarchy was due to a large extent to the Emperor's discouragement at his inability to win France's intellectual elite to his side.

With Fascist Italy, Nazi Germany, and Soviet Russia, we are in a different world from the comparative mildness and politeness of the two Napoleons. Twentieth-century authoritarianism is sharply distinguished from that of the nineteenth century by the scope of its control and the rigor of its methods. With the new media of mass communication at their disposal, the dictators of our own time have tried to indoctrinate the whole population under their rule—something that even in Napoleon III's time, a century ago, was a technical impossibility. And they have been correspondingly more severe in their treatment of the people to whom modern means of communication has given a dangerous new potential—the professional intellectuals.

We should be quite wrong, however, to view these authoritarian regimes in Europe as absolutely closed societies. Fascism, both in its Italian and in its German form, tolerated all sorts of autonomous centers of authority and competing loyalties—more particularly big business and organized religion. In Italy, Mussolini never even tried to curb the intellectuals completely: he gave a special status of privileged immunity to his country's leading philosopher, Benedetto Croce, and seems to have made no effort to bring into line the most influential of Italy's creative writers, Luigi Pirandello; the universities were full of independent spirits who only occasionally—as in the oath required of professors in 1931—were forced to give lip service to the regime. In Germany, intellectuals had a rougher time, but even here, a man who made only minimum concessions to Nazism or kept quiet on controversial subjects was frequently able to weather the storm. In Soviet Russia there have been no such autonomous centers of loyalty as in the fascist states gave comfort and shelter to dissident intellectuals: the Communist party very early achieved a monopoly of organized sentiment to which even Nazism was unable to attain. Yet in Soviet Russia intellectual control has never been total. The ups and downs, the alternations between rigor and leniency, in the official treatment of such major creative figures as Prokofieff and Eisenstein and Pasternak have suggested uncertainty on the part of the regime itself—a lack of clarity as to just how far it wanted to go in the molding of creative expression.

All these *European* authoritarian systems seem to have been skeptical of the possibility of actually changing people's minds. Certainly they have been suspicious of intellectuals. They have terrorized and persecuted them. They have imprisoned them or driven them into exile or reduced them to the silence of what the Germans call "inner emigration." Sometimes, as in the first years of the Soviet regime, they have temporarily exploited the talents of the established intelligentsia until they had time to train a reliable intelligentsia of their own. But these European dictatorships have seldom consciously tried to *convert* the intellectuals from an old value system to a new.

This, it seems to me, is the great innovation in authoritarian technique in Communist China today. An effort at reconversion—which formerly was restricted to dissidents within the party itself, as in the Moscow purge trials of the 1930s—has now been extended to the whole intellectual class. The great Chinese thought-reform campaign of 1948–1952 was unprecedented in human history in its range and intensity. Just as the goal was unique, so the method employed, the psychological pressures and the drumming up of enthusiasm in specially established "revolutionary universities," were novelties in the experience of authoritarian regimes. In the words of Robert Jay Lifton, whose recently published study is basic to the subject [2]:

> Though reform draws upon psychological skills of both traditional China and Western Communism; it . . . brings out the inquisitional tendencies of both worlds. From each of the two great cultural streams, it stresses what is most illiberal. Inquisitorial dogmatism, skillful human-centered manipulation, and ecstatic enthusiasm combine within it to produce an awesome quality. [The result has been the] most thorough and the most frightening type of mental pressure. As one victim of thought control has complained, his grandmother "could compel me to do things that I was not willing to do, but she could never make me say that they were good things."

Such is what we mean—or probably should mean—when we call some kinds of control over human beings "totalist" or "totalitarian." The absence of this ability to force people to say—and more important, to believe—that evil is good, has been the reason why a minority of us who have studied the subject have refused to apply the adjective "totalitarian" to such societies as Nazi Germany and the Soviet Union, indeed, why we have refrained from using the word at all. In the three decades from about 1920 to 1950, we believe, totalitarianism was an aspiration rather than a practical achievement. It was an "ideal" standard by which to judge the conduct of authoritarian states, rather than a description of actual conditions. Eloquent testimony to the margins of autonomy remaining even in the classic extreme situation of terrorist control can be found in the recollections of concentration-camp survivors, who have recorded the internecine struggles between criminal and political elements among the prisoners themselves, and the loopholes these left for individuals of moral strength and agility to preserve a tiny domain of undisturbed self-expression [3].

With Communist China, we seem to encounter something very different. Chinese thought reform combines "*external force or coercion* with an appeal to *inner enthusiasm through evangelistic exhortation*" on a scale and at a level of intensity far beyond the practice of previous authoritarian regimes. It makes a systematic assault on the inner identity of its victims, alternately bludgeoning and coaxing them into a mental confusion which blurs the lines between truth and falsehood, good and evil, inner self and external pressure, until in the end they realize that the only avenue of salvation is an acceptance of the thought-world of their tormentors. Mao Tse-tung has described the process with graphic simplicity [4]:

> The first method is to give the patients a powerful stimulus, yell at them, "You're sick!" so that the patients will have a fright and break out in an over-all sweat; then, they can be carefully treated.

It is not true, however, that the Chinese Communist treatment of intellectuals is totally unprecedented. Parallels can be found, as I suggested a moment back, in the Moscow purge trials of the 1930s and in the condemnation of Cardinal Mindszenty by the Hungarian Communists a decade later. These parallels may serve to remind us that the same kind of occult and irresistible powers that are now being ascribed to the rulers of China were earlier, although on a smaller scale, attributed to the inquisitions of European Communism.

Whenever one of the great show trials occurred, the press and even certain "experts" regularly speculated on the diabolical means that had been employed to extract confessions from the accused. And these confessions—in the detail of their fabrication and the apparent sincerity with which they were delivered—seemed to demand a sensational explanation. Invariably the rumor began to spread of a mysterious new drug that had paralyzed the individual's critical faculties. None of these assertions has ever been proved. The evidence is overwhelming that European Communists have extracted confessions by a simple alternation of terror and coaxing, and that pharmacology has played no part in them.

What induced Zinoviev and Bukharin and Mindszenty and all the others to "confess" seems to have been a combination of the threat of torture, a hope of saving their lives if they proved cooperative, and a longing to bring to an end an overpowering sense of personal loneliness by agreeing to what was demanded of them. The same is apparently true of the victims of Chinese thought reform. As Dr. Lifton's researchers have proved, the Chinese manipulators of human souls possess no occult powers. They have added nothing to the already existing armory of thought-control techniques, nor have they borrowed much from previous practice and theory. They have simply developed their methods pragmatically over a generation of trial and error. Coming from a people which has traditionally made a cult of carefully ordered human relationships, they have worked out a peculiarly effective succession of the conventional appeals and pressures available to anyone who is prepared to stop at nothing in his manipulation of his fellow men.

In brief, besides a certain amount of violence or threat of violence, the Chinese Communists have systematically exploited the free-floating guilt which is so prominent a feature in the psychological make-up of most intellectuals. They have gone to work on the implacably punitive element within the individual conscience. A denial of love—a threatened expulsion from a consensus of shared values—these are the central features of a process which seems mysterious but is actually quite simple. When parents resort to it in dealing with their children, we call it "emotional blackmail." In this process, confession occupies the crucial place. For those of us—most of us—who carry around a massive burden of guilt, the yearning for confession is bound to be intense. It is not so much the substance of what is confessed, but the purgation of the soul itself which counts. The trick is, then, to seize hold of the free-floating guilt and to direct it into channels of the inquisitor's choosing. And the way to do so is by first intensifying the sense of guilt until any way of escape seems preferable to continued emotional suffering, and then shifting over to a technique of mildness by pointing out where the path of "forgiveness" lies.

Two further parallels, one drawn from the European past and the other from our own very recent history, will suggest, I think, the universality of such emotional pressures.

The first derives from the experience of the Inquisition in the period from the thirteenth to the seventeenth centuries. In the traditionalist society of Medieval Europe, the problem of thought control was simpler than it is in a contemporary authoritarian state. It was as though the whole articulate population belonged to the party that incarnated the dominant ideology—a situation at which Nazi Germany or Soviet Russia never aimed and which Communist China has only begun to approach. In Medieval society, there were no conflicting ideologies; the only competition to Catholic Christianity came from a lingering animistic faith among the peasantry and from the satanic excesses of the literary underworld, which, in any case, was convinced of its own damnation. Thus thought reform went on *inside* the confines of a Christian culture: it was directed more especially at those within the fold who had lapsed into heresy.

The great ideological trials of these centuries—from the condemnation of the Knights Templar at the beginning of the period to that of Galileo at its end—had certain common features that strike us as modern indeed. There was the familiar alternation between violence (or threat of violence) and the promise of salvation (or love). There was the court's insistence that outward conformity was not enough; the inner assent of the victim was required. The final act of reconciliation symbolized a complete loss of identity by the sufferer himself—the whole-hearted delivery of his body and soul into the hands of his tormentors. George Orwell eptomized the process in the last lines of his *Nineteen Eighty-Four*: "He *loved* Big Brother."

When we shift from the closed society of late Medieval Europe to consider the open society of our country today, the parallel may originally seem far-fetched. Obviously the United States has no single religion or single political party that dominates its culture. But we have something that in time of stress functions in comparable fashion—the massive middle-class consensus which we sometimes call bipartisanship and sometimes "the American way." The most recent time of stress was the period from 1950 to 1954, when Senator McCarthy was riding high, and a host of precursors and imitators were reinforcing his authority. During this period ideological "heresy" was temporarily stamped out in the United States. That is, the free public discussion of truly burning and probing issues very nearly came to an end.

From the standpoint of what we are discussing here, the most interesting thing about the McCarthy era of American history was the comparative success that thought control achieved without resort to any kind of violence. McCarthy and his emulators did not have the authority of the courts or the police behind them, except to a very limited extent. For the most part, they were self-appointed inquisitors, arrogating to themselves an informal power whose legal basis was often extremely shaky. They could browbeat witnesses and terrorize them with threats that seemed worse for their very vagueness, but obviously they could not subject them to physical torture or the fear of death. Yet they were able to drive men to despair, to suicide, or to the comfort of the psychiatric couch. And even those whom they did not directly threaten they usually succeeded in reducing to silence.

The conclusion seems inescapable. Physical violence is a great help in thought control, but it is not essential to it. Reflection on the McCarthy era suggests that the widespread conformity of the early 1950s derived far more from emotional and psychological pressures than it did even from such a realistic fear as that of losing one's job. A loss of love, an expulsion from the national consensus—in short, social ostracism—these were the threats that really hit home in the inquisitorial phase of our own recent history—these, and the systematic exploitation of free-floating guilt that gave such weapons their cutting edge. If they searched their memories hard enough, most American intellectuals of originality and imagination who had lived through the 1930s and 1940s could find some ideological sin to be ashamed of—and this was enough for McCarthy and his fellows to work on.

There would be little point in recalling the political squalor of our immediate past were not some positive understanding to be derived from it. America, after all, *did* survive McCarthy. In terms of free, spontaneous discussion we have not yet returned to the level of the 1930s, but we are on our way to it. If, as I have argued, the prime engines of thought control are emotional rather than physical pressures, then there is hope for the autonomy of the human mind, not only in our country, where physical violence is very nearly absent, but even in the authoritarian states where it is an ever-present reality.

Let us look once more at the most extreme case of thought control known to recent history—Communist China. Dr. Lifton's data clearly suggest that the success of Chinese intellectual reform techniques has not in the end been as complete as it originally seemed to be. Among Chinese as well as Westerners who have been subjected to the "full treatment," whether in prison or in a revolutionary university, backsliding and defection have been frequent. It is far from true that the assent which once seemed so heartfelt has always stuck. When in 1956, following Mao's slogan, "Let the hundred flowers bloom, let the hundred schools of thought contend," the Chinese Communists experimented with a relaxation of ideological supervision, the result evidently shocked them profoundly. The sudden lifting of controls unleashed a torrent of criticism: all the doubts and resentments that had been kept just under the surface during the period of thought reform's apparent success came tumbling out, and the lid had to be clamped on again [5].

Lifton's work also suggests that the victims of the reform process, even those who were successfully "graduated" from prison or revolutionary university, were often able to hold back from manipulation and destruction some aspect of their thought that was particularly precious to them. Catholic priests, for example, succeeded in protecting their faith. Comparable examples from other countries and other ages spring to mind. We may think of Galileo muttering, *"Eppure si muove"*—"It still *does* move"—just after he had been forced to deny his new cosmology, or in the case of the Moscow purge trials, Bukharin winning his fight to keep a tiny corner of his revolutionary's honor intact [6]. Such examples remind us that even the worst rigors of contemporary thought reform fall within the range of man's experience in the past, and that if the tricks of the inquisitors are many and devious, so are the shifts and evasions to which the human mind can resort in its stubborn struggle for freedom [7].

So I suggest that a study of control of the mind needs to be complemented by an investigation of how the autonomy of the mind can and does survive. We need to know more about breaking points and points of desperate holding on. We need to study such episodes of dogged opposition to tyranny as the resistance movements of the Second World War. We should find out more about the ferment of new ideas that is currently emerging among the young people of Eastern Europe and even of the Soviet Union itself. The result, I think, would be to give us a new faith in the indestructibility of the human mind locked in a deadly struggle with the oppressors who, in different guises and under varying ideological labels, have pursued it unrelentingly through the ages.

References

1. Moraze, C., *La France Bourgeoise,* Paris, Armand Colin, 1946, p. 97.
2. Lifton, R. J., *Thought Reform and the Psychology of Totalism: A Study of "Brainwashing" in China,* New York, W. W. Norton & Company, Inc., 1961, pp. 298, 398.
3. See for example, Eugen Kogon, *The Theory and Practice of Hell,* New York, Farrar, Strauss & Co., 1950.

4. Lifton, *op. cit.*, pp. 13, 66, 380–381.
5. *Ibid.*, pp. 411–414.
6. Merleau-Ponty, M., *Humanisme et Terreur: Essai sur le Probleme Communiste,* Paris, Gaillimard, 1947, pp. 71-75.
7. See for example, David Riesman's speculative essay, Some Observations on the Limits of Totalitarian Power, *The Antioch Review,* Summer, 1952, pp. 155–168.

C. A. Mace

HUMAN MOTIVATION IN AN AFFLUENT SOCIETY

It would seem that sciences, like men, are apt to turn their coldest shoulder to their friendliest neighbors and to cultivate instead those who are least disposed to cultivate them; thus psychologists seek the society of physiologists, physiologists turn to biochemists, the chemists cultivate the physicists, and the physicists associate with mathematicians. There are very good reasons why workers in one discipline should exchange viewpoints with those in another, and there is no doubt that the major advances in psychology have occurred since the discipline was concerned to be a biological science looking to physiology, and indeed to physics and mathematics, for models and explanatory principles.

A case exists, however, for psychologists to take a look back over their cold shoulders to glimpse what is going on in the other sciences concerned with man, especially with man in advanced civilized communities. In sociology and economics, ideas are thrown up from time to time which can supplement and correct ideas based on the study of primitive societies and subhuman species. There are, for example, two ideas in recent and contemporary economic theory which may turn out to have important implications for psychology. A few years ago the economist Rostow described, in a happy aeronautical metaphor, the "take-off," that is, the transition of a country from a static preindustrial state to a growing industrial condition. More recently, Galbraith has excited the intellectual world by his analysis of the transition from the penurious to the "affluent" society. Both concepts can be given a psychological connotation. There is, indeed, a distinctive psychological "take-off" at a point in human evolution, and the distinction between penury and affluence is as much psychological as it is economic.

Affluence is, of course, a relative term. Absolute penury might be defined by the psychologist as a state in which 100 per cent of a man's waking life and 100 per cent of his energy are spent in effortful activity to secure the basic essentials needed to survive. Absolute affluence, on the other hand, may be defined as the state in which a man does not need to spend a moment of his life in such subsistence-level activities. Degrees of affluence or penury could be defined in terms of the percentage of this "energy spent in work," where "work" is, in turn, defined in terms of activities that men do not want to perform purely for their own sake but are compelled by necessity to do in order to live. For many centuries, and in many societies, there have been many men enjoying almost complete affluence. The distinctive feature of the affluence with which Galbraith is concerned is the increase of relative affluence in the lives of so many people in modern industrialized civilization.

The take-off from earth-bound penury to airborne affluence is also relative. In a condition of extreme penury all effort is directed toward making ends meet. After the take-off occurs, and ends are made to meet, there is slack to be taken up—longer and shorter periods of bumping along the runway. However, the point is that the transition can, as a psychological phenomenon, be as dramatic as is the biological phenomenon of metamorphosis; and an understanding of this dramatic transition is essential to an understanding of human motivation and incentives in the affluent society. What makes the transition dramatic is that this take-off is not only a release from anchorage to *biological* needs, it is the beginning of discovery of the ways of meeting distinctively psychological needs. The transition from penury to affluence may perhaps be interpreted in terms of a transition from a state of nature to a state of grace, "grace" being defined today as "gracious living." The state of grace implies, of course, in terms of contemporary conditions, good plumbing, washing machines, and air-conditioned apartments. But it means more than that: it means good food and good wine enjoyed in the company of good friends in an interior that is well designed; it means good hunting, good fun of all kinds; it means, in a phrase, what philosophers have for centuries described as "the good life."

Much work still remains to be done by psychologists, sociologists, anthropologists, and historians in describing and explaining the many and varied conceptions of "the good life" at different times and in different places. The heart of the matter is the explanation of the psychological take-off, that is, the transition from barbarism to civilization. The minor fact that the transition may be gradual should not obscure the major fact that this transition is not only the most dramatic but also the most important transition in human history.

Its dramatic nature has been enshrined in a passage in Hobbes's *Leviathan* (1651):

> . . . every man looketh that his companion should value him, at the same rate he sets upon himselfe: And upon all signes of contempt, or undervaluing, naturally endeavours, as far as he dars (which amongst them that have no common power to keep them in quiet, is far enough to make them destroy each other), to extort a greater value from his contemners, by dommage; and from others, by the example.
>
> So that in the nature of man, we find three principall causes of quarrell. First, Competition; Secondly, Diffidence; Thirdly, Glory.
>
> The first, maketh man invade for Gain; the second, for Safety; and the third, for Reputation. The first use Violence, to make themselves Masters of other mens persons, wives, children, and cattell; the second, to defend them; the third, for trifles, as a word, a smile, a different opinion, and any other signes of undervalue, either direct in their Persons, or by reflexion in their Kindred, their Friends, their Nation, their Profession, or their Name.
>
> Hereby it is manifest, that during the time men live without a common Power to keep them All in awe, they are in that condition which is called Warre; and such a warre, as is of every man, against every man. For WARRE, consisteth not in Battell onely, or the act of fighting; but in a tract of time, wherein the Will to contend by Battell is sufficiently known: and therefore the notion of *Time,* is to be considered in the nature of Warre, as it is in the nature of Weather. For as the nature of Foule weather, lyeth not in a showre or two of rain; but in an inclination thereto of many dayes together: So the nature of Warre, consisteth not in actuall fighting; but in the known disposition thereto during all the time there is no assurance to the contrary. All other time is PEACE.

> Whatsoever therefore is consequent to a time of Warre, where every man is Enemy to every man; the same is consequent to the time, wherein men live without other security, that what their own strength, and their own invention shall furnish them withall. In such condition, there is no place for Industry; because the fruit thereof is uncertain: and consequently no Culture of the Earth; no Navigation, nor use of the commodities that may be imported by Sea; no commodious Building; no Instruments of moving, and removing such things as require much force; no Knowledge of the face of the Earth; no account of Time; no Arts; no Letters; no Society; and which is worst of all, continuall feare, and danger of violent death; And the life of man, solitary, poore, nasty, brutish, and short.

To suggest that man can escape from, or transcend, biological needs might seem to be a fantastically exaggerated statement. To give more plausibility to this assertion one must first briefly recapitulate the main points of the first chapter of a representative modern introduction to psychology, then, second, suggest ways in which the second chapter needs to be revised.

The first chapter states that man (or any organism) is a sort of machine. The mechanical contrivance is an assembly of instruments of two kinds: (1) instruments for picking up signals from the environment (as well as similar instruments to receive signals originating within the machine) and (2) instruments for reacting to these signals in appropriate ways, chiefly by movements of limbs. The first type of instrument can be compared to the microscope, the telescope, and radar equipment; the second sort can be compared to tools such as hammers, pincers, and so forth. These two sorts of instruments are linked by a communication system comprising equipment such as intervening variables, hypothetical constructs, cell assemblies, storage systems, and—according to some—gnomes and ghosts which monitor the process and may intervene in disturbing ways. This discussion will ignore such control mechanisms; it will concentrate on the two sorts of instruments directly involved in the processes connected with input and output.

The behavior of the machine is normally, though perhaps not always, directed toward the attainment of certain goals. Since psychology is a biological science, the ends to which behavior is directed are the biological ends of self-preservation and the perpetuation of the species. What does this definition of human motivation mean? In one quite ordinary sense of the term "directed," ordinary behavior is plainly *not* so directed. Take species perpetuation. Ask anyone: How much are you concerned with perpetuating your species? Ask the historians: What historical evidence is there that men have been concerned with perpetuating their species? The historians will reply: "On the one hand, the founders of certain noble families in various societies genuinely wanted to perpetuate their families; they built family seats which they entailed, intending them to be occupied by their descendants for many generations. Among the common people, on the other hand, the ambition of perpetuating the species played little part." Nor, surely, one might add, does it play much part in the life of the man in the street today. There is an entirely different and more illuminating way of describing how the process of species perpetuation comes about. In his *Wealth of Nations,* Adam Smith developed the intriguing theory that, in the pursuit of their private interests, men, of necessity, through the operation of a hidden hand, promote the welfare of society; in other words, men and society are so constituted that by being allowed to follow their self-regarding impulses men are, so to speak, tricked into promoting the good of society as an unforeseen and unintended effect. The principle can be more widely applied. It could be argued with equal, if not greater, plausibility that in following their impulses men are tricked into perpetuating their species; this effect is both unforeseen and unintended. The same argument can be applied to the biological end of self-preservation. Although there are occasions when a man consciously acts to save his skin, in most cases actions which are in fact conducive to self-preservation are not motivated by so abstract an objective. By giving rein to appetite, man is tricked into nourishing his body. This analogy is applicable to his actions in general. While there are well-known exceptions, to a surprising extent what a man fancies also happens to be what is good for him.

Generally speaking, the abstract descriptions of the drives, instincts, or goal-seeking tendencies are incorrect or misleading; these descriptions include such abstract terms as self-preservation, sex, achievement, power, and so forth. What men want is always concrete and specific. A new approach is needed to the study of human motivation, and there is no better fresh approach than that suggested by Gardner Murphy's question: "How do we come to want what we want?" [1].

Two questions are, of course, involved here: What do we want? How do we come to want what we want? We must distinguish, on the one hand, between what a man does, which can be described in very many ways, and on the other, what a man is trying to do, which cannot be described in so many ways. It is odd, though very significant, that psychologists have found it impossible to agree about the basic motives, drives, or goals of the activities of animals and men. A part of the explanation is that the ends of goal-directed behavior are not definable in abstractions such as sex, power, achievement, and so forth. These goals can be defined—and this is a major hypothesis of this paper—only in the sort of way in which ethologists specify the perceptual component of innate releaser mechanisms. What releases instinctive behavior may be a relatively simple sensory stimulus, such as a blob of color, or it may be a rather complex pattern of stimulation.

What is suggested here is that for every releaser percept there is a corresponding goal percept, a sensory or perceptual experience accompanying or following the consummatory response; such a percept tells the organism, animal or man, once it has obtained what it wants, what it was trying to get. The percept specifies what a man wants to do, to be, or to have—say, to climb Mount Everest, to be a Don Juan, to have a speedboat. When a man finally gets what he wants, the fact that he has attained that particular objective is specified in a percept—that is to say, the perception of the world from the top of Everest, the percept of a social situation as it presents itself to Don Juan, the percept of the world as viewed from a speedboat, which itself is perceived as a "possession."

To improve on traditional statements of the goals of human endeavor we must specify these goals in terms of goal percepts either in the sort of way in which the ethologists specify releaser percepts or in the way in which experimental psychologists have for years specified the "equivalent" stimuli which release some response. As long ago as 1929, K. S. Lashley published an important paper which contained a figure illustrating "equivalent stimuli for a habit of jumping in the rat." Lashley stated [2]:

The animals . . . were trained to jump to a platform presenting a black surface and a white edge, seen against the background of the room. The appearance of the platform was then changed as indicated in the succeeding figures, by placing cardboard screens before it, or by substituting a large white screen on which paper figures were pasted. The animals jumped to any horizontal rectangle, whether black or white, but would not jump to a vertical rectangle or a plain figure. It seems clear that the stimulus here cannot be described as the excitation of such and such retinal cells. The elements common to the various situations are the proportions of the object seen against a varying background.

Equivalent stimuli in this case are, by definition, all stimuli which evoke the jumping response in the rat. If we ask what the common characteristics are of stimuli which evoke this response, we have, in the light of the experimental evidence, to find a rather complicated formula of the form of all combinations of black and lines and areas in which the horizontal dimension predominates over the vertical, and so forth, as described above. It is in this way that both releaser percepts and goal percepts must be defined; that is, the ends of goal-directed behavior.

The preliminary description of the machinery of goal-directed behavior may now be amplified in this way. The receptive part of the machinery picks up from the environment complex signals which function as releasers, that is, which instigate activity on the part of the tools of the organism, the parts used in the activities which organisms perform. The effects of these operations are reflected, by feedback, in the perceived field; the process is continued and may be redirected or varied by trial and error until the ultimate satisfying situation is presented; that is, the goal percept is attained—the food is enjoyed, danger averted, territorial demands satisfied, rivals put to flight, a mate successfully courted.

In the state of nature—the state before the take-off occurs—both the releaser percepts and the goal percepts are geared to biological needs: the releaser percepts are signals of danger or deprivation; the goal percepts indicate the removal of danger and the provision of the essentials for life. After the take-off, since the necessities are provided, there is no need for effortful activity. What happens then? The most relevant evidence is derived from the empirical studies of Munn, McClelland, and others, but it cannot even be summarized here. Relevant evidence also exists in the records and natural history observations concerning affluent peoples throughout the ages—oriental potentates, the lords and ladies and the landed gentry of Europe, and the great industrial tycoons.

In discussing the state following the take-off we can begin with a simple case, that of the domesticated cat. The life of the cat is almost a paradigm of affluent living. All the basic needs of the animal are satisfied almost before they are expressed: it is protected against both danger and inclement weather, and it is given food and drink before it has a chance to be hungry. How, then does it pass the time?

One might be tempted to say that, after taking its food and drink in its perfunctory way, it curls up on its cushion and goes to sleep; then it continues to sleep until awakened by faint interoceptive stimuli indicating the need for another meal, which it eats in a similarly offhand manner. This account of behavior under conditions of affluence might be taken as evidence supporting the Freudian hypothesis that all activity is directed to the removal of the stimuli, and that the truly normal state of the organism is the state of sleep; stimuli are forces that disturb sleep; we are kept awake only by physical pain or by the pain of unsatisfied desire.

Freud's theory, one feels, must be wrong. It is clear, even at the natural history level of observation that, once its basic needs are satisfied, the domestic cat does not just curl up and sleep; it prowls about the garden and in the wood, stalking and killing young birds and mice. The life of the domestic cat is a simple illustration of the reversal of the means-end relation which follows the transition to affluence. In the state of nature the cat kills to live. In the state of affluence it lives to kill. The phenomenon is even more marked in the domesticated dog. When its basic needs have been provided, it lives to hunt. But it does not hunt for the sake of hunting only. It lives in part for the enjoyment of social relations with man: it is not content with going for a walk; it requires to be taken for a walk.

The important principles concerning activity in a state of affluence are seen more clearly in the case of man in an affluent society. Affluent man does not need to work; he is not required to engage in any effortful activity. What is there left for him to do?

Broadly speaking, two kinds of activities remain for the affluent man to perform: he can play, and he can cultivate the arts. "Play" is an ill-defined concept, but in the present context the word is used to cover every activity which is engaged in for its own sake, without concern for the utilities produced. We can contrast work with play in this way:

work is activity in which effort is directed to the production of some utility by the simplest and easiest means; play is activity directed to the attainment of a pointless objective in a difficult way. As a paradigm of work we could take the production of so useful an object as an automobile in the easiest way; as a paradigm of play we could take the ridiculous procedure of guiding a small ball into a not-much-larger hole by means of awkward instruments in the face of obstructions deliberately devised to make the operation as difficult as possible. The point of the seemingly pointless activity of golfers can be classified under the formula of the reversal of the means-end relation. The goal, getting the ball into the small hole, is set up as a means for the true end, the enjoyment of the pleasurable activity itself.

This enjoyment of the activity for its own sake is what play has in common with the enjoyment of the arts. The enjoyment of the arts takes two forms: the supreme enjoyment of the creative artist who produces objects of beauty which can be enjoyed by himself and others purely for pleasure, and the comparatively minor enjoyment of those who enjoy the works produced by the creative artist. The advantage possessed by the creative artist, of course, is that he enjoys both the activity and the object created.

If an art can be defined in terms of the enjoyment of something for its own sake, without regard to its biological or economic utility, play belongs to the arts. Play ranks in all its forms—golf, baseball, cricket, and so forth—somewhere in the hierarchy at or near the apex of which we place music, sculpture, and poetry. This classification is indeed recognized in everyday language. We do not demur when someone describes fencing as an art, nor even when he describes cooking as an art. In a literal sense of the term "art," the lives of the affluent are restricted (if the word "restricted" is permissible in this connotation) to the cultivation of the arts. There is nothing else for them to do except to curl up and go to sleep.

Factual evidence to support this thesis could be adduced from major empirical studies such as those by McClelland and associates, reported in The Achievement Motive, and from minor studies such as those made at Birkbeck College, reported as the Aspirations of Young Persons in the Transition from School to Work. The most useful instrument for obtaining significant reports on human aspirations and sources of satisfaction is the projection test. Among its limitations is that it cannot be used to study the most affluent people, since they are, for obvious reasons, unwilling to subject themselves to "tests" other than those applied by their psychiatrists. There are, however, many affluent people who feel no need to consult a psychiatrist. The study of such people, like the study of animals in their natural environment, must remain for some time, if not forever, in the field of the natural history, nonexperimental fields of science. Just as the scientist must await the spontaneous occurrence of some meteorological conditions, so he must await the spontaneous expression of certain kinds of human motivation in, for instance, autobiographical writing. The following example is a passage from the autobiography of a representative member of affluent English Edwardian society:

> I suppose it would be true to say that I have had more enjoyment, a more vivid sense of the delight of living, with every faculty at full stretch, when pursuing and killing birds and beasts, than in any other activity. For sheer exhilaration, joined with the height of aesthetic satisfaction, I have known nothing to compare with deer-stalking. The hard physical grind, the constant exercise of craft and cunning, the breathtaking beauty of the high tops, the subtle and ever-changing colours of Scottish mountains, the solitariness and the silence, combine to exalt the spirit to the summit of happiness. The thrill of fox-hunting is ecstatic, but that has rarely come my way, and the pleasure is more physical than aesthetic. Grouse-shooting ranks high, for the mountains are there again, with the influence sweet as that of the Pleiades; the mountains, too, stand about the lochs, and make memorable many a day's fishing. But there is deep and quiet satisfaction to be had far from any hills; in waiting among the bracken, touched by the mild December sunshine, for the noiseless flit of a woodcock through a glade of ancient thorns, trailing Old Man's Beard; or in hiding among bulrushes, rustling drily, to ambush a flight of teal, or a wisp of driven snipe. Stalking grey-lag geese at dawn on South Uist, or slowly circling a flock of golden plover, in vain hopes of a shot, between Hecla and the green Atlantic, bring the same suspense, the same alertness of observation, the pitting of wits, the triumph or the failure which are the ingredients of delight; and always and everywhere is the feel of ambient air, of sun or rain or wind, sharp or caressing.

Three points may be noted in the above quotation to substantiate the present thesis. First, observe the close similarity between the life of a domesticated cat and the life of an English gentleman: freed from the need to obtain the basic essentials of life, they both no longer kill to live, they live to kill. Second, note the association in quality of pleasure between sport and esthetic experience—the enjoyment by the deer stalker not only of his art but also of the setting in which that art was practiced. The third point of interest is the transference of effortful exercise of skill from work to sport considered as an end in itself.

The transition from the penurious to the affluent society may be described in another way. When men are no longer compelled to work to satisfy their needs, or when work is turned into play, the machine begins to operate in a different way. Items which appear in the field of perception may cease to be treated as signals or simply as releasers and become, instead, objects of interest in themselves—for example, the scent of a rose or the song of a bird. The instruments of response can now work not merely to produce a goal percept signifying the realization of an innately determined biological end, but also to give enjoyment of the activity itself; in other words, the organism plays. These instruments also work to create *new* percepts which are enjoyed for their own sake. They work, that is to say, in the practice of an art. This can take the simple practical form of, say, landscape gardening, the object of which is to create a field of perception more satisfying than can be produced by nature left to its own devices. Trees may be planted not for their fruit but for their blossom. Houses are built not merely for protection against the elements but as objects of visual perception enjoyed as such. Man ceases to build like the mason wasp and becomes an architect. This happens, after biological needs have been provided for, in every modality of sense and in every way of exercising the muscles. This point may be illustrated by the following examples of the activities of civilized man:

To begin with an elementary case, take the transformation of hunger and thirst into the gastronomic activity of civilized man. Affluent people experience hunger and thirst only by accident, or when they deliberately set out to get hungry or thirsty by appropriate exertion or self-deprivation. Normally, they eat and drink before they are hungry or thirsty. No one could say that a man was eating caviar because he was hungry or sipping cognac to quench his thirst.

Take the physical activities of civilized man. Climbing a mountain and playing a round of golf are biologically pointless pursuits. Those who enjoy these forms of self-indulgence rationalize their behavior (quite needlessly) by telling themselves that these activities are good for their health. Biologists, and some psychologists, have supported their rationalizations in the interest of the theory that all such activities must have some biological function.

There are innumerable activities of civilized man for which no plausible biological justification can be given. One wonders what rationalization can be put, for example, for playing the bagpipes (an activity which is no doubt good for the lungs, but there are even better breathing exercises). Herbert Spencer suggested that listening to martial music faciliated the circulation of the blood. Presumably there are similar explanations for the human response to the "Dead March" or an "Air on a G String." But there is clearly a long way to go in validating this kind of esthetic theory.

Let us also consider sex. One might be tempted to claim that what Sigmund Freud, Frank Beach, and Alfred Kinsey do not know collectively about the "facts of life" is not worth knowing. This may well be so. Nevertheless, many human activities and human relations that are supposedly "explained" by reference to the sex drive remain biological enigmas, if not biological absurdities. There is, of course, a sequence of behavior to be observed in animals and men through which certain sign stimuli instigate actions which commonly have as their unforeseen and unintended effect the perpetuation of the species. However, love making in a modern, civilized, family planning community is only rather tenuously connected with this reproductive procedure.

The forms of behavior commonly attributed to the sex instinct and the goal situations are extraordinarily complex in the case of human beings and, to some extent, lower animals; the sign stimuli instigating this behavior are also exceptionally complex. Many biologists and psychologists have written about sex as a powerful drive, in virtue of which any male of the species is attracted by any female and vice versa. But what are the facts? There are, of course, some individuals of both sexes of whom this may be true. But these persons are deviants. The truth is that men and women living in civilized societies are so fastidious and exacting that they take a great deal of time to choose a mate, and many remain bachelors or spinsters forever. A man can be as carefully selective in choosing a wife as he is in picking a car. A woman can be as fastidious in selecting a husband as she is in the choice of a hat.

Both men and women are highly selective in respect of qualities which have no obvious biological significance. Speaking purely biologically, for example, why should a boy expect a girl to be pretty? Why should a girl expect a boy to be handsome? What is the *biological* significance of his demand that she be a witty, entertaining hostess interested in baseball, travel, and other subjects in which he happens to be interested? And what is the biological significance of her demand that he be sporting or musically talented? Their demands indicate that sex has become submerged under a vast overflow of social, esthetic, and other motives which possess little, if any, relation to sex.

There are innumerable forms of social relations commonly described as modifications of sex which have become detached from the biological requirements of procreation. Indeed, many are socially approved even though they are as biologically absurd as homosexuality. They may, in fact, be approved forms of gracious living. Examples are Darby and Joan affections, sibling affections, attachments aptly described as "natural affections," and human friendships which are valued and approved regardless of their possible biological function. They contribute to the social affluence consisting of the gracious living of a gracious social life.

Sooner or later it may be necessary to face up to the fact that many of the most important of human satisfactions, especially the pleasures known in civilized living, are derived from biologically pointless activities. When challenged to show the value of these activities from a biological point of view, one may be compelled to answer that they have no biological significance. Man has another distinctive set of needs in addition to physiological or biological needs—*psychological* needs. Self-preservation seeks to preserve a two-dimensional variable: the prolongation of life at a certain standard of living; that is to say, life which has quality as well as duration. What men endeavor to preserve and enhance is their standard of life and their style of living.

The argument of the thoretical part of this paper, comprising the first section, may be summarized as follows:

1. The transition from a state of nature to a state of grace, the

process of becoming civilized, is an important phenomenon in human psychology. This process may perhaps be adumbrated by the training and domestication of animals. Through domestication, wild animals came to have affection for man and to like his ways. In the same way, to put it as a theologian might, in the process of civilizing man, God domesticated him. Man came to love God and God's ways.

2. The essential condition of the transition to civilization was, first, the provision of the necessities of life, so that man (like the domesticated cat) did not need to work for a living, but could enjoy life.

3. Under these conditions there is a reversal of means and relations characteristic of the state of nature. Man no longer eats to live, he lives to eat. Man no longer builds to live, he lives to build. He no longer kills to live, he lives to kill. What he does he does no longer because he must, but because he *enjoys* it.

4. This reversal of relations involves a reorganization of the instruments of the organism. Signals are no longer received as signals for action required for self-preservation. The signals are enjoyed for their own sake.

5. The approach suggested requires a reinterpretation of goal-directed behavior. The goals of human behavior cannot be defined in terms of abstractions. Their meanings are set forth in terms of goal percepts which can be defined only in the sort of way in which the releaser percepts in innate releaser mechanisms are defined.

If the theoretical argument just put forward is valid, it must have implications for applied psychology, especially in connection with industrial motivation in an automated and affluent society. Those concerned with industrial management in Britain have been anxious about the effects of the welfare state, particularly full employment, upon the motivation of the worker. And they might well be concerned. Since the beginnings of the Industrial Revolution, the philosophy of management had been the philosophy of the carrot and the stick, that the basic motives of man are greed and fear. This philosophy is enshrined in the passage from Hobbes quoted earlier. That philosophy, written in 1651, has lived in the minds of business executives almost to the present day; it is now three centuries out of date. Like all simple, stark, wrongheaded ideas, it almost inevitably provokes reactions equally simple and equally wrongheaded.

The antithesis of this philosophy may take the form of an attempt to conceive an industrial order with an accompanying system of motivation based upon brotherly love. The reaction is reflected in utopian socialism and in the rather pathetic "experiments" that are tried, from time to time, to realize such aspirations in small societies based on the principle of idealistic communism. In fact, however, the collapse of the philosophy of the carrot and the stick has come about in quite another way. The collapse has come about less through the direct pressure of philosophies and ideologies than through the more humdrum procedures of empirical science. The religions, the social and ethical philosophies, and the ideologies have in general treated social motivation under two comprehensive rubrics: the concept of love, or benevolence (to use an old-fashioned and less emotive term), and the concept of duty, or obligation. In other words, social motivation has been taken to assume two forms, the tug upon the heartstrings and the prick of conscience. But both types of motivation had been treated in a too abstract and generalized way.

Love, benevolence, altruism, the brotherhood of man—call it what you will—had been thought of as impartial and all-embracing affection; and the patent failure to realize utopian dreams has been apt to lead by reaction to cynicism and disillusionment. The correction of both extreme views has come about through a slow but steady advance, through a variety of piecemeal and separate studies, in our understanding of the place of the "affections" in human motivation in concrete situations. Industrial psychologists have contributed to this advance, notably through the work of Elton Mayo in the Hawthorne experiment, which focused attention on the "informal organization" of working groups and the *actual* loyalties of groups. Clinical psychologists such as Moreno have mapped the forces in such groups. Freud and the "depth psychologists" generally have studied the natural history of the affections and have traced the far-reaching effects in adult life of the emotional relations between parent and child. Bowlby has produced evidence to suggest that traits often taken to be innate (for example, the disposition either to love or to be affectionless and selfish) may, in fact, be the effects of early relations between mother and child. Other workers are finding evidence that the pattern of relations in the home may later be reflected in the pattern of relations in a factory.

These and other studies have served to correct the too-abstract and generalized conception of the human affections. They have reminded us that Christianity begins with the love of one's neighbor, not with love for the man at the end of the street. They have taught us that the radiant warmth of the human heart varies inversely with the square of the social distance, so to speak. Those who give their unprejudiced attention to the natural history of the natural affections find it obvious that it must be nonsense to say that man is motivated only by self-interest, only by greed and fear. However financially hard-pressed a man may be, he will almost always find a dollar for a friend whose need is greater than his own. Instances really do occur when a miner, for example, will give his own life to save that of his mate. Although the motivation for such heroic sacrifices may be difficult to comprehend, nevertheless these incidents actually happen. These generous impulses operate in industry as elsewhere, but it would be a pity to take advantage of them, or to operate on the assumption that their automatic presence may be taken for granted. It would be unrealistic and unpsychological to expect the decent-hearted plumber, a loyal member of his firm, a good trade-unionist, and even a bit of a sentimental socialist, to display impartial and universal love. He cannot, even if he wanted to, feel the same regard for his boss, his firm, his union, or the benighted savage at the antipodes, that he feels for the devoted mate with whom he works. Brotherly love cannot be manufactured, nor can it be produced through the manipulation of "hidden persuaders." It is a fruit of civilized human relations and a by-product of the affluent society. When the basic needs are provided for, when a man feels secure—emotionally as well as financially secure—he is more disposed to share with others the goods he enjoys, just as affluent children are more prepared to share their candies than are those who are deprived. There are good as well as bad ways of "spoiling" children. And there are good as well as bad ways of "spoiling" adults.

The factual study of motivation in industrial situations seems to correct not only unrealistic and unpsychological conceptions of the natural affections, but also unrealistic and unpsychological conceptions of the sense of obligation. Freud has given us good reason to agree that "conscience" is not always the voice of God. According to him, it is the voice of the introjected parent, or a parent image which wags a warning or reproving finger at us all the days of our life. But it is also the voice of the primal herd and of a sort of primitive public opinion. In the industrial situation it is, so to speak, a sort of introjected shop steward who represents the will of the union or of the working group. It is the still small voice that tells the worker that if he works too hard he is a "rate buster," if he does not work hard enough he is a "chiseller," if he talks too freely to his foreman he is a "squealer," and if he fails to support his group he is a "scab."

Although great advances have been made in our understanding and appreciation of the power of social motivation, we must be on our guard against possible dangers. If the worker's fear of being dismissed by his boss is replaced by the fear of being "sent to Coventry" by his workmates, we shall not have made very conspicuous progress. Group loyalties are not enough to ensure harmonious industrial relations when they are on a purely emotional basis. They need to be augmented by the enlightenment of intelligence. We need to extend our understanding of the *intellectual* life of a group and of the place of rationality in human relations. We also need further to correct the balance by better understanding of what may be called the "third motive."

To explain what is meant by this additional type of motivation, let us take the case of a distinguished surgeon who is called upon to perform a difficult operation and who performs it with consummate skill. Why does he perform the operation at all? And why does he do it so well?

Part of this motivation, of course, is the lure of the fee he receives. Even a surgeon may like to get a fee, and no doubt, the larger the fee, the better he likes it, especially when he knows how much his patient can afford to pay. But to say that the fee is the most important motive would be plain nonsense, for the surgeon, we know, would be equally conscientious were his patient a pauper enjoying the benefits of the National Health Service in Britain.

We might be tempted to say that the distinguished surgeon is moved by a strong desire to alleviate pain in suffering humanity. This statement is, indeed, a perfectly correct assertion when one is writing the surgeon's obituary notice. But that is not a complete psychological analysis. Surgeons, no doubt, share with everybody else the natural and human desire to alleviate pain, but we must distinguish the performance of professional duties from philanthropy. The truth is that the surgeon performs an operation for the personal satisfaction of doing a good job; in other words, he does the job as well as he can because of an element in his make-up which compels him to feel that if his job is worth doing at all it is worth doing well. He does not do it from self-interest, in the proper sense of that term. He does not do it from interest in the welfare of others; he may, indeed, sincerely believe that it would be better both for the unhappy patient and for everybody else if the man were dead. He does the job for its own sake; this is the *third motive.*

How can we name this third motive—this performance of a job because of pride of workmanship? This additional motivation might be described as the "professional" motive, but this description would be misleading. It is true that we can see this motive in operation in the work of professional people; however, once we see it there, we can see it everywhere. In the years immediately following the Second World War, it was common to hear building operatives in Britain complaining bitterly at having to do a job below their self-imposed standards; because of their pride in their traditional high level of workmanship, they were dissatisfied at having to do shoddy work with substitute materials, at being denied the opportunity to exercise their skills to the full. This affront to their pride of workmanship does not mean, of course, that they failed to grumble about other imperfections; of course, they grumbled both at the lowness of their wages and about the conditions of their work. However, the point being made here is that they grumbled, too, at the frustration of their desire to do a job well.

In the present context the aspect of greatest interest is that the increasing dominance of the third motive is another characteristic feature of the transition from penury to affluence. It is not the case, of course, that man passes from the first to the second motive, then from the second to the third motive. It is rather that motivation becomes increasingly complex. It may well be true that in the state of nature or the state of penury man is activated chiefly by self-interest. As basic needs become more secure, he can afford to give rein to his natural affections. In the state of affluence his motivation is still more complex. He naturally keeps an eye on his own interests, but he begins to be generous, and in the state of greater affluence the third motive can become the most powerful of all.

In his working life in a modern civilized society a man passes through three phases. In the first stage, he works because he *must;* he has to ensure his basic necessities. He is near to the state of nature, perhaps activated in a high degree by avarice and anxiety. He works to live. In the second phase, following advancement, motivation changes. Essentials are secure. Effort is now sustained by the desire for some more or less clearly envisaged enhancement of the standard and style of life. Finally, in the third stage, as a man approaches the top of his particular tree or the branch on which he will be content to rest, there is a further change of motivation—a change which is overlooked because he continues to work as before and may continue to do so long after his colleagues have come to think that he ought to retire.

The reluctance to retire has not been properly understood. It is attributed to obsessive habit, to the unwillingness to relinquish power. Of course, these are factors in the situation, but there is another factor, perhaps of greater importance. The man has become subject to the law of the reversal of the means-end relation. Formerly he worked to live at the standard of life to which he aspired. Now he lives to work. Work has become play, an activity enjoyed for its own sake. This is obviously true of scientists and artists, but it is no less true of business executives; nor is it less true of technicians and skilled craftsmen.

There is, accordingly, a source of reassurance for those who are filled with gloom at the prospect of automation, through which still greater affluence will be assured for all by the work of the few who, through scientific and technological skill, produce and service machines. These scientists and technicians will be sufficiently well motivated by the tangible rewards of their jobs, their status, and the satisfaction of doing their jobs well. The displaced many—the relatively unskilled and ineducable—their needs secured by those who enjoy working for its own sake, will find *other* activities worthwhile for their own sake. Affluence is the soil in which perfection fluorishes. The scientist, the artist, and the obsessive business executive—each in his own way is a perfectionist. When men work only because they must—that is, when they work to live—it is not to be wondered at if they skimp their work. However, when they live to work, they are inevitably impelled to do the job as well as they can. The skilled workers will be perfectionists in their work; the displaced unskilled workers, on the other hand, will become perfectionists in their innocent recreational pursuits, breeding better and better pigeons or greyhounds, cultivating perfect auriculas, becoming better ballroom dancers, or pursuing in a perfectionistic way biologically pointless goals, but enjoying in these pursuits the good life. It is under conditions of affluence that man is revealed as what he is: an incorrigible perfectionist.

The views expressed in this paper are not, I submit, merely armchair speculation. At its worst, the paper has been an armchair exercise in the reinterpretation of the empirical evidence assembled by perfectionist experimental psychologists, ethologists, and motivation theorists. In the space available I have been able to state in an oversimplified way some of the conclusions. The corrections to objections to this overoptimistic, oversimplified thesis, as well as the qualifications, reservations, and the statement of the evidence, must be deferred to some other occasion.

References

1. Lashley, K. S., *Human Potentialities,* London, Allen & Unwin, Ltd., 1960.
2. Lashley, K. S., Nervous Mechanisms in Learning, *Foundations of Experimental Psychology,* Worcester, Mass., Clark University Press, 1929, chap. 14.

Martin C. D'Arcy, S.J.

THE INFLUENCE OF RELIGION ON SOCIETY AND THE INDIVIDUAL

In the foreword to this symposium religion is described as one of the more intangible forces which control our thoughts and emotions. I wish to say something on the role it has played and does play in the rise and decline of societies and in the life of the individual. That it has played a role throughout the long history of the human race must be admitted by all, for historical records and art reveal it as being the most dominating and formative influence in early societies. The Bible gives us the most familiar example of its influence on a race, but that story is paralleled by the history of India, Babylonia, Greece and Rome, Mexico and Peru, to choose names almost at random. Temples and statues confirm this; from afar mariners could see the gold on the statue of the Pallas Athena at Athens, and tribes met at the shrines of their gods to consolidate their unity and to renew their strength. The pilgrimages to Mecca and the passionate zeal of the Moslem, the clash of the Crusades and the later wars of religion, the part played by the orthodox clergy in national affairs and the inspiration of a Gandhi all bear witness to the continuing influence of religion.

These typical examples make another point immediately clear; namely, that religion has aroused such passion that evil and good alternate in its record to an extent which has made sundry writers fear and abominate the presence of religion at all: *Tantum religio potuit suadere malorum*. Lucretius and many others detested what they saw of religion, and the very strength of their detestation points to its potency. No doubt, high-minded men may grow disgusted with what they feel to be religion's bigotry and its occasional dark resistance to rational inquiries and discoveries, but such reasons do not fully explain the passionate debate for and against religion that has always gone on. It is the endemic influence, the passion of hate and love that religion excites, that makes the Marxist interpretation of it appear shallow. Religion is not just a sop for the unfortunate, an imaginary ideal to solace those who have no opportunity of benefiting from this world's goods; it ranks with sex in its power to set fire to the emotions and change man, and we must seek a partial explanation of this influence in the nature of man himself.

Some of the better descriptions of religion enable us to see the source of its enduring vitality and influence. Its common denominator, according to P. Sertillanges, lies in man's need to get into touch with that "mysterious reality, on which, so it is felt, our very personal life and the existence of the world around us depend." He goes on to say that we want to know it, to gain its protection, and to find in it an end and happiness. The mixture of abstract and personal terms is here a little confusing, but owing to the transcendence and mysterious character of what is worshiped, the mixture is perhaps natural. Cicero, for instance, in a well-known definition, writes of a divine power which encloses human life—*virtus quaedam divina vitam humanam continet*. It turns men's minds to images of the gods and the thought of a providence. Not very different is Joseph Maréchal's assertion that although we can have no intuition of the divine reality, we perceive it in the very movement of our being toward its source, we experience God by absence and want: "As one who knows water by thirst, God is anticipated by us; we have a prophetic sense of him." Maréchal is not saying that God cannot be shown by the mind to exist—he is one who believes that reason is not powerless before the mystery of God—but he is emphasizing what all seem to emphasize, what P. Gratry, for instance, tells us, that "the source of our interest and our power of passing from the finite to the infinite lies in a sense of the Divine. It is a call from the infinitely desirable and knowable, which is not a picture or thought or a felt state, but a disposition to act, to act on some primordial and metaphysical alliance of the soul with God, a disposition which is presupposed in every rational and free act."

Otto's idea of the numinous partly fits in with this picture, and so does the almost existentialist language of the French philosopher Louise Lavalle, that "God is the plenitude before which I am as nothing, and without which I would not exist nor feel my insufficiency." Tillich describes Negus as ultimate cause. More outside the chorus, but worth citing because it includes features so far not mentioned, is the view of Whitehead that "religion is a purifying force, an interior life, whose principal virtue is sincerity; it is a system of general truths, which transform our human condition and personality." Although this description is defective on many counts, it does give an explanation of why religion is essential to human living, whether in society or for the individual. When, too, he mentions solitude, he brings to mind the primordial relation of the self and God and the sigh of an Augustine to be united with God. Religion bears witness to the fact that man is profoundly aware that he cannot raise himself to the perfection which he seeks by pure human effort, even with the cooperative effort of mankind. There is an unbilical cord which ties him to God, there is a weakness in him which he can never totally overcome, and there is a bourne to which he moves that promises a love far higher than his own.

If this be near to the truth, then so much is contained in religion that we are closing our eyes if we classify it with that brood of fears which so often accompanies religion—I mean superstition, magic, animism, sorcery, serpent worship, the evil eye, and voodoo. These are like the diseases to which the human body is liable, and its witch doctors are what the quacks are to the medical profession and the Paracelsuses to the true scientist. They are still with us, though it is natural to have found them more successful in times when reasonable explanations of natural phenomena could not be given. But even in primitive times there were, as Mercia Eliade and other anthropologists agree, signs of genuine religion. Beset by forces around them which they could not understand, with nature now friendly and now hostile, tribes lived a more communal life and made of the divine idea a sectarian, protective deity. By the mask they could impersonate him and draw strength from him, and in the dance they could pass out of their weak condition into his immortal life. Eliade insists that the primitive believed in a paradisal state, in a day or moment which transcended time, and in the presence of the divine, especially at the center of the known world or in the city or on the mountain top. Whether this be true or not, it is undeniable that religion was the formative and dominating force, holding men together in a semimystical unity and helping to development of the individual conscience and consciousness.

With growing maturity the idea of God also became clearer, and as in India and in Greece, great literatures were born and philosophy and religion went hand in hand. However, to understand the lines followed by the great religions something more must be said about man's spiritual anatomy. The distinction between the masculine and feminine dynamisms, the *animus* and the *anima,* present and operative in every individual, has a place here. The *animus,* which is positive, life-promoting, life-preserving, is what Dr. Kurt Goldstein refers to in *The Organism,* when he writes that "an organism is governed by the tendency to actualize, as much as possible, its individual capacities, its 'nature' in the world. . . . This tendency . . . is the basic drive, by which the life of the organism is determined." The second dynamism, the *anima,* wrongly confined by Freud to a release from tension in the libido and to disintegration into the inorganic, lies behind the phenomena of the herd instinct, the sexual abandonment, self-sacrifice, and ecstacy. It is strikingly manifested in many religious phenomena. In India, as Arthur Koestler has recently argued, Yoga is a "systematic conditioning of the body to conniving at its own destruction"; and again, "the dreamless trance sleep of samadhi is a homage to *thanatos*—an exercise in death, while preparing for the final samadhi in which it is consumed." On the other hand, Zen Buddhism, he holds, while it uses techniques which should suppress self-consciousness, or to use its own language, while it seeks to throw itself over the precipice, is maneuvred in masculine fashion by the Japanese and subconsciously made an ally of enlightenment and enlivenment. The old books said that:

> Misery only doth exist, no one miserable;
> No doer is there; naught save the deed is found;
> Nirvana is, but not the man who seeks it;
> The Path exists, but not the traveller on it;
> But it may well be that the dynamism of abandonment
> And death has been subtly exploited

To increase the concentration of the warrior,
The business man and the strong ruler.

Be this as it may, much of the evidence from Eastern writings, techniques, and behavior points to the prevalence of the feminine dynamism. The self is in the way, it is an illusion, and only when it has been rubbed away will there come a light of fulfillment in some overself or cosmic consciousness. When a religious conviction of this kind enters into the individual's consciousness and habit of mind, and is furthered by long-tested techniques of self-denial, the whole attitude of man toward society and the individual is affected. Individual life is held cheap, crowds are at the mercy of a strong ruler, and there is manifest indifference to difficult conditions of life. Others will deal with this aspect of religion and will be able to evaluate the techniques used to condition the mind and prepare it for a form of suicide, so I need not stay upon it.

In the West the opposite dynamism has gained the upper hand. We watch for it in the struggle for existence, in all forms of growth, and in the ambitions of every individual. It is synonymous with Aristotle's *physis,* or nature in its process of becoming something, man developing his own perfection of mind and body. Its ideal is in the Apollo image, in which perfection of bodily health and athletic form go together with right reason and self-control. It is at the opposite pole from the frenzy or ecstacy of a Dionysius. By itself it is indifferent to moral good, though we translate the Greek word for excellence as "virtue." The weak go down before the strong in the cutthroat competition which this dynamism engenders. It breaks out in naked ambition or in enlightened self-interest; it can sanction mere power or turn to the high humanism of a Goethe. Whereas the feminine frenzy flows easily into religious cadres, its opposite tends to create its own form of living and has by education and training brought the art of living under moral and religious ideals.

In the balance between these forces civilization prospers, and it is in this balance or tension that religion has a necessary function. When Whitehead said that it had a purifying power and gave a framework to life by a system of truths and by transforming personality, he was describing this function. Undoubtedly, if either of these two dynamisms gets the upper hand, the results can be disastrous, for a culture passes into a sterile rationalism or a dark barbarism. Moreover, within a culture religion can be enlisted to serve evil ends; like the energy of matter misapplied, religious emotion misapplied has catastrophic effects. Some of the worst practices in history—human sacrifice, temple prostitution, suttee—are due to this untempered religious emotion. No wonder it has been equated with sex as the strongest of all the impulses of human nature. The writer of the *Crucifixion of Man* had his eyes on the horrors committed in the name of religion, and a Gibbon could make it responsible for the decline and fall of Rome. On the other hand, a Dante could see in it the expression of the will of God, which makes for our peace.

It is not the place here to dwell upon the failures of religion, for it could not be so powerful a factor for good were it not also subject to perversions. When clothed and in its right mind, it offers a philosophy of life, that is to say, a system of truths and an ideal which can transform personality. As stating unambiguously that man is no chance product of this earth and that he has a high destiny, it is the salt which gives savor to a civilization. Take away the truth about God and His providence, His love and what is taught of the beauty of personal relationship, and those emotions which are sublimated in religion attach themselves to some false god or ideal, to race or national ascendency, or to the dream of a classless society. The whole of life—its humdrum pleasantries and aims, its Newtonian grandeur, its mystery and ecstasies —are crushed into a program which soon bursts at the seams. The Christian religion, to take it as a paradigm, gives room for all that is human to grow and spread, and that is one reason why it has exercised such an influence in history. As Friedrich von Hügel argued, it allows for the exuberance of the senses and rejoices in their beauty, it stands for reason and the cool light of reason in science and philosophy, and finally, it encourages within the context of the other two, the imaginative and intuitive side of man which carries him toward poetry and mysticism. Without these parts of man cooperating freely there comes a miscarriage of religion and of the culture. Pasternak, living in an atheistic society, bore witness to this. He was forced into exaggeration as he looked around, but what he says has more than a trickle of truth. History, he said in *Doctor Zhivago,* centers in death and the mystery of it, with a view to overcoming it, and now Christianity has supplied the answer by its message of love and its two ideals of free personality and life as a sacrifice (the two dynamisms of self-realization and self-sacrifice): "The ancients had blood and beastliness and cruelty and pockmarked Caligulas, who had no idea of how inferior the system of slavery is. They had the boastful dead eternity of bronze monuments and marble columns. Only with the coming of Christ could men breathe freely."

That Pasternak is here unfair to many great men and women who lived before Christianity we must all agree, but much can be excused a poet who lives among pockmarked Caligulas and watches the sweated labor. His mind went back to the beginnings of Christianity and to the force which religion had in early times. I have already touched on the all-penetrating influence of religion in primitive societies, and when Christianity came it had an effect similar to what Pasternak depicts. The world was sick with a long fever. It had struggled to free itself from the foreboding that death ended all and that man was a victim of fate. Christian doctrines did bring a new hope and a new sense of the prerogatives and destiny of the individual. Few will deny that, however badly some of its representatives behaved and however forbidding some of the later doctrines may be thought to be, it gave play to the development of the individual and of a society in which the individual could work with others in justice and charity. Hospitals, universities, and the charter of the Common Law were the creation of clerics, and slavery gradually died out as the ideals of freedom and fraternity sank into men's minds. What had been a closed universe became an open one as a living God took the place of fate or necessity as the controlling power and providence.

It would take us too far outside the scope of this paper to show at any length the influence of religious ideas on Western society. It is to the point, however, to distinguish between its over-all influence for many centuries and the curtailed influence it now exercises. Both societies and individuals are conditioned in many differing ways and degrees. Once religion occupied the most prominent position, but that is not so any longer, and man's activities are now so numerous and complicated that the simple life of religion led by a primitive is scarcely possible. We must distinguish what can be called the vague or clear world view or attitude human beings accept or adopt. A child is constantly subjected to a barrage of impressions and has to come to terms with them, organically and mentally, and so it takes up an attitude and lives within a prearranged framework. This is its "world," a world vague in outline and emotionally enjoyed or feared or disliked. Each individual has his own milieu. A man may be an optimist or indifferent or sceptical almost without knowing it, and he settles down with his fate or providence. This outlook, however, need not be fixed. In early times it was usually religious. Second, the child comes to terms with the actual environment in which it lives as all day long it is exposed to the influences of its parents, companions, the country in which it lives, and its language, traditions, and food. We cannot help being the children of our time, separated in innumerable ways from those of past generations and countries. The *emigré* to the United States used to watch with mingled feelings the rapid Americanization of his children. This kind of conditioning has been increased in one way and lessened in another. The old caste or class distinctions have diminished, but in their stead have come the new outlooks of the white-collar clerk, the professional gamester, the specialist in industry or logistics, the university professor, the engineering technician, and the expert physicist. Each of these has his own conditioned way of seeing what is happening around him. None of these attitudes is pure and undefiled, and after a time the diffused attitude of a modern city and capitalist life creates disquiet, and the young are stirred to a partial revolt.

This leads to the third type of attitude, one which rests to some extent upon a person's own initiative or decision. It can be called the moment of decision, or the taking on of a personal philosophy of life. All accepted standards and outlooks are liable to revision, for there is a law of tedium and of diminishing returns. Even religion, when it rests its case on reason and good sense, has to expect this kind of revolt and should shape its policies accordingly, as Hans Sachs advised the Meistersinger to do. But in our present age the appeal of religion—and some would say the danger—is the unfortunate conditioning to which all the young have to submit. They feel like a Laocoön caught in the coils of a vast serpent. Knowledge and techniques have gone ahead too fast, and everything can now be done on such a vast scale that the individual sinks into insignificance. Only a Christian sentiment stands in the way of his enslavement or use as a perishable instrument. I need not dwell on the complicated machinery now of the state and industry, big business, and bureaucracy. More frightening to those who have to face a long future is the intrusion into the formerly sacrosanct chamber of the human person, the supersession of specifically human work by machines, calculating cybernetic machines, and new techniques for measuring human intelligence and work. Still worse is the threat that citizens may lose their private lives when instruments can read off what they are thinking and new drugs can so change their character that they may become unrecognizable and willing servants of those in charge of the state.

Dismayed by so much that is happening and by the growing impersonality of human existence, many have reacted in a way which has come to be called by the general name of existentialism. The existentialist takes seriously the old saying that there is nothing of which man is certain save death. This is the human predicament. Confronted with extinction, a man asks why this should happen and what is man that he should have such dreams and such disillusioning experience. He ponders whether there be any meaning in life, who he is, and what he should be doing. The sensations which accompany this state of mind are anxiety, dread, nausea, loneliness, and nostalgia. What increases the dread is the spectacle of so many who have lost their souls within living memory—the spectacle of the Hitler youth baying before their idol the Führer, of those entering the ovens of the concentration camps, and of the hordes who gather round those lustful for power or those with quack remedies for the salvation of man.

It is in this crisis that religion finds again its entrance and its *metier* after it has been ignored by a society too confident of its own strength and virtue. The condition diagnosed as existentialism is like that of the religious outcry in the psalms and in other religious writings. "What is man that thou art mindful of him?" "Out of the depths I have cried unto thee." Religion brings back the lost framework of life and gives a meaning to confused voices sounding in the soul. As sense and reason and emotion and aspirations are brought together in one heading, confidence is restored not only in general but in the significance of individual achievement. Moreover, the specter of death vanishes. Here then should be the remedial effects of religion. I say remedial because a man does not so easily come to terms with life now as in primitive times. There are too many competing interests, too much business to do which cannot easily be translated into a religious context. That is why even among those who practice their religion assiduously and faithfully, religion appears to be but one factor in their outlook. They would have to be saints to see everything, as the primitive did, through the eyes of their faith. It begins as a decisive catalyst and sets a new system of ideas going, but this falls short at first of the category I mentioned.

Like all the other factors distinguished above, religion helps to condition a society and the individual. It remains now to ask in what particular way and by what methods this conditioning is brought about. A partial answer has already been given in the statements about the life-giving quality of a faith which is reasonable and rich in aspiration. For proof of this one has only to look around and consider what faith and hope went into the making of so many fair monuments in the arts, into philosophy, and into the leveling up of society. More relevant to the questions before us, however, are the methods and means which the church, and in particular the Catholic Church, has used to instill into its converts and adherents a knowledge and love of the God of the Christians. These methods are best seen in the education of the young and in the rules which are imposed upon the members of the Christian body. And here I am faced with a difficulty. There are many Christian denominations, and they differ in no small degree on the subjects of their teaching and on the stresses used in the teaching. Obviously, when St. Bernard took a group of his young friends off to a solitary place in the mountains called Clairvaux and taught them there to think as far as possible only of divine things and to regard the world as a distraction in their prayers, he was treating them very differently from a nun who does teaching in a parish school in Chicago. Again, many of those who descend spiritually from the reformers of the sixteenth century hold the belief that the human race was corrupted radically by original sin, whereas the Catholic teaching is that human nature has remained radically good, though it is no longer in proper concord with itself and is biased toward selfishness and sex. Overemphasis, too, can creep in and spoil the simple meaning of some doctrine, and we have with us always, let us remember, those who are puritanical by disposition and those who are easygoing and kindly in their judgments. One can turn God into a monster, while the other makes of him a good-natured parent.

An error in stress can be very costly and lead to an antipathy to all religion or to the psychiatrist's couch, and it has been claimed that much of the power exercised by the Calvinist and Catholic Churches comes from their having paralyzed the minds of the young with warnings against sin and threats of the punishments of a wrathful God. Such kinds of teaching were perhaps more suited to a rougher age, when warriors did not care for namby-pamby gods, but they must be the exception now. Authority is, for the time being, out of favor, and general opinion is against the punishment of the young. The Bible, nevertheless, offers abundant evidence of the need of keeping a true sense of God alive, and a true sense of God begins with awe and fear: *Initium sapientiae timor domini.*

It is possible to keep the balance between awe and love and joy, but they must all be present if one is to sup with God. The attitude of the Christian Church is often misunderstood. Fear is but a subsidiary element in the Christian teaching, which is after all a Gospel, that is to say, good news, tidings of great joy. True religion is an exclamation of joy at the liberation of the spirit and the promise of living at the top of one's bent in the presence of absolute love. So great is this treasure that it must not be lost, and at times drastic means are taken to prevent its being lost. Such means are adopted especially on behalf of those who are simple and weak, the children of the Gospel who must not be scandalized. Let us admit that to protect them the Church at times may appear to disapprove of what is harmless to grown-ups. What is good in itself is not always opportune, as we have seen in our own day in the too-rapid concession of complete democratic liberty to tribes still fonder of vengeance on their neighbor than of freedom.

The aim of the Christian religion is to produce free personalities, because only *persons* can worship in truth and love. Hence, if we look more closely at the methods followed in teaching, we shall find great stress laid on reason and the ability to think out for oneself what is worthwhile within the divine order of providence. The mind should be prepared to have an answer to the main questions which life raises, and the will, too, should be disciplined to take the hard with the soft, the adventurous with the domestic. The soul is made acquainted with mystery, with the transcendent reality which by its infinite perfection measures a person and sets him in a position to understand his own status. A hero or a demonic power has from time immemorial been one of the means of drawing the best out of the young. He is the legendary figure who so often stands in the mists behind the story of the beginnings of a city or a tribe or a family—the household gods and Anchises and Aeneas who meant so much to the Romans; Abraham and Moses, who were sources of inspiration and hope to the Jews, and led them to expect a still more wonderful hero in the Messiah; Christ, who is to the Christian a historical figure, a man, and more than a man or hero, because he is the Logos, the wisdom of God, and the love which makes the stars. To walk in sight of such a being, to be taught to learn his ways and fall in love with Him, cannot on any count be called a dangerous conditioning of the mind. It is more likely to liberate the mind and set it toward perfection.

But it may be said that Christian practice, while it can aim high, has also fallen very low, and there have been more than whispers of how the Jesuits, for instance, have tried to condition youth. There is, indeed, another type of conditioning which is unscrupulous and deadly. We hear tales of it from those who suffered under Hitler and at the hands of Soviet officials. Enough is known about the methods to make the stories plausible, and there is natural fear that as more and more is discovered in the science of medicine, the easier it will be to depersonalize human individuals and substitute other characteristics for the familiar ones. There are many new arts of persuasion besides the customary ones of slanting history and advertising propaganda—new pressures on the nerves, new forms of persecution in the cell, and drugs to turn the martyr into a compliant tool of a party or a dictator.

Has not Catholic teaching descended to a kind of brainwashing at times, and have not the Jesuits even boasted that if a child of four is put into their hands they can make of him what they want? I can only say that such a boast would be a monstrously foolish one, seeing that so many of the products of Jesuit education have been moderately or immoderately critical of their teachers. If we look at the book on which all the Jesuit methods and techniques are founded, the famous book of the *Exercises* of Ignatius of Loyola, we see how baseless is this charge. The *Exercises* come the nearest in Western Christendom to the techniques elaborated in the East. In the West the *Rule of St. Benedict* set the pattern of religious behavior amongst Catholic religious, and a host of spiritual books followed in the Middle Ages. It is hardly an exaggeration, however, to say that St. Ignatius started a more scientific training in the spiritual life, and the *Exercises* are as exact and as practical as a military handbook. No one, nevertheless, could say that they prescribe a conditioning of the mind or put undue pressure on the will. St. Ignatius does use what may be called stage properties to get his effects—when he asks the exercitant to mediate on sin and death he suggests that fasting and darkness may help the mind—but the whole end of these meditations and exercises is to produce a free choice unencumbered by lazy feelings and a sticky will. He begins with a consideration that is wholly rational and intended to be logically convincing, and most of the book is taken up with meditations on the splendors of Christ as an example and an inspiration. Let us admit that in the rules written for the Jesuits themselves obedience is preached as a virtue, and to an outsider some of the images used, such as that of a corpse or stick in the hand of a master, may sound extreme. They are not so, however, in the context of the whole rule, which is founded on love, and in view of the freely chosen vocation of the Jesuit to be ready to take up any duty which the greater glory of God demands.

A little later than St. Ignatius, the two Spanish Carmelite mystics St. Teresa and St. John of the Cross explored more scientifically the higher regions of prayer. Most high religions have had their mystical paths, and a clear philosophy of ascent is to be found in the neo-Platonic Plotinus as well as in the Hindu writings. St. John of the Cross, however, is detailed and exact, and in his teaching the senses first suffer a dark night, then conceptual thinking, until in the end there is left what another writer has called the fine point of the spirit. What here looks like a method for abrogating the self turns into an enthronement of it amid flames of love. Neither then in these Spanish mystics nor in the Ignatian exercises and rule is there loss of personality. Quite the opposite, and Von Hügel was surely right when he contrasted a mystic saint such as Catherine of Genoa with a psychopathic case. The latter grows more and more narrow as interest in the self fills the horizon of the patient's mind; the saint and the true mystic, on the other hand, grow more and more generous in thought and feeling until his or her world is almost identical with that of mankind: "Who is hurt, and I am not hurt?" Moreover, there is evidence to show that the moral and the religious sense is so part and parcel of the personality that it cannot be successfully eradicated. Patients who have been hynotized are, as a rule, obedient to the suggestions and orders given to them. If, however, an order runs counter to a deep moral conviction, resistance stiffens. The same has been known to happen to those who have been drugged or have had pressure put upon their will. Though they may be beside themselves, they nevertheless balk at the attempt to rob them of their moral and religious values. Those who are bent on changing them have either to disguise what they are doing or to attack their convictions circuitously. The religious dye colors the whole person, as if the person were so constituted that its selfhood were in communication with God or enjoying some ultimate and radical relationship with God.

If this be so, then religion should not be ignored in any debate on the meaning and basis of selfhood, and we should expect religion to provide a clue on how to preserve the personality against the threatened invasion of it by forms of brainwashing and by drugs. A theologian or philosopher cannot take the place of the physician and psychiatrist. He can do little more than give the groundwork, and even here he is handicapped by the varieties of religions and their varying tenets. According to some, there are no genuine persons to preserve. For this reason I shall confine myself to the Christian religion. But even here there are differences which affect our judgment on the character of the individual. Julian the Emperor and many Romans of the later Empire accused Christianity of failing the people in the national duties and of speeding the dissolution of the Empire because of the preoccupation of Christians with another world. The accusation has been repeated most eloquently by Nietzsche in his diatribe against the servile mentality of Christians and their other-worldliness. Many of the early Christians, living during time of persecution and hoping for a quick end of the world, did pay little attention to the worldly life around them. Nevertheless, Christianity has always managed to combine an ideal of other-worldliness with a duty to use talents in earthly tasks and with a love for one's neighbor. The Christian does not regard these differing purposes as contradictory; they provide that tension which makes for a full life and, by the meeting of challenges and the overcoming of resistances, leads to the advancement not only of the individual but of society.

The philosophy behind this is that man is more than a living material organism. He stands on the horizon of two worlds; he sets before himself a spiritual ideal which has to be realized through his psychophysical organism, and his part is to make reason control the feelings and passions and sublimate the lower desires and loves into a high human love which has a kinship with the divine. Hence, every individual is of great worth and is unique. The West has so taken to heart this teaching that the value of the individual has served as the cornerstone of social, legal, and political betterment.

At this moment, however, a great question mark has been raised in many minds by what is happening around us and by what is being prepared in the laboratory. We all think that our minds and will operate on their own steam. Language bears this out as well as judgments on behavior in courts of law. But the psychiatrists have made some of the old claims for freedom dubious, and the modern empirical philosopher cannot find a place for the self of his system. Dr. Kurt Goldstein, in his *The Organism,* gives us valuable information on the working of the organism as a whole and on the relative constancy of the organism. He maintains that in spite of the many changes which a man's character may suffer, and the unfolding and decline in the course of the individual's life, a relative constancy is maintained. "If this were not the case, it would never be possible to talk about a definite organism as such. It would not be possible to talk about a definite organism at all." Here is something relatively unchanging in an individual, and Goldstein in another place admits willingly that "all creative activity originates from the living impulse of the organism to cope productively with the environment," and that "consciousness is prerequisite in order that productivity may find its manifestation. . . . It is ultimately consciousness which determines direction." He clings, however, to the idea that it is an abstraction to think of consciousness plus organism. But how, we may ask, could an organism create standards which make it possible and permissible for that which organizes life to give up its life for an ideal?

Austin Farrer, in his Gifford Lectures for 1957, examines the arguments for and against the existence of the self and of freedom. He points out that when I lift up my pen or think aloud of what I have written, there is no good reason for supposing that in each of these actions or steps the part played by the brain changes radically. The action is controlled by the brain, but the action is in the organ, in the hand or the mouth. This is the part of me which I am using, and I am conscious of what I intend in using it. When we are carrying out a project or intention we often improvise and go on without a prefigured or fixed plan, so that it is almost impossible to think of the intentional act as prefigured in the workings of the brain. Furthermore, in the higher forms of organization, there is present a real power to bewitch the lower forms. The small-scale patterns are set to a new dance by larger-scale patterns. Again, the activity of a given pattern of action and the transition from one action pattern to another go beyond physical laws. What this comes to is that our intentional life calls the tune. The neural action patterns themselves have no name of their own; they are identified only as physical patterns corresponding to ordinary human actions. On the other hand, the action of our intention is independent of any purely physical theory. Minute physiological patterns go on without correlation with conscious human intentions, and conscious human intentions go on without correlation with nervous patterns. The regularities deploy themselves. The minute physical energies, of course, go on working regularly, and we should be grateful for this, for it would be a serious handicap if we could not acquire bodily habits, such as walking, talking, and reading, and cease to worry about them.

So Mr. Farrer acknowledged that human beings are to some extent controlled by breeding, physical conditions, interest, and superstition and prejudice. Such conditioning, however, leaves a margin of sheer aspiration which goes out toward the object of a creative choice, and it is this creative choice which makes for advances in estimates of value, and for a stretching of inculcated principles until they are virtually transformed. An electronic machine, for instance, may do wonders within definite limits, but it is not going to change its basis of action, repent its destructive mission, and immolate itself by plunging into the bowels of a volcano.

P. F. Strawson, in his valuable analysis of *Individuals,* to some extent supports the argument of Farrer. We cannot avoid, he tells us, falling back upon the primitive idea of a person. Most empiricists limit the connotation of a person. We must say, for instance, that "*I* am bald; *I* am cold," as well as "I see a spider on the ceiling." Such facts explain why a subject of experience should pick out one body from others and give it a name. Strawson insists, however, that this limitation of the meaning of a person will not do, for it does not explain why the experience should be ascribed to any subject at all, nor again, why the I or the subject of the reference *and* the corporeal features should be attributable to the same thing. That is to say, they fail to explain the use of the word "I," or how any word has the use which that word has. In other words, they have failed to explain the concept we have of a person.

The problem of the person will be brought out if we suppose, as many have done and still do, that the person is a kind of compound with two kinds of subjects, the one an ego or pure consciousness, the subject of experience, and the other a substance with corporeal attributes. But if we started from the very beginning with such an idea or picture, we could never arrive at this compound idea of a person. If the ego, the pure subject, came first, we could not think at all of other subjects of consciousness, each distinguishable and identifiable. We should be stuck with our own ego in an inescapable solipsism, that pit which the modern philosophical positivist knows he is always in danger of slipping into. We could never assign our experience as such to any subject except ourselves. Worse than that; we could not do it to ourselves, because we could not identify ourselves without others. This means that the pure subject or ego cannot exist as a primary concept, on the strength of which we explain ourselves, others, or a person. The concept of a person* must be logically prior to that of an individual consciousness. This latter may have a logically secondary existence, for we do speak of a dead person, a body, and we do speak of a disembodied person, which retained the logical benefit of individuality from having been a person.

I do not think that this analysis is quite complete, because it presupposes that we cannot go behind the ascription of person to what is subject-consciousness and body. It has the merit, however, of removing some prejudices about the meaning of a self and bringing together in the human self both mind and body. It is this notion of the self which is such a matter of concern at present, owing to the spiritual power over others which is increasingly being put into the power of our bosses. This sense of the self must be carefully distinguished from another sense

* Strawson means by a person one who is both conscious and corporeal.

which is becoming very common both in scientific journals and in ordinary language. In the latter sense, person and personality mean little more than character, and so psychologists like Block and Petersen will entitle an article Some Personality Correlates of Confidence, etc., and Janet A. Taylor writes on A Personality Scale of Manifest Anxiety. Freud, too, has, as everyone knows, his language of the ego and the superego, and Jung has a set of distinctions of his own, which nevertheless, it can be argued, imply a permanent, subsisting self, which is even an *anima naturaliter Christiana*.

Ever since Descartes's time there has been a tendency to treat the self as a mind in a machine, what Ryle called the "ghost in the machine." This tendency goes back a long way before Descartes, perhaps because the presence of the spiritual side in us is so striking and because it is so easy to form a picture of it as imprisoned in the body, or driving it, or half in love with and half despising it. This Platonic and Eastern fashion of thought is harder put to it to explain the incursions of medicine and pharmacology into what was regarded as strictly private to the spirit. In the Catholic religion, on the other hand, partly owing to the dissemination of the Aristotelian outlook, the discoveries of medicine and pharmacology cause little alarm. The theory of the intimate interaction of soul and body allows for such discoveries. If the soul be the form of the body, and a human being has to be defined in terms of his being essentially body as well as mind, what affects the body should affect the mind, and mind and brain should function together. The difficulty here is to justify the high estate of the soul and its relative independence of the body. It is harder, that is, to find a self, and a self which is not completely covered by its organic activities. Why, in fact, look for something beyond what the psychologists call the character?

The reason is that organic behavior does not of itself tell the whole story; it leaves over the mystery of the self, which is there in the precious individuality of each person we know and love, and it does not account for the heights of aspirations and the acts which make up the life which man most treasures. There is a relation always between spirit and body in this life, but this relation must allow for the aspirations of which man has shown himself to be capabale. To clear the situation Farrer gives us an allegory from playing the violin. Violin music may be freely and personally produced. But it cannot exceed the capacities of the violin, and however competent the performer, if we loosen the strings equally, he cannot play in pitch; if we loosen them unequally he cannot play in tune; of if we knock holes in the sound box, his music will lose resonance. "At some point a degree of interference will have been reached such that he can reproduce no semblance of music. Just as some men go mad, and all of us die; though it be that God will raise us up and put instruments of a new music in our hands." Few are surprised to find that when they have a headache they cannot think well, and from the beginning of history men and women have seen the effect of wounds and diseases on mind and character. There is nothing new, therefore, in the information about drugs which can send men mad or condition them to docility. The Aristotelian type of answer covers this situation; from this viewpoint the solution in terms of a pineal gland has always seemed ridiculous.

The Aristotelian framework has, however, many varieties. There are some philosophers who see great possibilities in the suggestion of Bergson that the brain is more a protective or economic instrument than a creative one. All day long we are bombarded with impressions, thousands and thousands of them impinging upon us as we encounter an ever-varying reality. Were our brain not like a model secretarial machine, sorting out what is to the point and letting past only what we can control, we could never grow and have a flexible and ordered mind. Another image of the brain is that of a telephone exchange. Reality strikes upon our consciousness, but for us to be able to report it to ourselves and docket it, we need the brain. It enables us to talk to ourselves, to be not only conscious, but self-conscious. When the exchange breaks down, because of a blow or illness, we are still conscious, but we are unable to catch our thoughts and call them our own. The thought is there, as the dream which vanishes just as we awake, or as with the very old who cannot remember from one moment to another what they have said.

Still another view deserves mention to offset what is feared by some to be happening now: the coming of the era of the faceless man, what has been called a revolution in administration when the privileged *faubourgeoisie* in contemporary subtopias exercises a faceless and standardizing influence on an increasingly lulled and affluent proletariat.

Is something worse than this to happen? Is a man as proud as Julius Caesar to become as gentle as a sucking dove and an Abraham Lincoln to reveal the habits of an Al Capone? Granted that there be the most intimate union between character and selfhood, must there not be some selfhood which is inviolable and continues in one stay all throughout the changes it may have to endure? A static, unchanging self is out of the question, but to even any kind of self the empirical psychologist may give short shrift. He may say that there is no need to invent such hypotheses, for all that happens in experience can be sufficiently examined without the addition of such a self.

One kind of answer to this lies in pointing to the fatal flaw in materializing the mind or the will. J. B. S. Haldane was quick to see this flaw. If the mind is determined by matter and not by truth, then whatever I say has no value as truth. To use Haldane's words, "In order to escape from this necessity of sawing away the branch on which I am sitting, so to speak, I am compelled to believe that mind is not wholly conditioned by matter." In fact, the operations of the mind cannot be put into the same category as matter; a nebular hypothesis and stars are not the same kind of material. The same landscape can be painted again and again and can be thought of by different people without anything happening to the landscape, just as the earth existed long before Plato or Aristotle thought that they understood something about its nature. Aristotle talked about species and genus and the relation between them, but never could a genus devour a species as a cat devours a mouse. Not all these operations, which we call mental, are the acts of someone or something, and the effect cannot be higher than the cause.

If we examine the nature of these operations of the spirit we shall see still more clearly that the presence of some acting and subsisting self is required. In every judgment we make an assertion, and an assertion is more than a conclusion; it is an assent, and an assent means that we make what we are saying our own and commit ourselves, and sometimes our future life, to it. In the law courts I swear to tell the truth, and it is in its very essence a personal act, for which I am responsible. (In a more profound analysis it could be shown that there is contained in every statement an act of self-identification.) Kent tried to reduce this assertion to a mere formal unity, but this is denied by the acclamation with which every original act or expression or work of art is greeted, and later recognized as ours. What is true of judging holds also for acting and deciding. Any analysis which omitted the very special way in which we make one of two or more alternatives our own, when any one of those alternatives lay within our power, would be far from the mark. It is thus that we grow and become ourselves and achieve the ideas we aspire to, and all the language we use in descriptions of this process involve the presence of a subsisting self. This may be called the existentialist self, the one which has, down below the ordinary anxieties of living and choosing, that of a concern with itself and the desire to continue to live. In a paper read before the Aristotelian Society, P. T. Geath pointed out that there are statements in which the word "exist" is a real predicate. When Jacob in the Bible cried out, "Joseph is not and Simeon is not," it would be quite absurd to say that Jacob in uttering these words was talking not about Joseph and Simeon, but about the use of their names. Moreover, here the reference of a name admits of no time qualification; names are tenseless.

The poet Gerard Hopkins, who was no mean philosopher, called the self a positive infinitesimal. He had an unusually vivid sense of himself, both for what he was as a character and as a singular, subsisting being. In his notebooks this passage occurs:

> I find myself both as man and as myself something most determined and distinctive, at pitch, more distinctive and high-pitched than anything else I can see; I find myself with my pleasures and aims, my powers and my experiences, my deserts and guilt, my shame and sense of beauty, my angers, hopes, fears, and all my fate, more important to myself than anything I see. And when I ask where does all this throng and stack of being—so rich, so distinctive, so important—come from, nothing I see can answer me. And this, whether I speak of human nature or of my individuality, my self-being.

Still more is this the truth in the experiences of the mind and self-consciousness:

> When I consider my self-being, my consciousness and feeling of self, that taste of myself, or *I* and *me* above and in all things, which is more distinctive than the smell of walnut leaf or camphor, and is incommunicable by any means to another man . . . nothing else in nature comes near this unspeakable stress of pitch, distinctiveness, and selving—this self-being of my own.

Hopkins explains this distinctive self-being as a kind of positive pitch which every self has from the beginning, a positive infinitesimal or will, which has its own way and inclination. From the beginning it follows its own line, and this line cannot with certainty be predicted. This freedom of pitch is integrated always so as to make one being in experience with a nature determined by heredity and environment. This nature is the area of its actvity, the stuff which it has to mold, the Sparta given to it which it must adorn. Such a self is present in time of sleep as in time of awakening, and even if its field of operation were changed by drugs there would remain not only the same body, the same language, some similar memories and ideas, but the subsisting active subject which makes sense of there being any change at all. The self preserves the identity, which normally is apparent to those who love the person. In small matters the signature tune may be faint and recognized only by lovers and friends, or it may be as loud and distinguished as a Dante's or Shakespeare's, as determined as a Winston Churchill's. In our liberty we are always creating and so becoming what we already might be, but of the many things we might be, what we do become is the fruit of our liberty and very much our own. Such a self, while at home in the body and one with it, is represented at its best in what is fresh and new and in the discovery of truths and in the choice of love. It is this self also which, as E. I. Watkin, in the *Philosophy of Form,* says, "has a radical orientation of the will towards eternity and the world of spirit—in the last analysis towards God, which is so distinct from the lower psychological impulses that it struggles to achieve freedom from their yoke."

There is a sense, then, in which the self can sustain many attacks upon it and continue always in being, in growth or decline, despite changes of the body, disease and a damage to the brain, or conditioning of its dispositions by drugs. In his *Autobiography,* the late Edwin Muir wrote:

> I realized that immortality is not an idea or belief, but a state of being in which man keeps alive in himself his perception of the boundless union and freedom which he can faintly apprehend in time, though its consummation lies beyond time. . . . I think there must be a mind within our mind which cannot rest until it has worked out, even against our conscious will, the unresolved questions of our past; it brings intense contemplation.

Put with this what Marion Chase recorded of her mentally ill patients: On being persuaded to try her therapeutic dances, they would sometimes cry out, "This is me." A nice puzzle is given to logician and psychologist by the remark made by an old woman who was out of her head, when a friend came to visit her: "You should not have come, as I am out of my mind."

All images fail us in describing the complexity of the self which is fundamentally simple, for if we say that there is a self within a self, we are giving a false picture of a unique relation which has not even a far-off counterpart. There is this self-being, and it cannot have a true view of itself without an external world to keep it down to earth and the criticism and idealism of others to improve standards. As one of the characters in Compton-Burnett's *Mother and Son* remarks: "You can do as you will with solitude. It does not take you on equal terms." Gilbert Chesterton said on one occasion, "A mirror is a wonderful thing, but not half so wonderful as a window." Some are called to live the life of vestal virgins, but too much solitude for most leads to idiocies, aberrations, and misconceptions of one's own nature. Only by contact with others and by living in the presence of those worthy of the admiration of others can we change those two dynamisms which I have already mentioned, turning the centrifugal one into generosity and self-spending for others and the centripetal one away from self-glorification and the lust for power to self-respect, honor, and integrity.

In our fears of what may happen to us and those to follow us through the abuse of drugs and brainwashings, we forget not only that such fears have been shared in the past by those who thought of renaissance poisoners, of sorcery and evil eyes, and of love philtres, but also that countless peoples have been in every generation slightly or seriously mistaken in their ideas about themselves. There will always be Don Quixotes, Malvolios, and Peer Gynts. Today the mask is a symbol of what people who are uncertain of themselves pretend to be. As Yeats wrote in 1909, "I think that all happiness depends upon the energy to assume the mask of some other self; that all joyous or creative life is a rebirth of something not one's self, something which has no memory and is created in a moment and perpetually renewed." Fortunately, in the majority of cases we do not mistake ourselves so much as certain characteristics of ourselves. In judging who we are we act, to use another and a biblical image, like those who look at themselves in a mirror, "Like a man," as St. James says in his Epistle, "looking at his natural face in a mirror; for he looks at himself and goes away and presently forgets what kind of a man he is." Even more commonly, he sees a face which is not his at all, a face which is suited to his desires or is distorted by his fears.

The problem created by the transforming power of drugs is not entirely different from this problem of our true self and our quest to find ourselves and integrate our personality. The heart of the matter lies in our being able to go below the superficial impressions and standards we tend to live by, and in our being honest and truthful, steadfast and loving. Religion, perhaps, can help us here most of all. Socrates recognized that the true wisdom which so few possessed depended upon the precept "Know thyself." It is this kind of wisdom which the Christian religion lays down as the foundation of virtue and self-development; it says that without humility no progress can be made. Humility has been described as knowing the truth about ourselves and facing it. It is better perhaps, because the appeal to self-knowledge may seem to beg the question, to say that humility is the recognition of what we are in the light of and by comparison with the absolute standard of divine justice and love. The affect of this is seen in the *Confessions* of St. Augustine, and the inspiration in the saying of St. Paul that "I can do all things in Him who strengtheneth me." The self abides in *conspectu Dei.*

Arthur Koestler

SOME ASPECTS OF THE CREATIVE PROCESS

My purpose is to show that art and discovery have more in common than is generally assumed, and to isolate the common denominator. I propose to approach the problem through the back door of humor; for comic art is the only domain of creative activity where a stimulus on a high level of complexity produces a massive response on the reflex level which can be used as an indicator. Allow me to quote a single example:

A marquis at the court of Louis XV entered his wife's boudoir and found her in the arms of a bishop. After a moment's hesitation, he walked to the window and went through the motions of blessing the people in the street. "What are you doing?" cried the anguished wife. "Monseigneur is performing my functions," replied the marquis, "so I am performing his."

If the story is told in a less dehydrated manner, it creates a certain tension which mounts as the narrative progresses (Figure 1, left). But it never reaches its climax; the marquis's unexpected gesture decapitates the logical development of the story, and the tension is exploded in laughter. The crucial factor is the marquis's behavior, which is both *unexpected* and perfectly *logical,* but of a type of logic—the division of labor, the *quid pro quo*—not usually applied to this kind of situation.

I must proceed from this single example to the following generalization, which I have tried to substantiate elsewhere [18]. All experiences that tend to produce laughter have a common element: *the*

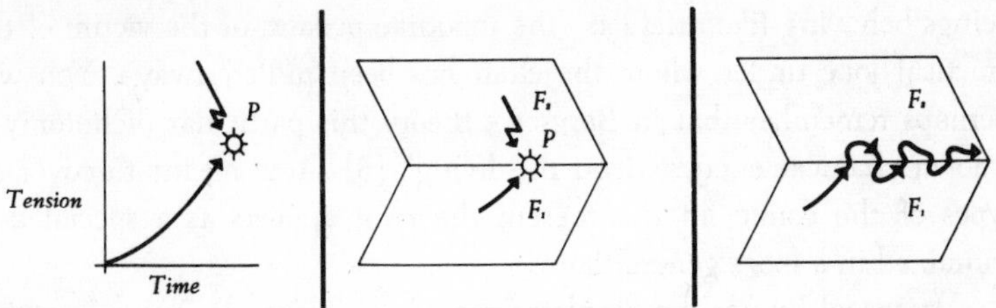

Figure 1

perceiving of a situation or idea, P, in two self-consistent but habitually incompatible associative contexts or frames of reference, F_1 *and* F_2 (Figure 1, center). I shall use the term "frame" rather loosely for a while, and define it later. The pivot *P,* the mental event in which the two frames intersect, is made to vibrate on two different wavelengths, as it were, or translated into Hebb's terms, to participate simultaneously in two independent phase sequences [13]. While this unusual situation lasts, the event is not merely associated with one behavioral pattern but *bisociated* with two. I have coined this barbaric neologism in order to make a distinction between the routine skill of thinking in closed systems [2], on the one hand, and the creative act, on the other. The latter I believe to be based on those transitory stages of unstable equilibrium which the term "bisociation" is meant to imply. The creative act may lead to the integration of the previously separate frames; I shall return to this when we get to the process of discovery. For the moment I am concerned with processes in which the two frames preserve their separate identity—even if they are brought into contact quite often. Figure 1 (right) is meant to represent what happens when a narrative constantly oscillates between, say, the fantasy world of Don Quixote (F_1) and Sancho Panza's universe of hard, obstinate facts (F_2).

Let me briefly mention some of the most common types of the comic. In the *pun* a single sound is bisociated with two different meanings. In the various types of *witticism* a word or situation serves as pivot; the same applies to the comedy of errors. In all forms of *disguise* the impersonator is simultaneously perceived as two beings, himself and somebody else. This applies to the animals of Walt Disney, who behave like human beings; it applies to children at play imitating adults; it applies to artifacts imitating life (Punch and Judy) and to human beings behaving like artefacts (the robotlike pedant, or the victim of the practical joke under whom the chair has been pulled away). You will perhaps remember that in Bergson's theory this particular dichotomy—"the mechanical encrusted on the living" [3]—was meant to cover all types of the comic; in the present theory it appears as a special case contained in a more general law.

In visual humor the simplest form of the *caricature* is the distorting mirror. It reflects one's body elongated or compressed, as if it were nothing but an elastic surface. The caricaturist, however, distorts selectively, by the exaggeration and simplification of relevant features. The result is at the same time visually convincing and biologically impossible, a malicious confrontation of percept and concept (the "narrative" here is of course compressed into quick visual scanning). The *satire* is a verbal caricature of society. For the discussion of other types of the comic I must again refer you to a previous work.

To give one more detailed example, the stumbling block of all theories of the comic is *tickling*. It calls forth the squirming reflex, a striving to withdraw the tickled part, apparently a built-in defense mechanism to escape a hostile grip on vulnerable areas of the body not usually exposed to attack—the soles of the feet, the neck, armpits, belly, and flanks. Tickling a small child will call out a wriggling and squirming response, but the child will only laugh if a second condition is fulfilled: it must perceive the tickling as a mock attack, a caress in aggressive disguise. Mothers and nurses know that battle cries like "peekaboo" and "bow-wow" are as effective as the comedian's imitation of the lion's roar. The element of surprise is also important: the expert tickler never lets the victim guess where the next pressure of pincer movement will occur. Experiments at Yale on babies under one year old showed that they laughed 15 times more often when tickled by their mothers than when tickled by strangers. The mock attack will cause laughter only if the infant recognizes it as a mock attack; even with its own mother there is a slight feeling of uncertainty and apprehension, and it is precisely this tension between two tickles which is relieved in the laughter accompanying the squirm. Thus the process falls under the heading of comic impersonation. The tickler impersonates an aggressor, but is simultaneously known not to be one. In adolescence, erotic elements may replace infantile apprehension, and tickling may become a mock sexual attack. Besides, as in all other forms of the comic, laughter may become a conditioned response to certain standard stimuli.

The sudden bisociation of an event with two habitually incompatible frames of mental organization is a necessary condition of the comic. The element to be added to make it both necessary and sufficient is a grain of adrenalin. The man who slips on a banana skin—the prototype of Bergson's theory of humor—is a comic figure, but he is instantly transformed into a pathetic figure if, in the spectator's mind, aggressive malice is replaced by sympathetic identification. The same applies to Don Quixote and to every other category of the comic. There is only a step from the sublime to the ridiculous, but that step is reversible—and it is surprising that no theorist of art has thought of reversing it. This explains the reason for the back-door approach, for I shall try to show that there is a point-to-point correspondence between humor and art—that the same bisociative patterns provoke comic or esthetic experiences according to the type of emotion which is aroused and the process by which it is discharged.

The characteristic reflexes of comedy and tragedy are laughter and weeping. Laughter gives the impression of a sudden detonation; it explodes energies which have become redundant owing to the abrupt transfer of thought from one associative context to another. Thought is capable of performing such leaps, emotion is not—I mean the aggressive-defensive type of emotion which enters into the comic. It acts as resonance body to the cortical strings of thought; the adrenal-sympathetic system, with its glandular and visceral machinery, has a more massive, persistent, and unidirectional action than the cognitive processes in the neocortex. In a word, this type of emotion has a greater inertia than thought. As a result, the sudden switch to a different kind of logic dissociates emotion from cognition, and the emotion deserted by thought is discharged along the channels of least resistance in the laughter reflex.

In the sustained comic narrative, the oscillation of attention between the two frames results in a continuous discharge of redundant tension in mild amusement. Laughter is a luxury reflex which emerges at an evolutionary level where reasoning has gained a certain degree of autonomy from the utilitarian urges of emotion.

The reflex character of laughter has been demonstrated by Duchenne [6], Charcot, and Richet [26]. Duchenne used galvanic currents to innervate the zygomatic major, and by varying the intensity of the current, produced corresponding facial expressions from faint smiles to the mimicry of loud laughter confined to the innervated half of the face, the other half remaining expressionless. Raulin's serial photographs of tickled babies and of hysterics to whom tickling was conveyed by suggestion showed the reflex swiftly increasing from feeble contraction to the paroxysm of shaking and choking. Concerning the reasons why these specific muscular contractions should serve as a channel of least resistance, Freud [7] suggests the following:

> According to the best of my knowledge, the grimaces and contortions of the corners of the mouth that characterize laughter appear first in the satisfied and satiated nursling when he drowsily quits the breast. . . . This primal sense of pleasurable satisfaction may have furnished the smile, which ever remains the basic phenomenon of laughter, with the later connection with the pleasurable processes of discharge (de-tension).

The breathing action of laughter, with its repeated explosive exhalations, seems designed to "puff away" surplus tension in a kind of respiratory gymnastic, and the vigorous gestures and slapping of thighs obviously serve the same function.

It could be objected that the faint malice aroused by a joke or a caricature would not suffice to bring the adrenal-sympathetic machinery into play; but laughter shares the anachronistic character of other autonomic-nervous-system responses to stimuli which were once biologically relevant (e.g., developing gooseflesh at a screeching noise to make our long-lost body hair bristle in defense against some screeching beast). Such built-in responses may be called "overstatements of the body" and seem to be capable of being triggered off by certain stimuli in quasi-homeopathic doses. Other factors facilitating laughter are conditioning and the socially infectious nature of emotive display.

Weeping, too, is a discharge reflex which relieves emotion. But first, the secretion of tears is activated by the parasympathetic system; second, sobbing—short, deep, gasping inspirations followed by long sighing expirations—is the opposite of the respiratory action in laughter. Third, laughter tends to produce exaggerated gestures and heightened muscle tone, including the coordinated reflex contraction of about 15 facial muscles; in weeping, muscle tone is lowered, the body slumps, the face droops, the head sinks forward. Finally, in laughter tension is suddenly exploded; in weeping it is drained away in a gradual manner which *does not disrupt the unity of thought and emotion.* The emotion discharged in weeping is devoid of the galvanizing quality of the hunger-rage-fear class; instead of begetting muscular activity, it tends toward quiescence and catharsis, lowers respiration and pulse rate; it neutralizes adrenal excitation and, in extreme cases, produces trancelike or comatose states.

Typical situations which elicit emotions of this kind are listening to Mozart, looking at a majestic landscape, and being in love or in bereavement. Each of these activities—or shall we say, passivities—may cause a welling up of emotion and its overflow in tears, while the body is becalmed and its tensions are drained. The common denominator of these heterogeneous experiences is a feeling of participating or *identification* or belonging; the self is experienced as part of a whole—which may be Nature, Mankind, a personal bond, or the *anima mundi.* This is sometimes accompanied by a sensation of the expansion and depersonalization of awareness—Freud's "oceanic feeling"—in which the self seems to dissolve like a grain of salt in a lot of water. I propose to call these the *participative* or *self-transcending emotions (STr).* This is not meant to carry any mystical implications, but merely to convey that in these emotional states the need is felt to behave as part of some real or imagined entity which transcends the boundaries of the individual self, whereas in the hunger-rage-fear type of emotions the ego is experienced as a self-contained unit and the ultimate value. The latter could accordingly be called the *separative* or *self-assertive emotions (SA).*

Extremes apart (e.g., rage tantrums or religious trance), emotive behavior is a compound in which both types of emotion participate. In love—sexual or maternal—the aggressive or possessive SA element and the identificatory STr element may reinforce each other. In restrained animosity they inhibit each other. In the explorer and scientist, ambition is nicely balanced with devotion. In outbreaks of fanaticism, devotion to a creed serves as a catalyzer for destructive mass behavior. Even the elementary activity of feeding has an STr component—expressed in the mystic belief of primitives in sharing the virtues of the devoured animal or enemy, in the communion with the slain god (Zagreus, Orpheus, the Eucharist), and in the rituals of conviviality. Again one is reminded of the various modes of interaction between the two branches of the autonomic nervous system—antagonistic, synergic, catalytic, or overcompensatory, according to circumstances [8,10]—and the term "ambivalence" appears as an oversimplification.

The STr emotions are, of course, not always pleasurable. Pleasure and unpleasure seem to form an independent scale of affective values superimposed on both types of emotion (as brightness values are superimposed on color), indicating satisfaction or frustration of the emotive drive. Crying in bereavement, for instance, may be said to express the frustration of a STr bond.

In a previous work already referred to I mentioned some biological arguments in support of this classification, and suggested that the SA and STr emotions may be related to the interlocking processes of differentiation of structure and integration of function in biological evolution. Be that as it may, and independently of such speculations, the hypothesis of the "polarized" nature of the emotions is based on observable and oft-described phenomena of common emotional behavior, such as the contiguity of the tragic and the comic. In the present confused state of the semantics of emotion, it seems that the criteria to be applied to a new classificatory hypothesis are its heuristic value and its compatibility with neurophysiological data. Regarding the former, the hypothesis seems to yield a unified view of the creative activities in a single continuum. Regarding the latter, the correlation between the SA emotions and the sympathetic nervous system seems to be firmly established and made more specific in detail by recent attempts to discriminate between the hormonal processes in rage and fear [10,11]. To assume a symmetrical correlation of STr emotions with the parasympathetic nervous system would be tempting, but the subject is full of pitfalls. More than 30 years ago, Cannon [4] wrote: "The sympathetic is like the loud and soft pedals, modulating all the notes together; the cranial and sacral innervations are like the separate keys." Since then, the significance for psychology of the anatomical and physiological contrast between the two branches of the autonomic nervous system has become more evident, to the extent that "rage is called the most adrenergic, and love the most cholinergic reaction" [5]. A further correspondence between patterns of emotive behavior and modes of interaction between the two branches of the autonomic nervous system emerged when it was shown that the vagoinsulin system may act, in different circumstances, as an inhibitory or a catalytic agent in the glucose-utilization process and may also produce overcompensatory aftereffects [8,10]. Hebb [13] suggested that a distinction should be made between two categories of emotions, "those in which the tendency is to maintain or increase the original stimulating conditions (pleasurable or integrative emotions)" and "those in which the tendency is to abolish or decrease the stimulus (rage, fear, disgust)." Whereas the latter have a disruptive effect on cortical behavior, the former have not. A few years later, Olds [21,22] and others demonstrated the existence of "positive" and "negative" emotive systems by electric stimulation, and further showed that they were activated respectively by the parasympathetic- and sympathetic-nervous-system centers in the hypothalamus. These hints all seem to point in the same general direction but are not sufficiently precise to allow us at this stage to coordinate the STr emotions with the parasympathetic nervous system. Old's self-stimulating rat, for instance, cannot be said to display any participatory type of emotion—but then it is only a rat, and we can hardly expect to find a platonic component in its sex drive. Finally, it bears repetition that neither the STr emotions nor the parasympathetic reactions are always pleasurable [9,10,21]; the only description which does not lead into self-contradictions seems to be that pleasure and unpleasure (discomfort, frustration, as distinct from pain) are specially coded signals indicating progress or otherwise toward fulfillment of the emotional need—which seems to resolve von Neuman's paradox that "a sadist is a person who is kind to a mascochist."

To sum up, impulses generated by the SA emotions tend toward overt muscular activity; those of the STr emotions seem to be consummated in internal behavior, in visceral and glandular processes, with a general tendency towards quiescence and catharsis. The former act through a coordinated, massive machinery; the latter have no comparable physiological apparatus at their disposal, and above all, they do not tend to fall out of step with the cognitive process. When the schoolmaster's chair collapses under him, one of two things will happen. If my attitude toward him is dominated by aggression and apprehension, emotion will persist in its course, and the sudden debunking of authority by gravity will make it explode in a giggle. If, however, my attitude is one of sympathetic identification, it will be instantly transferred to the teacher's new behavioral field, and the sprawling figure will become

Aggression, dissociation, detonation	*Identification, integration, catharsis*
Impersonation	Illusion
Comedy	Tragedy
Coincidence	Fate
Caricature	Character portrait
Pun	Assonance, rhyme
Comic simile	Metaphor, image
Satire	Allegory
Man and artifact	Puppets of destiny

Self-transcending

Self-assertive

Figure 2 The SA emotions dominate humor; they are aggressive, lead to the dissociation of thought from emotion, and to sudden discharge. The reverse is true of the STr emotions, which dominate art: they tend toward identification, integration, and catharsis. The empty column in the center will be filled in later.

an object of anxious compassion. Rage is immune to reasoning; but sympathy rcmains attached to understanding, whatever surprises understanding has in store for it. This distinction assumes basic importance when STr emotions are fed into the same bisociative patterns I have discussed before.

The counterpart of comic impersonation is *dramatic illusion.* It is the simultaneous presence and interaction in the mind of two universes, one real, one imaginary. It transports the spectator from the trivial present to a field remote from self-interest. This is achieved by the lure of heroes and victims with whom the spectator identifies himself in varying degrees, forgetting his own preoccupations. Thus illusion excites STr and inhibits or neutralizes SA emotions. Even when fear and anger are aroused in the spectator, these are vicarious emotions, derived from his identification with the hero, which in itself is a self-transcending act. Vicarious emotions aroused in this manner carry a dominant element of sympathy, which facilitates catharsis—in conformity with the Aristotelian definition—"through incidents arousing horror and pity to accomplish the purgation of such emotions."

The *plot* of a drama or novel is, broadly speaking, based on situation and/or character. In the first case, the entanglement of two independent causal chains in a focal event creates coincidence or misunderstanding or conflict, as the case may be, all of which are mainstays of both tragedy and comedy. In the second case, the conflict is between incompatible temperaments, or scales of values, or codes of behavior; it is fought out either within the same person, or between different persons, or between hero and society. In all these variants the author aims at compelling his audience to accept both conflicting frames as valid within their own terms of reference, which leads to a clash, in the spectator's mind, between two simultaneous and incompatible identifications.

There is no sharp division between *caricature* and portrait; Daumier's and Leonardo's character sketches fit either column, depending on attitudes of sympathy or derision. The technique of stressing relevant aspects by exaggeration and simplification is common to both; the artist calls it stylization. When Picasso shuffles about the eyes and limbs of his figures in a manner that is biologically impossible and yet visually convincing, he operates, like the caricaturist, through the bisociation of perceptual and conceptual frames. I am using the term "conceptual" loosely, meaning that the artist superimposes a selective filter F_2 on his visual field F_1 (Figure 1); he sees in terms of his medium—stone, clay, charcoal, or pigment—and in terms of his preferential emphasis on contours or surfaces, angles or curves, stability or motion. Moreover, in painting a landscape he transposes experienced space into the confines of a wooden frame, whereby the ratio of focal to peripheral vision is increased about a hundredfold, which may be one of the reasons why nature is so much prettier on picture postcards. Man has always looked at nature through some frame—mythological, anthropomorphical, or metaphysical. A hexagon on the drawing board does not strike one as beautiful; nor does a snowflake; but when we discover that a snowflake is made up of perfect hexagonal patterns, we marvel at the "cleverness of nature."

The *rhyme* is a glorified pun, the confluence of two rhythmically patterned streams of thought. It developed out of rhythm via alliteration and assonance, as primitive melody grew out of unmodulated beats. The function of rhythm, according to Yeats, is "to lull the mind into a waking trance." According to Richards [27], "We do not merely perceive the pattern, but are becoming patterned ourselves." Like the shaman's tomtom, the rhythmic beat awakens archaic resonances. So does the rhyme. It echoes the tendency to vocal repetition in the language of primitives and children (kala-kala, ma-ma) and the tendency to associate by sound, reflected in the prevalence of puns in juvenile humor and Freudian dreams. The subjects of Luria and Vinogradova [20], who normally associated words by meaning, when made drowsy by chloral hydrate regressed to association by sound.

A further case in point is Foerster's patient [1], who, during an operation on a third ventricle tumor, burst into an apparently manic flight of punning which, however, contained a meaningful request to the surgeon to proceed carefully. When the surgeon asked for a *Tupfer* (tampon), the patient yelled, "*Tupfer, Hupfer, Huepfer, huepfen Sie mal. . .*" On hearing the word *Messer,* he burst into "*Messer, messer, Metzer. Sie sind ein Metzer, ein Metzel, das ist ja ein Gemetzel, metzeln Sie doch nicht so messen Sie doch, sie messen ja nicht Herr Professor, profiteor, professus sum, profiteri.*" These responses were dependent on manipulation of the tumor and could be elicited only from the floor of the third ventricle. The patient functioned, as the poet does, under the dual control of two different levels in the neural hierarchy.

This applies not only to thinking patterned by rhythm and rhyme, but also to the sources of *poetic imagery.* Pictorial thinking precedes conceptual thinking; poetic statements are projections of conceptual thought into the ancient "picture-strip language" [19] of the bushman—and the sleeper. The creative act always involves a *regression* to older levels in the mental hierarchy while a simultaneous process continues in parallel on the highest and most articulate level—it reminds one of a skin diver with a breathing tube. To put it another way, the artist bisociates frames of common, everyday experience with frames of greater emotive potential, a procedure which facilitates catharsis, the earthing of the emotive current. At the same time, the transposition of a familiar experience into a different frame makes it appear in a new, unfamiliar significant light; and this simultaneous occurrence of *intellectual illumi-*

nation and *emotional catharsis,* which are complementary aspects of the bisociative process, seems to be the essence of the esthetic experience.

This process is, I suggest, also the essence of scientific discovery. When a datum of experience is abruptly transferred from its habitual context F_1 into a new context F_2, it will be perceived from a different angle, and attention may fasten on some aspect of it which is irrelevant in the terms of reference of F_1 but relevant in the terms of F_2. This shift of emphasis, or *displacement effect,* is a crucial feature of the bisociative act in all three domains of creative activity. Koehler's chimpanzee Sultan discovered the making of tools when, for the first time, he broke off a branch from a tree and used it as a stick to rake in a banana. In its habitual frame F_1 the branch was seen as part of a visual and functional whole, the tree. However, Sultan was occupied with searching for a stick, and this occupation provided the frame F_2, so that when his glance fell on the branch, attention was displaced onto the previously irrelevant and unnoticed aspect of its sticklikeness. The branch was wrenched out of its context and made part of another context. Thus, when Sultan discovered the hidden similarity between twisted branch and straight stick, he confirmed the old saying that discovery consists in seeing an analogy where nobody had seen one before. And that, of course, applies equally to the discoveries of the poet and the humorist.

At this point it becomes necessary to give a more precise meaning to the term "frame." A frame of behavior in the present hypothesis is defined as an innate or acquired skill governed by a code of invariant rules. The common spider will suspend its web on three, four, or more handy points of attachment, but the radial threads will always intersect the laterals at equal angles; the performance is thus adaptable to environmental conditions, yet governed by a fixed code. The pianist who transposes a tune into a different key, the chess player, the physicist, all display a flexible strategy while obeying the rules of the game.

The term "code" is not meant as a metaphor, but to refer to a schema of neural organization. The difference between the concept of "behavioral frames" and such old friends as "*Aufgabe,*" "set," "determining tendency," "*Gestalt,*" etc., lies in the postulate of a hierarchy of codes which govern the principles of behavior on all levels, i.e., limit the degrees of freedom to permissible variations of strategy within the confines of invariant rules. A frame (e.g., a verbal skill) is not defined by the sum total of components (words, syntactic units) which have been recruited into its service in the past, but by its code. In the various aphasias and kindred disorders, it is not this or that component of a skill which is affected, but the master switch which governs the entire skill. Similiarly, *en continuant cette phrase en français* and then reverting to English, millions of neural assemblies are simultaneously affected by "throwing the switch." The same applies to verbal tests in naming synonyms, antonyms, etc., or to Foerster's patient and the experimental subjects of Luria and Vinogradova, who switched from semantic to phonetic association.

Vice versa, a component (e.g., a word) is a member of several established frames of reference governed by different codes. Metaphorically speaking, it is a member of several clubs, but it likes some clubs better than others, where the atmosphere is more familiar or relaxing than in those governed by highly formal codes; the effort of concentrating on a process of sustained complex reasoning is probably expended on inhibiting drift into frames with higher energy potentials. From the neurophysiologist's point of view, a model for a code presents the same, but probably no greater, headache than a model for a trace; on the other hand, the altered approach may simplify some aspects of the neuropsychology of thought.

When the same task is repeatedly set under unchanging conditions, the skill will tend to degenerate into an automatism. Vice versa, a variable environment will tend to create flexible behavior. But variation may reach a point at which the situation, although it still resembles *in some respects* other situations encountered in the past, contains some new feature which makes it impossible to solve the problem within the confines of the behavioral frame applied to those past situations. If this happens, the situation is *blocked*—though the subject may realize this only after a delay, or never at all.

A blocked situation increases the stress of the frustrated drive. When all hopeful attempts have been exhausted, thought runs in circles like the cats in Thorndike's puzzlebox, and random trials make their appearance, accompanied by rage behavior—or the distractedness of creative obsession. At this stage—the "period of incubation"—the whole personality, down to the unverbalized and unconscious layers, becomes saturated with the problem, so that on some level of the nervous system it remains active even while attention is occupied in a quite different field—such as the chimpanzee's looking at a tree, or Archimedes's watching the rise of the bath water displaced by the immersion of his body, or Darwin's reading Malthus's essay on population while searching for a cause of natural selection. Thus a favorable chance event may provide the opportunity for bringing a new frame to bear down vertically, so to speak, on the problem blocked in its old horizontal context.

In the cases that I mentioned, chance consisted in hitting on a pivot, and triggered off the fusion between the two previously unconnected frames. But countless other chance opportunities in human history must have passed unnoticed; for the fusion to take place, a further condition is necessary, which one may call *ripeness*. The chimpanzee's ripeness for his discovery is given in the primate's manual dexterity, its oculomotor coordination, and so forth; a dog may carry a stick between its teeth, but will never learn to use it as a rake. Thus the statistical probability for a relevant discovery is greater the better established and exercised each of the still separate skills. This may account for the recurrent phenomenon of simultaneous discoveries, and for the independent development of the same techniques and styles of art in different cultures.

But the role of chance is a subordinate one. In searching for an appropriate new frame to unblock the blocked situation, the mind does not grope completely in the dark; it often proceeds in a vaguely sensed direction, guided by nascent, unverbalized analogies which run approximately like this: "Something reminds me of something, but I don't know what reminds me of what and why." This groping toward each other of the two mental processes in solving a problem, described, for example, by Polya [24,25], oddly reminds one of Kappers's suggestions on neurobiotaxis [16]. At any rate, the creative stress seems to set up energy gradients of some sort in the unconscious. An intuition may be likened to an immersed chain of which only the beginning and the end emerge over the surface. The diver vanishes at one end of the chain and, as if by miracle, comes up at the other end, because he had the underwater guidance of the invisible links.

The nature of these links is intimated by the language of the dream, when the codes of disciplined thinking are suspended, and the stream of association is free to drift, by its own emotive gravity as it were, from one frame to another each time an appropriate pivot offers itself. Hence the prevalence in dreaming of the familiar bisociative patterns—punning, shift of emphasis, displacement, disguise, double identity, the discovery of hidden similarities. But since the reasoning codes are dormant, there is no simultaneous juxtaposition of logical frames, whereas in the waking state the same bisociative processes will cause comic, tragic, or illuminating effects. A broomstick serving as a phallic symbol is, after all, but an optical pun—one visual form bisociated with two functional contexts—just as the chimpanzee's discovery that a branch is a stick, or Newton's discovery that the moon is a falling apple. Thus in the dream the creative techniques are reflected upside down, as it were, like trees in a pond. The most fertile region seems to be the hypnagogic borderland, where the frames of reasoning are operative yet still sufficiently hazy to allow a dreamlike freedom of thought [*cf.* 23, 12].

This leads to another aspect of the creative process. The code of rules which governs the performance of a skill functions on a lower level of awareness than the performance itself. The paradox of the centipede applies not only to motor skills such as bicycling, but also to perceptual skills such as recognizing universals, and to reasoning skills. In ordinary conversation, the rules of grammar, syntax, and common or garden logic function below the conscious level because they have been learned "by ear," as the gypsy learns to fiddle without knowing musical notation. Hence the difficulty of defining the rules which define our thinking; and semantic analysis is a pretty sterile procedure. But when two universes of discourse suddenly meet in the creative act, what was taken for granted no longer is, and implied assumptions are dragged into the daylight. Thus discovery often consists in uncovering what has always been there, but had been ignored (like the rise of the water level on getting into a bath) or masked by prejudices and fallacies woven into the texture of orthodox schemata. Each creative act has its destructive side; it disrupts codes of behavior and patterns of thought which have outlived their usefulness and reshuffles the data of experience into a new pattern. It is a *reculer pour mieux sauter*, a dedifferentiation as a condition of reintegration, a mild form of shock therapy. Ernest Jones [15] has remarked that the creative genius seems to be a mixture of scepticism and credulity. Of course he must be; he must take nothing for granted and read a camel into the shape of a cloud.

The sudden illumination of the creative act is usually followed by the laborious work of elaboration and verification. If all goes well, the two frames, after undergoing certain modifications, will in the end fuse into a single one. When two wave fronts meet, we get interference. When two frames of reference interpenetrate, we gain new insights by mental synthesis—and this, I believe, is the essence of free learning, as opposed to stamped-in conditioning, the differential factor being the organism's ripeness for that particular synthesis to occur. Once the child has made the fundamental discovery that everything has a name, the attaching of verbal tags to things becomes a routine and sometimes a compulsion, because unnamed objects now appear incomplete, like molecules with free valences in the integrated field. Not the chaining of reflexes or the association of individual concepts, but the integration of autonomous subwholes, or innate or acquired behavioral patterns, seems to be the method of the nervous system of adding 1 and 1 together in the integrative hierarchy of mental evolution. The meaning of a concept is defined by its contexts, and not the other way round; it is not a mental atom, but rather something like a Schroedinger electron, a blur traveling in a wave packet.

To sum up: routine thinking, according to the codified rules derived from past experience, can solve problems only within its own frame of reference. Creative thinking, on the other hand, involves a "thinking aside" [12] on a different plane. In the various forms of art, the two planes always remain in lively juxtaposition without merging—which provides an added dimension to experience; in the emotionally neutral arts of science, they become eventually integrated into a more complex level of the hierarchy. This difference is reflected in the quasi-linear progress of science, as contrasted with the quasi-timeless character of art, its continual restatement of certain basic emotional experiences in changing idioms but without cumulative effect.

By calling science the emotionally neutral art, I did not mean absence of emotion, which would be the equivalent of apathy, but that particularly well-balanced and integrated blend of emotions which is the driving power behind exploration and research. The exploratory drive is a mixture of self-assertive motives such as ambition, competi-

	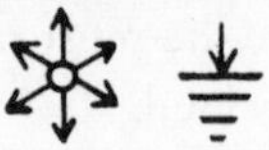	
Pun	Anagram, crossword	Assonance, rhyme
Witticism	Epigram	Parable
Satire	Social criticism	Allegory
Comic simile	Hidden analogy	Poetic image
Comic displacement	Change of conceptual frame	Change of perceptual filter
Debunking	Implied assumptions revealed	"Fauvism"
Coincidence	Trigger action of chance	Deus ex machina
Impersonation	Empathy	Illusion
Imitation by mechanisms	Investigation of human mechanism	Puppets of destiny
Caricature	Schema	Portrait

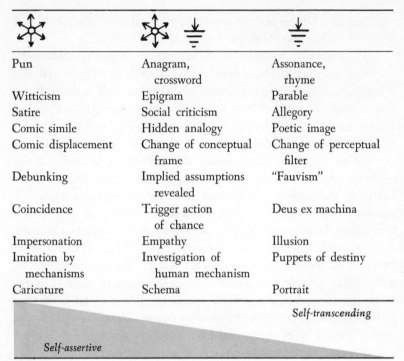

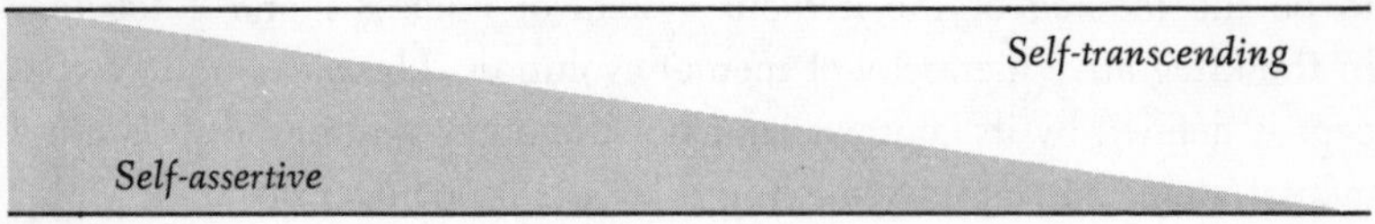

Self-transcending

Self-assertive

Figure 3

tion, and financial necessity, on the one hand, and on the other, a disinterested, self-transcending absorption in, shall we say, the wonders and mysteries of nature, based on an act of faith—the belief that there *is* a harmony of the spheres, a cosmic law and order waiting to be discovered and named. Accordingly, there are two sides to the manifestation of emotion at the moment of discovery: first, the triumphant explosion of the self-assertive stress, which has suddenly become redundant, precisely as in the joke and for the same reasons—so you jump out of the bath and run through the streets laughing and shouting *Eureka!*—and second, the gradual catharsis of the self-transcending component due to the fact that the particular problem has been "earthed," that is, resolved into a more general frame of greater explanatory power—just as in art tension is drained by transfer into a frame of greater emotive capacity. The Greek ideal of beauty was a body of perfect geometrical proportions, the physicist's ideal of truth is a unified field theory; both aim at earthing particular experiences in a universal frame of order.

Thus we arrived at a kind of triptych, the three panels of which show a horizontal point-to-point correspondence of logical patterns, and superimposed on it a continuous emotive spectrum from the aggressive through the neutral to the integrative arts—a kind of two-dimensional continuum of the creative processes. The pole at the left in Figures 2 and 3 stands for sudden discharge, that at the right for gradual catharsis. The continuity between the left and central panels can be demonstrated, for instance, by the gradual shading of coarse joke into subtle wit into epigram, then into metaphor or parable. The more subtle the joke, the more it approximates the riddle of the *New Yorker* cartoon type. When we have "seen" the joke, the aggressive or sexual voltage that it carried is detonated in laughter and gloating, while the glow of intellectual satisfaction derived from solving the riddle ebbs slowly away, as in discovery. The higher forms of art, which hint rather than state, also speak in riddles; and we get a symmetrically reversed transition towards the right end of the spectrum, from the highly intellectualized forms of art towards the more sensual and emotive, ending in the thought-free beatitude of the oceanic feeling—the cloud of unknowing. To take another example, the Bergsonian confrontation of the mechanical and the living becomes in the neutral panel the subject matter of the biological sciences and of the philosophical inquiry into free will and determinism; in the right-hand panel we get man as the tragic puppet of his gods or chromosomes. The comedy of characters changes into the analysis of character, then into drama—with psychodrama therapy as the latest link. The continuity and spatial order of the three panels is borne out by the fact that in all Indo-European languages "witticism" is derived from "wit" in its original sense of ingenuity, derived via *videre* from *veda,* knowledge. On the other side of the triptych, the fluidity of the boundaries between science and art, in chess or architecture, psychiatry or historiography, is equally obvious. The pre-Socratians wrote their philosophy and science in verse; and adjectives like "beautiful," "elegant," "witty," etc., are applied to all three domains. The panels should really form a hollow half-cylinder to indicate that you can, of course, take short cuts from the tragic to the comic diagonally, without passing through the neutral zone.

Finally, the caricaturist's technique of exaggerating relevant features and simplifying or ignoring the rest is applied by the scientist whenever he draws a graph or a topographical map or constructs a model. Every schematic or symbolic representation is an unemotional caricature of reality, and the type of model that results depends very much on the temperament of its maker. There is, of course, the criterion of verifiability, but that is a matter of gradations.

You can verify a prediction, but not the theory on which the prediction is based. Consider, for instance, the precise predictions made by Babylonian and Ptolemaic astronomy, or those which pour out of that welter of contradictions which is modern physics. Thus we get a continuous curve of increasing verifiability in this limited sense, from the vaguely predictable effect of a joke or poem, through historiography, the social sciences, psychology, biology, up to mathematical physics, where the

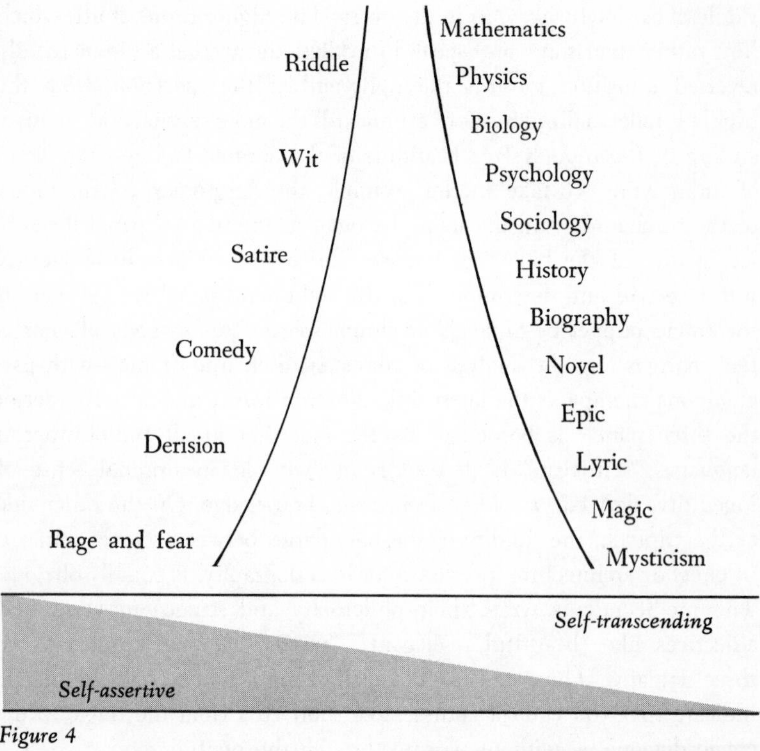

Figure 4

curve becomes an asymptote—or so one hopes; but it remains a continuous curve which does not indicate where witticism changes into wit, nor where science stops and art begins.

References

1. Association for Research in Nervous and Mental Diseases, *The Hypothalamus and Central Levels of Autonomic Function,* Baltimore, The Williams & Wilkins Company, 1940, vol. XX.
2. Bartlett, Sir F., *Thinking: An Experimental and Social Study,* London, George Allen & Unwin, Ltd., 1958.
3. Bergson, H. L., *Le Rire,* 15th ed., Paris, F. Alcan, 1916.
4. Cannon, W. B., *Bodily Changes in Pain, Hunger, Fear and Rage,* 2d ed., New York, D. Appleton & Company, Inc., 1929.
5. Cobb, S., *Emotions and Clinical Medicine, New York,* W. W. Norton & Company, Inc., 1950.
6. Duchenne (De Boulogne), G., *Le Mechanisme de la Physionomie Humaine,* Paris, P. Asselin, 1862.
7. Freud, S., *Gesammelte Werke,* London, Imago Publishing Company, 1940, vol. VI.
8. Gellhorn, E., *Autonomic Regulations,* New York, Interscience Publishers, Inc., 1943.
9. Gellhorn, E., *Physiological Foundations,* New York, Interscience Publishers, Inc., 1953.
10. Gellhorn, E., *Autonomic Imbalance,* New York, Interscience Publishers, Inc., 1957.
11. Gellhorn, E., Recent Contributions to the Physiology of the Emotions, *Psychiatric Research Reports of the American Psychiatric Association,* January, 1960.
12. Hadamard, J., *The Psychology of Invention in the Mathematical Field,* Princeton, N.J.: Princeton University Press, 1949.
13. Hebb, D. O., *The Organization of Behavior,* New York, John Wiley & Sons, Inc., 1949.
14. Hebb, D. O., The Problem of Consciousness and Introspection, in *Brain Mechanisms and Consciousness: A Symposium,* Oxford, Basil Blackwell & Mott, Ltd., 1954.
15. Jones, E., The Nature of Genius, *British Med. J.,* 1956 (4):8.
16. Kappers, A., et al., *The Evolution of the Nervous System in Invertebrates and Man,* New York, The Macmillan Company, 1936.
17. Koehler, W., *The Mentality of Apes,* London, Kegan Paul, 1925.

18. Koestler, A., *Insight and Outlook,* New York, The Macmillan Company, 1949.
19. Kretschmer, E., *A Textbook of Medical Psychology* (trans. with introduction by E. B. Strauss), London, H. Milford, 1934.
20. Luria, A. R., and Vinogradova, O. S., The Objective Investigation of the Dynamics of Semantic Systems, *British J. Psychol.,* May, 1959.
21. Olds, J., Studies of Neuropharmacologicals by Electrical and Chemical Manipulation of the Brain in Animals with Chronically Implanted Electrodes, *Proceedings of the First International Congress of Neuro-Pharmacology,* Amsterdam – London – New York – Princeton, Elsevier Publishing Company, 1959.
22. Olds, J., Positive Emotional Systems Studied by Techniques of Self-stimulation, *Psychiatric Research Reports of the American Psychiatric Association,* January, 1960.
23. Poincaré, H., Mathematical Creation, in *The Creative Process: A Symposium,* Berkeley, Calif.: University of California Press, 1952.
24. Polya, G., Wie Sucht Man die Losung Mathematischer Aufgaben? *Acta Psychol.,* 1938, IV:2.
25. Polya, G., *How to Solve It,* 5th ed., Princeton, N.J.: Princeton University Press, 1948.
26. Raulin, J. M., *Étude Anatomique, Psycho-physiologique et Pathologique sur le Rire et les Exhilarants,* Paris, J. B. Balliere & Fils, 1899.
27. Richards, I. A., *Principles of Literary Criticism,* London, Kegan Paul, 1924.

INDIVIDUAL AND GROUP DECISION

This is an actual transcription of the formal but spontaneous panel discussion of the papers immediately preceding. Only minor editing has been done where continuity and clarity required it. The editors feel that the spontaneity of the actual discussion gives a particular value to the panel in this form.

Moderator: Seymour M. Lipset
Panel Members: Martin C. D'Arcy, S. J., H. Stuart Hughes, Arthur Koestler, C. A. Mace

Prof. Lipset In his new book *The Two Cultures* C. P. Snow described the problem of the cause of the presumed absence of a dialogue between those who have been more involved or interested in the humanistic disciplines and those involved in what we call the natural or physical sciences. One of the purposes of this symposium is to bring together people from the humanities, including religion and the social sciences, on the one hand, and people from the biological and medical sciences, on the other. I think this panel will enable us to begin to bridge in straight face-to-face dialogue some of the problems that Sir Charles Snow has argued must be bridged if we are going to resolve the key political and social problems of our era. I felt that Mr. Koestler and Professor Mace tried to bring together the world of science and the world of the humanities and their separate approaches and concepts. But I think one way in which we might start this discussion would be to take up the challenge which Father D'Arcy has posed to most of us who have been involved in one way or another with a very scientific approach to the study of human behavior. He suggested that by attempting to explain human behavior, particularly the behavior of the mind and brain in terms of materialistic assumptions, and by limiting our variables to more or less physically measurable and quantifiable factors, we are somehow missing what is the essence of the human being. There is something else there which is involved in the process of reason and in the person and soul that presumably cannot be measured. I think that by not considering truth as a variable one does violence to an understanding of how people behave and what makes them behave as they do.

Prof. Mace In considering the subject which we have come to discuss, individual and group decision, I am naturally predisposed to start with the small problems, the sort of problems that can be tackled in the laboratory and in experimental committees. There are many suggestions to be found in the working of groups and in the study of the kind of mixture of groups and different approaches which come nearer, I think, to a philosophical problem in the constitutional committees. I take the view that nothing goes on in the individual mind which cannot go on in the collective mind of a group, such as a committee. The worst type of committee, I think, is a homogeneous committee. Ideally, a committee requires two types of members: what I would call the creative members and the critical members. The best kind of thinking comes about in both the individual and the group in a situation where you get the right sort of mixture of creative and critical activity. I think the kind of problems with which Father D'Arcy and Arthur Koestler are concerned are those in which the emphasis is perhaps on the creative type of thinking. But creative thinkers, I suggest, are not at their best when they are just alone as creative thinkers. Again I go back to a committee. I suggest that a committee of management, for example, requires men of vision, creative people full of ideas, but it also needs the humdrum, cautious accountants and people who calculate and say, "Be careful; you can't do this." I suggest that if you have a committee or a group composed entirely of creative people, the ship will soon be on the rocks; if you have a committee composed entirely of cautious accountants the ship will never get launched. I think that was the sort of starting point for the consideration of the rather larger forms of the creative thinking with which Father D'Arcy and Arthur Koestler were concerned.

Prof. Hughes I am impressed with the fact that Father D'Arcy does not seem to differ from most of the speakers here as much as he had suggested. If I am correct, we have been using four or five terms, all of which can be connected with equals signs, and the vocabulary depends to a considerable extent on whether one is a religious believer or not. Soul equals self equals mind equals spirit equals human being. Roughly it seems to me that we have been using these terms interchangeably, with the religious using certain terminology and the irreligious another. I would say that there were two basic statements made previously in this symposium which again bear out the fact that in one sense or another we are all with Father D'Arcy. The first was Dr. Penfield's introductory statement, that mind and brain are different and that nobody yet, as Freud and many others have said, has been able to trace the exact connection between the two. Brain is the raw material, the machinery of the mind, but how the mind works the brain nobody knows. The other basic statement, it seems to me, was that drugs act on the brain, but we don't know how they act on the mind. They seem simply to have a physiological reaction on the brain in terms of slowing it up or slowing up some physiological process, speeding up certain other processes, in extreme cases cutting off processes entirely, but they do not affect thought in the sense of contributing new thought. Perhaps they jumble thought, but they do not put new thought in. As I understand it, the drug has not been invented which can put a new idea into the brain that will, in turn, enter the mind. So I think that what I would call a spiritual interpretation of our proceedings seems to be agreed upon by virtually everybody, and that the mind-brain dichotomy is not a serious one in our transaction.

Prof. Lipset Mr. Koestler, would you like to comment?

Mr. Koestler I think you were too moderate, Professor Lipset, in making a parallel between the cold war of the humanities versus the sciences and the tension between religion and both. The relation of religion to the humanities, on the one hand, and to science, on the other, is really a triangular problem, but we can treat it as one here. When you look at creative individuals, whether poets or scientists, with a religious conviction, you find that religious conviction has acted as a motivation—and when I say "religious" I mean it in a very broad sense. A classic example is Johannes Kepler. He set out to discover India and he found America. He wanted to prove that the arrangements of all the planets obeyed, first, certain geometrical rules, and second, certain musical rules, the "harmony of the spheres." Now, neither of these happens to be the case, yet in pursuing this he found his own new truths. So let's leave the personal, mystical convictions of an individual alone; psychotherapists have accepted that for a long time. On the other hand, let's not have dogmatic religion staking claims in a different universe and creating discords. At the time before the Galileo scandal, when the leading astronomers in Europe were Jesuit Fathers, they did not try to discover the seat of the angels; they were playing the mathematical game of astronomy. They didn't cheat. So let's have a peaceful coexistence between the two domains and in individual exchanges never touch the deep convictions of the other. I should go one step further: don't even touch the deep religious convictions of an atheist. I have seen people of a materialist persuasion who, when they got some evidence that extrasensory perception might exist, reacted in a way that almost amounted to loss of faith and a nervous breakdown.

Father D'Arcy I hold strongly that each pursuit has its own terrain and that there should be full liberty within it. If one is true to one's own conviction and true to the theory of life which I hold, one ought to be insistent on saying, "I welcome all knowledge and welcome every developing science within its own limits." What I think is a great danger always is that you can become conditioned merely by finding out, by treading so long in your own particular field that it becomes your whole universe. Just as you deal with mathematical methods, so you deal in qualitative things. After a time you deal with material things, that is the serious part; so that within your line—it used to be called your degree of abstraction—you deal with it; you are completely within your right. I would say that belief in the Christian religion can be proved by reason and has its own authenticity. But the actual dogmas which arise out of a feeling are not susceptible to scientific questions. Nor have religious men any right to interfere with scientific questions; the case of Galileo was complete folly. I would rather speak as a philosopher. I brought in theology more as it always used to be—not a dogmatic theology, but a theology which belongs to mankind, which you can think out, such as a belief in providence, a realization of God's looking after you, and the existence of an afterlife. All those matters I hold not to be dogmatic but to belong to thinking. You may think I am wrong there, but I would not be afraid to argue on it.

Prof. Mace I would say that the most effective types of groups in thinking are those with rather sharp and contrasted differences. I think it is very important to have conferences to get scientists, philosophers, and religious thinkers together. Conferences such as this one give such mixed groups time to establish some kind of communication.

Father D'Arcy Theology until quite recent time was always considered a part of philosophy. Aristotle went on to metaphysics after dealwith the physical world. He thought it quite necessary to perceive the idea of a thinker who thought his own thoughts. I hold that every discipline has its own special training. But the religious philosophy gives, I suggest, a complete picture of the world which no other philosophy can give. This philosophy explains questions such as those raised by existentialists about death, about concern, and about objects of permanence of your pursuits, the ending of your life, and what the values are. I shall give you an example of what I mean. I was brought up at Oxford with really strict analytical philosophers who would say, "This is the notion of duty that nothing else could explain," because already you knew what that duty was and what the knowledge was. So it was useless to talk further about it; everything else was rubbish. I always felt there was a gap there. You may say to yourself, for instance, "I know it is wrong to tell a lie, I know it is wrong to be unjust to someone else," and if this is unmeaning, isn't it really just a feeling or a sentiment, and why should I follow that moral code? But if you have a whole constructed universe to support your view and a theory of life which bears it out in every kind of way, then you have a philosophy of life.

Prof. Lipset In former times, religion dealt with science or matters taken up by science in ways in which it now no longer deals; for example, formerly it dealt with astronomy, physics, and the like. The reason Father D'Arcy reacted as strongly as he did is that there is a moral conflict posed between certain assumptions about human behavior and motivation inherent in any religious thought and the way in which pharmacologists, social scientists, or psychologists analyze human behavior and, in particular, tackle the study of the mind. In dealing with this problem, I suggest that in a certain sense Father D'Arcy—who is perfectly correct in rejecting my assertion if he wishes to do so—is considering certain variables and making certain assumptions about the factors affecting the mind and reasoning which are ignored by social scientists, pharmacologists, chemists, and physiologists dealing with mental processes. Now, can, and should, these be introduced into the study? In the same way, Prof. Leo Strauss, a political philosopher, has argued that one of the troubles with social science analyses, or solutions such as group decisions as discussed by Professor Mace, is that the social scientist ignores truth. Professor Strauss would argue that the truth is a factor in the determinant of any situation, and that if the historian, sociologist, or psychologist wants to explain how and why people behave, he should assume that a rational person would be more likely to choose what Professor Strauss calls the "true" solution to any problem This would be that solution most congruent with divine or natural law, or which permits one to adapt to a given situation. He and some of his intellectual disciples have been most critical of so-called behavioral sciences for ignoring the truth as a variable. There is a real split in that the philosophers and the theologians speak largely to themselves, and the scientists on the whole, simply ignore the problem altogether. I may be interpreting incorrectly, but I think in a sense Father D'Arcy was reacting strongly to that today. Would I be right?

Father D'Arcy I am too pugnacious. Yes, I do very much agree with what you are saying. You see, I was raised in the analytic philosophy of the old Oxford. I was brought up by Wilson, the ablest man I can think of. What his school intended to do was to find logical inconsistencies in a scientist when he went outside his scientific statements. For example, I remember a letter written to the *London Times* which said, "It is high time we all acknowledged as certain that there is no such thing as absolute truth." To point out his logical inconsistency, I wrote a letter saying, "Would you rub out the first part of that sentence, please." In other words, his own statement was put down as an absolute: he said that it is an absolute truth that there is no absolute truth. In that sense you cannot have a variable: you can't make a statement at all.

From the Floor I would like to refer back to Professor Mace's "aimless biological activity." What would be the consequences to an organism, in the light of isolation experiments, if such an organism, instead of engaging in this aimless activity, were to do nothing?

Prof. Mace Well, I don't quite like the question; I would rather answer it in a different form. I did not say anything about aimless biological activity; I think on the whole I am prepared to say that all behavior is goal-directed; that is, it has an aim. What I was trying to say was that the goals are not restricted to what is ordinarily called survival; there are all sorts of biologically useless activities. They do not conduce either to self-preservation or race preservation or to what are ordinarily stated as the biological needs of men, but they are goals. I wished to stress the point that we want either to note a category of goals, which I should be prepared to call psychological goals, or we have to extend and liberalize the concept of biological goals. I was prepared to compromise on that and say that perhaps the simplest way of doing it is to define the biological ends as two-dimensional: not merely the prolongation of life as such, but the prolongation of life which has a certain quality. At the human level, this quality of life is probably much more important than the duration of life. In other words, most human beings would prefer to have a shorter life of a certain quality than a longer life of no quality. If pharmacologists could produce a drug to put one into a gentle, comfortable, and dreamless sleep for 200 years, I would not be awfully excited about the prospect.

From the Floor Mr. Koestler, I want to refer to your concept of self-transcendence—which implies one's merging into something greater than one's self. Does not that include an element of religion?

Mr. Koestler I made a specific warning not to take this term in any mystical sense. I said I used this term in a purely technical sense. The individual behaves as if the supreme value were not himself, but as if he were part of a higher unity, whether this unity be society or the beloved one or the *anima mundi* or God or the Atma; which of these he chooses is irrelevant in this context.

PART FOUR

THE IMPACT OF TECHNOLOGY ON THE MIND

Chairman: William R. Dennes

In the fourth and final phase of the symposium, attention turned to the particular problems raised by modern technological advance for students of the mind and its operation, again with special emphasis upon the extent to which control of human thought was implied in such technological innovation. The principal points considered in the papers were the significance of new techniques for processing information, and especially the immense potential of the electronic computing machine; the relation between mass media for disseminating information and control of the mind, particularly in the political sphere; and the significance of ideology, with its concomitant myths, on the development of human thought and on the ability of society to control thought.

The panel discussion centered on the evaluation of the effect of computing machines on future investigation of human thought processes and some of the uses currently being made of computing machines in social or political situations.

Herbert A. Simon

THE CONTROL OF THE MIND BY REALITY: HUMAN COGNITION AND PROBLEM SOLVING

I shall be concerned in these remarks with the impact of technology on our understanding of the mind and on our knowledge of how it works. The central conclusion is a very simple one, and perhaps it is best if I state it first and then show in general terms just what it means: At the present time, with ordinary general-purpose electronic computers, we can simulate many kinds of human thinking. By simulating human thinking we can provide an explanation for a number of the important processes that take place in the brain when thinking is going on.

What do we mean by "explanation" in this context? How can we explain human thinking or explain the processes that go on in the human brain by simulating those processes with an electronic computer? We can explain phenomena at many levels. This is a familiar enough procedure in the natural sciences. In genetics, for example, the pioneering work of Mendel explained the statistical frequency of certain varieties of plants in terms of the crossing of the parent plants. It was only a rather long time after Mendel that the same phenomena were explained at the next level, in terms of underlying biological mechanisms, the genes and the chromosomes. Thus, the explanation of observables took place first at a macroscopic or gross level, to be followed after several generations by explanation of the same behavior at a biological level, in terms of biological structures and their processes.

Table 1 Levels of explanation in genetics, chemistry, and psychology

	Genetics	*Chemistry*	*Psychology of thinking*
Level 1	Mendel: statistics of plant variety	Molecular reactions	Information processing
Level 2	Genes and chromosones	Atomic theory	Neurophysiology
Level 3	Biochemistry of genes	Nuclear physics	Biochemistry of brain processes

The same phenomena are now being provided with a third level of explanation, which we heard discussed here, a level of explanation in which chromosomes and genes are shown to obey the laws of chemistry (see Table 1).

Similarly, the science of chemistry itself at first had chemical theories expressed in chemical equations that described gross molecular reactions. Chemistry had explanations for what was going on in the test tube in terms of chemical equations long before we knew what those equations meant in terms of the structure or planetary picture of the atom. It was not until Mendeleyev had put those equations together in an orderly fashion, and had shown that numerous regularities could be codified by the periodic table of the elements, that we began to see the possibilities of the next level of explanation. Again, several generations after that, chemistry moved from the atomic level, the picture of the atom as a little sun with electronic planets about it, to the subatomic, nuclear level of explanation.

We see, therefore, that levels of explanation are familiar enough in science, and I am going to talk about one such level here—the *information-processing* level. I shall indicate how we can explain human thinking by reducing it to a set of information processes, or symbol-manipulating processes, if you prefer. These processes are presumably carried on by that biological organ we call the brain and by the neurological elements in the brain. Hence, at the lower or more fundamental level—whichever term you prefer—we presumably want to have a neurophysiological explanation of thinking which will tell us how the brain performs the information processes that we are postulating at the higher level. Again, as we heard previously, we might hope that in time we would be able to explain, in turn, the neurological mechanisms and the neurological processes in terms of underlying chemical processes, the biochemistry of the brain.

I am speaking now, however, of the explanation of human thinking in terms of information processes. If we succeed in such explanation, we create the usual division of labor in the sciences. We will expect our friends in neurophysiology to provide, in turn, a reduction of these information processes to neurological processes and mechanisms. There are only a few hints at present as to what is involved in that reduction. Finally, we hope that our biochemical friends will provide the other link between the neurological level and the still more fundamental chemical level.

We have seen that the idea of building theories from the top down is not unfamiliar to the sciences. I have already given two examples in which the gross behavior was in a certain sense understood and explained long before we had even an inkling of the existence of the more microscopic level. Long before we had any direct evidence of the existence of genes and chromosomes by looking at them through an electron microscope, we had indirect evidence of their existence, because certain peas turned out to have certain colors and certain fruit flies turned out to have certain deformities when they were born. Before we had any direct evidence through the electron microscope or otherwise of the existence of atoms or of the planetary structure of atoms, we had indirect evidence of these things. Chemists and physicists had postulated their existence on the basis of the gross behavior of material as it was observed in the laboratory. So here, too, we might expect to obtain some notion of the kinds of underlying mechanisms that are required through a study of gross behavior and through the development of theory at this information-processing or symbol-manipulating level.

In a sense we are in a rather peculiar position in psychology, because, in contrast to the other examples I have cited, here we do already have some direct evidence about the nature of the underlying mechanisms. The study of the brain as a biological organ has been going on for centuries. We know what some of its structures look like, we know a good many of the processes going on in it, and therefore we might expect that the arduous task of linking the biological and the information-processing levels of psychological theory might be a less difficult problem than was faced by the chemists or the geneticists, who really had no direct evidence at all of the nature of the underlying elements.

Now where does the computer come into all this? I have talked about information processes or symbol-manipulating processes, but I have not talked about computers. The computer provides us with the essential tools for building the kind of theory to which I refer, and for testing the theory. Just as many advances in the sciences had to wait for the invention of the telescope or the microscope—a history of the physiological and biological sciences could be written to a considerable extent in terms of the development of tools of observation and tools of analysis—so in this area the study of anything as complex as human thinking had to wait until we had instruments available which were worthy, so to speak, of the complexity of the subject matter. It appears that the electronic computer is such an instrument.

In the first place, the computer is an instrument which facilitates our formulating the theory. The theory is most easily stated, in fact, as a program for a digital computer. Again, let me explain this statement by analogy. In physics when we want to explain something—why the planets go around the sun at the particular time they do—we write down some differential equations. These equations are the theory, and we make predictions from the theory by integrating the equations, manipulating them in various ways, and saying, "If the planets are here now, then according to these equations they're going to be there tomorrow." But the theory itself is most accurately, most rigorously expressed as a set of differential equations—Newton's second law, Maxwell's equations, and so on.

In the same way, an information-processing theory will be expressed as a computer program which will give a rigorous description of the processes that a mechanism goes through when it is doing that activity which we call thinking. Again, in order to test this theory, we do the equivalent of integrating the equations in order to predict where things will be a minute from now if they are at a certain place now. We use the computer as a device that can simulate the thinking organism—that can behave like the thinking organism by carrying out the instructions of the theory, that is, by following the behavior postulated in the computer program. So we use the computer, on the one hand, as a basis for formulating the theory in formal language, and we use a computer at a later stage to test the theory. Because the theory is complicated, it is very difficult to see what behavior it predicts. The easiest way—and almost the only way—to see what behavior it predicts is to turn the computer on and see what it does, see whether the computer then does in fact simulate the thinking human subject as the theory asserts and predicts that it will.

Later, I shall try to explain a bit more concretely what I mean by a program, but I think you have already had an example or reference to a program in an earlier talk. A program is a sequence—often a very complicated and branching sequence—of instructions, which states: "If the system is here now, then it will do such and such, and when it reaches its new position at the next moment, it will do something else," and so on. The program gives a series of instructions for the system to follow, just as the differential equation gives a set of instructions for the physical system to follow.

You will observe that I am not talking about a crude analogy between a computer and a brain; I am not talking neurophysiology. If you open up a computer and look inside it, it looks very different from the inside of the human brain, at least from the pictures of the human brain that I have seen. They look very different, and from all the evidence they are organized at the "hardware" level in quite different ways. Hence, I am not talking about an analogy between brain "hardware," or I should say brain "software," and computer "hardware."

In Figure 1 we have a human being, let's say the college sophomore at the psychological laboratory, who is the human being about whose behavior we have the greatest knowledge at the present time. Here is our sophomore, and over on the right we have a computer that already has a program in it. This program is written in a computer language that allows us to describe some basic information processes, elementary processes for manipulating symbols. Thus, we have some elementary information processes which allow us to write this general problem-solving program for the computer. In anticipation of this, we have done a little work on our computer so it is capable of executing these ele-

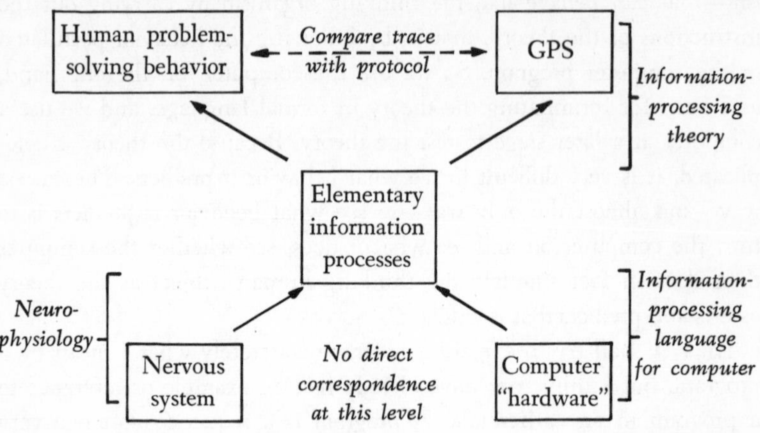

Figure 1 Levels in an information-processing theory of human thinking.

mentary information processes; we have provided the computer with a so-called information-processing language.

The theory asserts that human thinking behavior, what this sophomore does when he is confronted with problems in the laboratory, is to be explained by a program which is identical with or, more modestly, similar to the program we have put into the computer. We are asserting that the sophomore does what he does because he too is governed by a program of elementary information processes stored in his brain. Of course, no one wrote an information-process program for him. Underlying his elementary information processes are some neurophysiological processes, and underlying these is the biological structure we call the brain.

We are not proposing an analogy at the neurological or biological level; we are talking about the extent to which we can write a computer program that, when we turn it loose on the same problems that we present to the human being in the laboratory, will, step-by-step and minute-by-minute, produce the same stream of verbal behavior as the college sophomore does when confronted with these problems, and hence will predict his behavior if we turn the computer on a little before we start him on the problem.

We test this theory now by comparing the stream of computer behavior, what is technically called a trace of the computer's major processes, with the tape-recorded verbalization of the sophomore, whom we asked to think aloud while solving the problem. This is the major basis for testing a theory of this kind.

Since we do have in this field, as distinguished from the early days of chemistry and of genetics, some direct ways of observing the brain and its processes—ways that were described to you previously in the symposium—we have another way of confronting the information-processing theory with evidence. The theory asserts that the human being is behaving in a certain way because of the structure of his program of information processes, and this assertion presumably implies something very general about what the underlying neurology must be like, what kinds of things must be there. Sooner or later the neurologist is either going to find the kinds of things that will allow the brain to carry out the information processes, or he is not. In this way we will also have a neurological confrontation of this theory with evidence, just as after the electron microscope came into being we had a direct confrontation of atomic theory with the evidence of that instrument and other instruments that allow us to observe at lower levels. At present, however, our theory is largely tested by confronting it with the stream of human behavior and seeing whether this stream can be predicted or not. Thus, the theory explains certain species of complex thinking, problem solving, learning, and memorizing behavior by showing how such behavior can be synthesized from organized systems or programs of elementary information processes.

Now, let me provide a little detail about one example of this theory. By an example I mean a program that purports to explain one area of human thinking behavior. There are now in existence at least a half-dozen computer programs that are intended as theories or explanations of various areas of human thought process. I am going to talk about one of those, and then merely mention two or three others.

The particular program I want to describe is the general problem solver, or GPS, which was developed by a joint RAND–Carnegie Tech group, beginning in about 1956 [4,5].* Let's consider a person con-

* This is a suitable point to record my debts to my coworkers Allen Newell and J. C. Shaw. What I am describing is our joint work, which is reported more fully in the references listed at the end of this paper.

fronted with a relatively novel problem, that is, a problem in an area where he does not already have a cut-and-dried solution. I will first characterize the problem abstractly: You are placed in some situation, situation *A;* your task is to change that situation to situation *B.* You are permitted a certain set of operations *Q* for changing the situation. In summary, you have *A,* you want *B,* you have some operations *Q,* and you want to make *A* into *B,* using *Q.*

This very abstract formulation really covers a wide range of the matters, both everyday matters and laboratory matters, that we call problems. For example, in discovering a proof for a mathematical theorem, you are given certain axioms and previous theorems. The object you are supposed to find is a string of propositions logically connected, the last of which is the theorem you are trying to prove. Your job is to change these axioms and theorems into a proof of the desired theorem. In composing a sonata you have certain musical means at your disposal, and your problem is to write down a piece of music that has the characteristics of a sonata and that will be pleasant to listen to. In making a chess move, you have a certain position on the board, and you would like a certain other position, preferably one in which the opponent is checkmated. The problem is how to bring this about. Another example is the problem of getting to the airport—I am sure you are all familiar with that problem. Still another example is the old problem of how to get the missionaries and the cannibals across the river without any missionaries being eaten in the process. We can add to the list of examples some very practical problems. In investing a $100,000 trust fund, you have $100,000; you want a portfolio of stocks and bonds that will yield a profitable income. How do you transform this $100,000 into stocks and bonds?

These are all problems that come under the general formula. I wish I could say they are all problems the GPS in its present form could solve. That would be a rather strong claim. In fact, the GPS at present will discover proofs for mathematical theorems in some areas of mathematical logic; it will solve the problem of missionaries and cannibals. Other computer programs not very different in structure will do such things as play chess and produce, if not sonatas, at lease some contrapuntal music more or less in the style of Palestrina. Special-purpose computer programs of this general sort are available for a wide range of these tasks, and the GPS will, in fact, handle a restricted range of such tasks.

Let me make one other observation before I say just a little bit more about the program itself. We usually think of a computer as a device for doing arithmetic, because this is what computers were originally invented and designed to do. What I am talking about here is a nonnumerical use of the computer. Getting to the airport is not an arithmetical problem—at least we don't usually solve it by setting up equations or computing numbers, although we may do a little subtraction in terms of how much time we allow. When we use a computer for this kind of research we do not use its arithmetic powers. We use instead the general procedures, its so-called logical instructions that any general-purpose computer has for manipulating symbols. In effect, you can disable the fast arithmetic processes of a computer and still cause it to behave in the manner we are describing. We are using the computer as a nonnumerical, symbol-manipulating, symbol-processing device to simulate as closely as we can the symbol-manipulating processes that we think are going on in the human brain.

Now why do we call the program I have mentioned the general problem solver? If you examine the set of instructions that it embodies, and by means of which it allegedly describes how people tackle relatively novel problems, you will find that these instructions make no specific reference to any subject matter. They are not instructions for solving geometry problems, they are not instructions for playing chess, they are not instructions for composing music—they are instructions for getting from here to there if you are told in general what some of the ways are of getting from one place to another.

If you examine the GPS program, you will see that it has the following general structure. You will pardon me if I anthropomorphize a bit; it is the easiest way to describe the program and the description can be turned back into more proper terms readily enough. At the outset the program says, "Well, I am given *A*, and I am supposed to produce *B*; what is the difference between them?" It examines the situation *A*, it examines the situation *B*, and it finds certain differences between *A* and *B*. Then it says to itself, "Now we have this difference, *D*; what operators have I been provided with, what means are at my disposal, that have some relevance to differences of this sort?"

If the problem is to get to the airport, then the problem, the "difference," is one of geographical distance. We are some 15 miles, I suppose, from the airport. What means do we have at our disposal? Well, there are legs, not very relevant to this particular problem, there are busses, there are taxicabs, maybe even helicopters. These are the means available for doing this job. Let's take one of those means and see if we can apply it to produce a new situation, which may be the one we are seeking, or may be closer to the one we are seeking than the situation we are in now. Then we have simply set up a new problem of getting from our new situation *A* to the desired goal *B;* and we can apply the same apparatus all over again.

This is a simple example of reasoning about ends and means. You start with an end, you see in what respect your present situation differs from the end, you ask yourself what relevant means you have, you try to apply some of these and you produce a new situation. Then you ask yourself whether you are any better off than you were in the first place. One of the means of getting from here to the airport is to take a taxi. If we take a taxi and are dropped out there, then we have the new problem of getting from where the taxi leaves us to the particular ramp where our plane leaves.

This is a very oversimplified skeleton of the GPS program. The GPS also includes other processes that say, "Well, I cannot apply this operator now, but maybe if I change something I can." For example, "We can't find a taxicab; maybe we should phone the taxicab company —of course, they won't answer the phone—but at least this is a possibility." We might have to do some preliminary things before we can actually apply the operator.

Likewise, we might be confronted with a problem that has too much detail in it—a very complex, complicated problem. Suppose we not only have to get to the airport, but we have to meet somebody there who is coming on a particular plane and taking another plane, and we have to change a ticket in the meantime. We don't try to deal with this problem in all of its detail but throw away a lot of the detail and first deal with the problem of getting to the airport. After we get there we worry about the rest of the problem. Again the GPS program has means at its disposal for doing this—for taking the original problem, throwing away much of its detail, producing thereby an abstraction of the problem—or if you prefer, an image of the problem—solving the problem in this abstracted space and then going back and putting in the details.

To a certain extent the theory embedded in the GPS has been tested in the psychological laboratory by giving it problems from various domains that it can tackle, giving students the same problems, and comparing their traces step by step. The only general statement I can make, since there exists almost no relevant statistical theory for circumstances like this, is that in some cases we are able to produce a parallelism of their behavior for periods of time ranging up to 5 minutes. That is, for 5 minutes or so the computer will notice the same things about the problem, will consider the same subproblems, will go down the same blind alleys, will back off for the same reasons as the human subject. In these cases the GPS will often reach the same solution the human being does, and in some cases it will be buffaloed for the same reasons and will be unable to solve the problem.

Notice that we are not trying here to get the computer to solve problems well; we are trying to get it to solve problems the way people do, and that is sometimes well and sometimes badly. The program must simulate the failures as well as the successes if it is to be a theory of human thinking.

So much for the general problem solver and the program that embodies it. Given a little more time, it would be interesting to see to what extent the mechanisms that Mr. Koestler was describing yesterday afternoon in his very interesting paper on the creative processes are in fact simulated by the GPS. I think I could produce for you an example of an "aha" experience, which it had. The GPS didn't say "Eureka," but I think it clearly had an "aha" experience.

Among the other programs of this sort in existence today, two have been produced by men who are now on the Berkeley campus, so you can go to them after this lecture and find out about their programs. A program called EPAM, elementary perceiver and memorizer, produced in its first version by Prof. Edward Feigenbaum [1], is a theory, again formulated as a computer program, of the processes that human beings use in the kinds of rote-memory tasks that psychologists subject them to in the laboratory. Perhaps some of you have been subjects in such experiments. You are presented with certain stimuli, usually in the form of nonsense syllables, and you are supposed to give an appropriate response, which is also usually nonsensical. This experiment is done in several forms, including the so-called paired-associate method, and the so-called serial-anticipation method.

EPAM is a program that simulates the behavior of laboratory subjects in rote-memory experiments of both the serial and paired-associate variety and in certain other types of experiments of this general kind. What we are doing with EPAM at the moment is trying to replicate with it some of the classical psychological experiments on rote memory. It turns out that the EPAM program, although not constructed with this in mind, is able to simulate some of the processes that the child evidently uses when he is acquiring oral language and subsequently when he is learning to read. You can perform the following kind of experiment: You present EPAM with some stimuli, which are supposed to represent or simulate certain characteristic objects of the environment —balls and cats, say. At the same time you present EPAM with responses to these stimuli, in the forms of phonemes or sequences of phonemes, oral syllables. That is, you point to an object in the environment, for example, a furry object which we know as a cat, and at that time you present to EPAM a simulation of the oral syllable "cat." After a number of trials, when you present the furry object alone the computer will respond "cat" with the appropriate phonemes. (It will not actually pronounce the word orally, but it will print out the phonemes.) A little later you present as a stimulus the printed word "cat," and as a response the oral phoneme "cat." After a few trials the computer is able, when the written syllable CAT is presented, to produce as the response the phoneme "cat." Now you present the computer with the aural word "cat" and with a series of objects in the environment or simulations of objects in the environment, and on the first trial, without additional practice, the computer will select the furry object out of the set of objects. It will be able to point, in effect, to the cat, thus demonstrating that it has not only learned to pronounce the phoneme syllable corresponding to the printed word, but that it knows the "meaning" of that term. If you wanted to take the quotes off the word "meaning," that is your privilege. I am personally inclined to do so, but I would not at the moment really want to argue the point at length.

Finally, there are some other programs in existence at present which simulate other kinds of human behavior: A program by Professor Feldman [2] simulates some of the classic psychologic experiments in binary choice, or so-called partial-reinforcement experiments with which some of you are familiar. There are some programs produced by Hovland and Hunt [3] at Yale which seem to simulate very well certain simple forms of human concept attainment, again in psychological laboratory settings.

Let me then conclude and summarize. We all are aware that the electronic computer is beginning to have vast effects on our economy through automation—which may be the subject that our program committee thought I would talk about. At the same time the computer provides us with a powerful new tool for understanding the human mind. We now have at least a first approximation to a clearly defined and testable, if only slightly tested, theory of thinking. We soon will be able to obey that ancient injunction, "Know thyself," and obeying it we may be able to use more wisely the tremendous powers over man and over nature that the very rapid advances of our technology are giving us.

In thinking about and evaluating the implications of computer simulation, I wish that we would keep this aspect of it in the forefront of our minds. The power to understand the mind through imitating it in no way subtracts from the dignity of man. Our dignity does not reside in the fact that we don't understand ourselves, that we are mysterious. Man has really nothing to lose, and he may have a great deal to gain by understanding himself, and this potential gain may serve to moderate the fears, which I think we all sometimes experience and sometimes express, at the vision of a robot that imitates nature a little bit too closely for our comfort.

References

1. Feigenbaum, E., The Simulation of Verbal Learning Behavior, *Proceedings of the 1961 Western Joint Computer Conference,* Los Angeles, May 9–11, 1961, pp. 121–132.

2. Feldman, J., Simulation of Behavior in the Binary Choice Experiment, *Proceedings of the 1961 Western Joint Computer Conference,* Los Angeles, May 9–11, 1961, pp. 133–144.
3. Hovland, C. I., and Hunt, E. B., Programming a Model of Human Concept Formulation, *Proceedings of the 1961 Western Joint Computer Conference,* May 9–11, 1961, pp. 145–155.
4. Newell, A., Shaw, J. C., and Simon, H. A., Report on a General Problem Solving Program, in *Information Processing, Proceedings of the International Conference on Information Processing,* Paris, UNESCO, June 15–20, 1959, pp. 256–264.
5. Newell, A., and Simon, H. A., The Simulation of Human Thought, in *Current Trends in Psychological Theory,* Pittsburgh, University of Pittsburgh Press, 1961, pp. 152–179.

William E. Porter

POLITICAL EDUCATION AND CONTROL OF THE MIND

There is much mutual benefit for both medical and nonmedical men in this kind of meeting. The nonmedical men acquire a luster reflected from white coats, and their vague pursuits almost seem an orderly accrual of wisdom as they rise from their armchairs and stand alongside the laboratory sink. The medical men, for their part, stand to gain something of a reputation for horizon viewing—a remission from accusations of always seeking truth at the bottom of a test tube.

But we share more than the willingness to improve each other's status. The men who work in both the behavioral and medical sciences are generally credited with knowing things they don't know at all. They are the twentieth century's largest gainers, perhaps, from the benefit of the doubt.

Of these two, the nonmedical are the greater gainers. It is true that our society has a remarkable faith in medicine as a science. We seem to believe, as a people, that if you put money in, cures come out, and that there is a quantitative relationship. This is an astonishing endorsement of one application of the scientific method, as well as the happy-go-lucky empiricism which may accompany it.

Society has paid an even more striking compliment, however, in the persistent belief that there is such a thing as manipulation of the mass mind, and that opinions and attitudes can be altered and controlled to predictable ends by those in the know. This is a most irrational idea, but it is found among the sophisticated as well as the naïve. The medical experimenter who, in reporting the action of a drug upon a laboratory animal which has spent its lifetime alone in a small wire cage, will qualify his findings heavily on the ground that there are many variables beyond his control—that same man may accept without argument the idea that the rise and rule of fascism was primarily the work of propagandists who lifted hoops through which the German and Italian people could not but jump.

Some of the belief in this kind of power must grow out of that astonishing moment when it was first possible to believe that man was orderly enough to be perfectible, some of it from observation of the interlocking growth of cause and effect in applied science. If man can throw an object into what 20 years ago was an inviolate emptiness and make it rise and set as predictably as the sun, he surely must also be capable of controlling the opinions and conduct of other men. To deny it is to deny the rationalism which has been the first article of faith, in one way or another, of Western thought for almost 300 years.

There may be another kind of belief in manipulative control of the mind which grows out of disappointment. If our failure to construct a society that never produces pain or cruelty can be attributed to villains who pull psychological strings which move us in spite of ourselves, we can find consolation; if Americans find themselves unpopular abroad, there is comfort in blaming it all on Communist propaganda. This feeling probably is too vague to be described as rationalization; it's a kind of intellectual analgesic. We seem to have an almost morbid interest in assurances that we are really mere pawns in the hands of calculating deceivers.

The terrain in which these people work is vast and ill defined; it ranges all the way from the "hard sell," through Joseph Goebbels, to brainwashed PFCs in North Korean prison camps. Since the only thing which holds the image together is the concept of people pushed into attitudes or actions against their will, its proper study must involve many disciplines and many methods. This paper deals with one obvious part of this complicated public image. I take the phrase "political education" to refer to the process of producing changes in attitude or action affecting the relationship between the individual and his government, or among governments. I take it, further, that most of us associate this kind of persuasion, this kind of making of public opinion, with the media of mass communication. Thus, it is with the effect of mass communication upon political life that this paper is concerned. Suppose we begin with a summary look at what we know about the nature and dimensions of such effects.

What we know does little to justify any fear of control of the collective mind, if there is such a thing. The truth of the matter is simple. If control of the mind means making people take certain actions contrary to their rational conclusions, their real desires, and their moral convictions, then there have been no demonstrable examples as yet of control of the mind through mass communication. If control of the mind means the functional directing of a society toward ends which are contrary to its cultural inheritance and its collective beliefs, there have been no demonstrable examples of collective control of the mind.

This should not be taken as an assertion that all research in communications have come to nothing. Much has been learned about many things. Some significant concepts about propaganda and what I, at least, would call political education were set forth by Lasswell in the early 1930s. They have been investigated and substantially documented. Much has been learned about voting behavior and the sources of influence upon it—for example, that family and group ties are highly important, and personal influence more important than the media. There is a very large amount of information about such things as reader, listener, and viewer habits—for example, that we tend to expose ourselves to that which will reinforce rather than contradict what we believe. There has been elaborate mapping and analysis of public opinion on literally thousands of issues; some things, at least, of significance have been learned about the effects of exposure to certain kinds of messages in specific, controlled situations—for example, that attempts to move people through frightening messages often results in their simply avoiding the messages.

The most useful developments, perhaps, have been in the area where mathematics and communication meet—information theory, information storage and retrieval, and remarkably quick and comprehensive data analysis. All these have helped get notable utility out of a modest increment of fundamental knowledge. (It has also meant, of course, the rise of a group of subspecialists in communication who can hardly communicate with anybody else at all.) The device currently being described as Mr. Kennedy's "people machine" is a good example of this marriage of mathematics and machines. It is, in effect, a massive filing system for a hundred thousand interviews, a way of consulting past public opinion on many issues. Within this context, the development is of great importance. Prediction becomes better grounded in knowledge than before; synthesis of possible reactions can consider a greater number of variables, and the real predictor, which is a man—or a group of men—is better equipped than before for his leap of faith. But it is still a leap; we remain a long way from the "social pathology" which Rudolf Virchow thought he saw from the top of the nineteenth-century wave of confidence in science.

A summary of dimensions of our knowledge is provided by Joseph Klapper in a recent book called *The Effects of Mass Communication.* This volume is a succinct shaking-down of the first-rate research to date on, in the words of its subtitle, "the effectiveness and limitations of mass media in influencing the opinions, values and behavior of their audiences." In the terminology of medical literature, it is a review article, of book length and excellent quality.

Klapper does not refer to the five points which follow here as a summary, but rather as a set of generalizations about the field. As generalizations, they are drawn from research findings but also include some synthesis and well-grounded intuition. Klapper himself describes them as "attempts to account for an order in existing research findings." For this reason, they seem to me to provide a particularly sharp assessment of where the field stands. They are as follows [1]:

1. Mass communication ordinarily does not serve as a necessary and sufficient cause of audience effects, but rather functions among and through a nexus of mediating factors and influence.

2. These mediating factors are such that they typically render mass communication a contributory agent, but not the sole cause, in a process of reinforcing the existing conditions. (Regardless of the condition in question —be it the vote intentions of audience members, their tendency toward or away from delinquent behavior, or their general orientation toward life and its problems—and regardless of whether the effect in question be social or individual, the media are more likely to reinforce than to change.)

3. On such occasions as mass communication does function in the service of change, one of two conditions is likely to exist:

a. the mediating factors will be found to be inoperative and the effect of the media will be . . . direct; or

b. the mediating factors, which normally favor reinforcement, will be . . . themselves impelling toward change.

4. There are certain residual situations in which mass communication seems to produce direct effects, or directly and of itself to serve certain psycho-physical functions.

5. The efficacy of mass communication, either as a contributory agent or as an agent of direct effect, is affected by various aspects of the media and communications themselves or of the communication situation (including, for example, aspects of textual organization, the nature of the source and medium, the existing climate of public opinion, and the like).

There seems no need to comment upon the modesty, or humility, of those conclusions to anyone who is concerned that control of the mass mind is all but upon us. The gains have been small, their accumulation considerable. Perhaps the breakthroughs will be produced by those eager, esoteric new diggers who deal in psychopharmacology. I hope I sound not rude, but only old-fashioned, if I admit that I view with mild horror the possibility of a chlorpromazine bomb. Better, almost, the hydrogen kind.

Meanwhile, we must make do; we must tackle the problem of political education with what is at hand. In doing so, we will be constantly reminded of some fundamentals which are much too obvious to be regarded as the fruits of research. Yet they shape all research in political influence and propaganda, and the understanding of them is the first step toward sophistication.

The first of these fundamentals is the inescapable connection between what we might roughly call the facts and their exploitation for political ends. To pick a conspicuous example, this country's efforts at political persuasion among African and Asian nations must live with the fact that we have a history of discriminatory practices against Negroes. The most artful practitioner cannot explain this away for colored people in other parts or induce them to believe that it is insignificant. We can attempt with some success to arrange more favorable perspectives and wait hopefully for the eroding effects of time and short memories; we can benefit at others' expense when such episodes as the Notting Hill riots demonstrate that this is not a uniquely American state of mind—at least until somebody tries to integrate another school in New Orleans. But we must begin with the fact that it exists.

In very much the same kind of way, the Soviets must live with the fact of the suppression of Hungary. The circumstances vary somewhat here; because they have complete control over the formal channels of dissemination of information in their own country and the satellites, the Soviets could keep the details of the story from reaching at least their own people, at least for a time. But the word gets out, and one of the fictions that the Soviets have tried hard to sell—that such drill fields as Czechoslovakia and Albania are sovereign principalities—goes unsold.

Every major national power has a whole catalogue of happenings which have made some nations hate and distrust it, as well as a list that makes it respected and emulated. The more major the power, the longer and more dramatic both the lists.

It is from these events, these attitudes, the reputations thus made, that those concerned with political education, or persuasion, or propaganda work. Effective propaganda, indeed, could be described as the art of elaborating or minimizing the facts of the case. An affair in progress at the time this paper was written demonstrated the Soviets at work in the classic fashion. A report originating in the United States indicated that the Israelis might be developing, with French help, an atomic weapon. The United States expressed concern and asked reassurance. The Soviets exploited this simultaneously in several directions—to encourage alarm and belligerence in the Arabs, to suggest to the Israelis that the United States was interfering in its internal affairs, and to hint to the French that a presumed ally, always highhanded, was now downright insulting. All these approaches apparently showed, in varying degrees, some success. But none of them would have been possible without the reality or, in this case apparently, a convincing facsimile.

One aspect of this relationship between reality and effect needs comment. Reality may be misrepresented by a lie, but it has great effect only when the lie is taken for the reality. One of the first and best known pieces of research in the effects of mass communication [2] concerns Orson Welles's radio adaption of an H. G. Wells story, which brought some of the more impulsive citizens of Connecticut into the streets with fowling pieces to fight off an invasion from Mars. This was, of course, a fiction; and if this fact had been clearly understood, there would have been no panic. But this is irrelevant; the thing that produced the panic, in effect, was an invasion from Mars, and in a sense what Mr. Cantrill was really studying was not radio as a psychological weapon, but the variety of ways in which people might react to such an invasion. The carefully built lie, big or little, has been of much importance in political persuasion and control, but its effective use must follow more or less the same rules as the exploitation of the facts.

The question of the lie brings us to the second of those contextual fundamentals. Usually there is an inescapable moral context within which the attempt to exert influence operates. I do not refer to the vague horror that a certain kind of professional humanist finds in the very idea of calculated persuasion, but to practical problems in making decisions. Let us suppose, for example, that the United States government learns that unrest is approaching the flash point within some country in the Soviet orbit. A false report of a clash and a promise of immediate aid to the rebels in the event of an uprising would be enough to ignite it. Any such revolt would be greatly to our advantage; it would either cost the Soviets a satellite or bring them to a display of force that would outrage the rest of the world. Either way, we win—at least in short-range terms. But we would win by gulling several thousands of people into dying for the sake of a propaganda ploy. How much is too much? The answer is not to be found in research, or "people-predictors," or a fine structure of rationality. It is essentially a matter of morality. So is the following, but in a much less obvious way: Since public acceptance is increasingly important in the conduct of foreign policy (witness, for example, the strong consumer-oriented pronouncements of the United States government in the Suez crisis), how far should our government go in trying to convince its own citizens that an authoritarian regime abroad which serves our interests by suppression of Communists conforms to our idea of what proper government should be? The question sounds rhetorical, but it is not meant to be. Obviously, several answers might be given. One might be a declaration, along with withdrawal of support, that this country cannot countenance the police state in any form. Such a decision clearly is on a moral basis. Another possible answer would lie in going all out to convince Americans, along with the rest of the world, that such a regime actually is true to the traditional Western concepts of democracy. This, too, would be a decision in a moral context, although somewhat more involved than the preceding one. The violation of conventional morality in propagating a lie would be justified on the grounds that the need is extreme and immediate, and that the opposition does worse things every day. A third possibility might be the seeking of a decision as far removed from the moral context as possible, something like this: "Look, we need this guy; let's use him as inconspicuously as possible and not talk or think about it." But—if you'll forgive me for what might remind you of your sophomore course in logic—the attempt to make a decision of this kind outside the moral context is itself a question of morality. In matters affecting persuasion and control of the mind, the only decisions which can be made on an amoral basis are small ones.

Neither science nor scientism can provide a bypass. The scientist may, and often does, declare himself uninterested in such woolly issues, and he may have good sense on his side when he does so. The accumulation of hard knowledge is enough obligation for any man, and sometimes it can be performed in an amoral context—to which, interestingly enough, the adjective "pure" is sometimes applied. The big problems arise when knowledge has to be applied for something other than pragmatic, short-range ends. The scientist can declare himself uninterested and still be a wonderfully useful man, and the society will be grateful to him. It is even further indebted to him, however, when he decides to go all the way.

There are close connections between morality and social objectives, and between those two and political issues, and between all of these and political education, as we have been discussing here.

There are signs that our biggest future problem in political education lies in strengthening our own establishment. We need more political vitality, more specific direction, more sharply defined political morality. These things might be presumed good in themselves, but there also are functional reasons for their desirability. If we are concerned with having influence on the political development of new nations, if we are concerned with the spread of whatever we mean by the democratic ideal, we need clearer political objectives and commitments. One of the things that has been repeatedly demonstrated in communications research is that the specific is more quickly comprehended than the general, the precise idea more easily transferred from one mind to another than the vague. The clearer this country's commitments, the more understandable it will be to the rest of the world and to its own citizens.

Unfortunately, this means more than simply drawing up a list of catch phrases which translate with equal ease into Amharic and Urdu. The involvement of much of the society is required, because if the society does things one way while its propagandists cheerily insist that it believes in a different way, the audience is more likely to believe the act than the assertion. This seems to leave us with the nakedly evangelical idea that the only way to improve our political persuasion is to improve society, at least in its politics.

And this, perhaps, is now beyond us, or any industrialized Western democracy. As many writers have pointed out, we no longer have any deep enthusiasm for the kind of issue-against-issue, ethic-against-ethic controversy which breeds missionaries, makes the populace take sides, and ends with a national commitment. The last of these, perhaps, was the great debate over what we then called "isolationism." That was 20 years ago. Since that time we have been little inclined to argue things out. We still have moral values, a kind of self-conscious dilution of the Protestant ethic, but these seem most often to operate as a list of things not to do; they do not drive us forward. We obviously have a great consensus about the general circumstances under which we want to live, but this hardly constitutes a clear idea of national objectives. We have issues manufactured, with some signs of strain at campaign time, but the candidates and their strategists must wonder if anybody is listening.

I'm a conscientious reader of *The Guardian* (formerly *The Manchester Guardian*), and my chief reason for being one is that the 1,000 to 1,500 words it gives to United States affairs every week often seem more perceptive than almost as many pages in our own press. There are times, however, when *The Guardian* seems spectacularly off base, and one of these was an editorial written shortly after Mr. Kennedy's election (written, significantly, in Manchester, not by one of their correspondents in this country). The article was concerned about Mr. Kennedy's mandate, and it rejoiced in the fact that Americans had chosen the New Frontier. Never mind the thinness of the margin, *The Guardian* said, in effect, rubbing its hands together before this rekindled fire, the people have rejected their own curious passivity of the past several years and the United States is once again on the move. In other words, the editors believed that Americans primarily had voted for the ideas which Mr. Kennedy expressed in his speeches. There is something wonderfully childlike about this notion; we could all wish that American politics still worked this way.

But apparently it does not. The analyses of last November's results began almost simultaneously with the first returns. During the night, television's official deep thinkers talked about urban and rural votes, and somewhat more gingerly, about Negro and Catholic votes. I, at least, have no recollection of a single word spoken concerning either candidate's program. Since the election, the Gallup organization has issued a series of reports on the voting behavior of many groups. None has referred to approval or rejection of either candidate's programs.

This is not to say that research yet to be reported may not indicate something about the importance of the issues. Nor is it to say that the candidates were disinterested in a clash of ideas; indeed, in retrospect, this campaign at least presented a clearer cleavage about fundamentals than its predecessors of 1948, 1952, and 1956. The interesting point is that no one even seems to consider it a possibility that the New Frontier, or the old one, had anything to do with the result.

The lack of real difference between American political parties is an old subject for American humor, and there seems to be an increasing tendency for nature to imitate art. British politics have taken on more of the same look, and there are signs of this, it seems to me, in much current British comment on the split within the Labor party over unilateral disarmament. Outside of Mr. Cousin's and Mr. Foot's own in-group, there apparently is little discussion about unilateral disarmament as a national policy—but there is a great flap about what this honest-to-God big issue is doing to the Labor party and to British politics in general; and a casual reader of the British press is tempted to generalize that more words have been printed during the last 6 months about whether the trade union's executive should have control of Labor's parliamentary delegation than about the implications of Britain's renouncing atomic weapons. Meanwhile, the intellectual distance between the majority of the Laborites and the Tories steadily shrinks. Similarly, it is increasingly difficult to guess what the alternative to De Gaullism might be, or what the Social Democrats would really do if they whipped Dr. Adenauer.

Basic political issues no longer seem to stir us very much in the West, and particularly in the United States. This is an oversimplification, of course, and should be held suspect despite its familiarity (I encountered it first when the public library in my small Kansas town bought a copy of Oswald Spengler). Some of this blurring inevitably takes place when big political issues are decided; the losers move toward the things with which the winners won. Or perhaps the whole business is cyclical (it might be possible to make a case for a complete cycle since Spengler's time), and Senator Goldwater is the first item tossed up by the wave of the future. There are reasons just as convincing, however, for believing that the highly industrialized democracies have reached a plateau in which basic drives for change are lacking because we can no longer visualize a society which would be a great improvement over this one. Perhaps we are in a kind of velvet trap from which no wise society would want to escape. We have in this country a remarkable freedom, as individuals, from authoritarian government. We have a level of personal comfort for most of the population beyond even the dreams of the nineteenth century. We have a society which is far from classless, but which has a high degree of social mobility and movement from class to class. It is constantly said that we are soft, materialistic, lacking in ideas, but what is there to be hard for? What other ideals are there that are universal enough to move a great body of us? Injustice, and pain, and poverty remain with us in detail, of course, but they are no longer so gaudy that we cannot stand their sight. (One wonders, incidentally, if part of the decline in quality, as well as numbers, of medical students is chargeable to a conviction that the big battles have been won.)

The life we lead as members of this society represents the fruition of the Enlightenment and the rise of rationalism and secularism which went with it. It also represents a remarkable accomplishment when examined in perspective. So far as the good government of men is concerned, this is pretty much the way the men of the eighteenth century, armed with new intellectual tools and a great secular evangelism, saw it. When the disenchanted urge the mass of us to press forward, we are rather like children who, having satisfied their hunger, are told to clean up their plates because clean plates are nice. When it is cited that the satisfaction is a delusion and the food false, we can point out placidly that it seems to serve the purposes of men and cultures everywhere. Moslems gravitate toward ballpoint pens, Chevrolets, monogamy; and even the Chinese Marxists, whose value system is the most clearly opposed to our own, measured their accomplishments against our standards —to catch up with the British in 5 years and with the Americans in 10.

This is not a situation which creates political issues of significance; in the title phrase of a new book by Daniel Bell [3], which examines these questions at length, it signifies an end of ideology. The question of how we break out of this amiable torpor raises subsidiary questions of considerable moment, beginning with this one: Why try? Isn't this what we've been after?

And the beginning answer, at least, is that we're obliged to. The system which is chiefly competitive with Western democracy still has great energy derived from literally millions of people who are still hungry and cold and sick, to whom the belly argument has an overwhelming appeal. That system, or loose clusters of systems, can overwhelm us—or, in the words of one of our more conspicuous critics, bury us.

Another part of the answer rests in the fact that it is relatively easy to talk people out of things about which they do not deeply care. It is a truism of communications research that lightly held opinions often can be changed, while deep commitments almost never can. As our lack of concern about the intellectual and spiritual apparatus which produced this society grows, so does our vulnerability to persuasion toward other systems of regulating men's affairs. The democratic system needs the exercise of dialectic. It had it once, and with it swept the Western world.

These are partial answers of a sort, but functional answers have to come from the involvement of the whole people. They mean the working out of a sharper sense of national purpose and values and objectives. And since this is not a meeting about the national purpose, it might be appropriate for this discussion to settle for the short-range clinical view—the establishment of a state of readiness. The immediate job of political education through mass communication must be the development of a livelier political life and a deeper sense of involvement.

This is the precondition for refining further what we already have, or protecting ourselves, or facing up to Armageddon. There may be something surprising in the idea that the greatest need for political education is not in the wooing of uncommitted peoples, or in whatever is meant by that grandiose phrase "the battle for men's minds," but in the improvement of our own participation in what we already have. But the sense of surprise is an excellent example of the symptomatology of the affliction.

Stirring up new concern is steadily more difficult. Comfort makes it more difficult; so does an environment full of ingenious diversions which make it possible to keep the mind busy with trivia throughout the waking day. So do some of the instruments which we will have to learn to use more effectively. For a single, small example, take one aspect of television as a factor in political life. The idea of face-to-face confrontations of the candidates for President within intimate viewing range of almost the entire population is exciting to the most pedestrian mind. But the face-to-face quality may represent more of a corruption than a strengthening of political participation. Research has shown repeatedly that face-to-face communication is the most effective; and the television screen gives a most deceptive reproduction of the face-to-face situation, which means that the viewer can react in terms of his personal chemistry. And some people are much more likable on the tube than others; irrelevant personal idiosyncrasies may take on great weight. It was thus possible last November that many people voted for Mr. Kennedy's smile, or against his Massachusetts "a"; for Mr. Nixon's habit of saying "let me make this crystal-clear" as he launched into a point which might not, in all nonpartisan objectivity, prove to be exactly that, or against his looking tired during the first debate. The thought that the Presidency might have been settled by cumulative judgments about such nonsense is chilling, but the possibility is a real one. There are research findings which suggest that the decline of Senator McCarthy's influence began with the televised Senate hearings because it was felt that a man like Joseph Welch could not but represent the forces of light.

This kind of attitude formation was almost impossible 100 years ago. The voter of 1860, if he attempted any kind of assessment at all beyond his geographical and familial inheritance, was almost forced to think about secession or slavery; his impression of the candidates as personalities was necessarily so vague—and so easily manipulated by their partisans—that his personal chemistry was useless. Leading us to vote from our considered judgments rather than from our reactions to somebody's dimples is clearly a responsibility of our future political education. It is also a sample of a long and complex list.

I suppose the most useful kind of paper in a meeting such as this is the revelation of significant new information which represents careful research, and it is the hope of finding this, perhaps, which has stimulated so much interest in this symposium. There is a second, lower order of usefulness in the orderly review and summation of material already known. The next level, in descending order, is the discussion which contributes nothing new in information or convenience, but which points up problems and calls for more research and more consideration. There are some other levels, of course, all too distressing to think about, but I should like, in closing, to try to put this monologue in that modest third category. If we are to strengthen our society's involvement in political life, we need research in the epistemology and dynamics of mass persuasion through mass communication. We need to find more answers and develop new techniques.

For example (and at random), it has been well established through investigation that political discussion tends to move chiefly along sympathetic, partisan lines; Democrats talk to Democrats, Republicans to Republicans, in orgies of reinforcement. How do we go about developing more real, individual examination of issues and candidates?

There is some evidence and much theory indicating that mass communication has its influence through a so-called two-step flow; that is, it influences certain kinds of key people—hundreds of thousands of them, perhaps—on national issues, who, in turn, influence the rest. There is reasonably convincing evidence that these opinion leaders are exposed more to the media of mass communication; they are wider readers, listeners, viewers. But how do they use this additional experience; in what ways can they be induced to use it more effectively? There is evidence that they often have a critical role in modifying opinion or moving to action—but what about their capacities in the other direction, as resistors to change?

There is a good deal of experimental evidence that information can be communicated without changing attitudes, even when it is designed to do so. What does this do to the old notion that democracy functions best when people know the facts and then make up their own minds?

There is some evidence that on some issues a certain amount of exposure to the subject is sufficient to produce a feeling of being well-informed, regardless of content. For example, foreign students coming to the United States for study often indicate that they made no particular effort to gain information about this country because they already knew all about the United States from movies and their own publications—when this material actually is not related to what they need to know functionally at all. Is the same thing true of exposure to political talk? If it is, what can be done about it?

There are hundreds of such questions to which systematic investigation may provide answers. As the answers come in, a new major question will arise: How do we put this knowledge to work in a system of mass communication which is largely in private hands and operated primarily for profit?

Not all qualified opinion would agree with this view of the possible fruits of research, as some of you know. One of the half-dozen most distinguished men in the short history of mass-communications research has left it and pronounced it dead. He feels that its concepts have been on a sterile plateau for several years, and that most of its methods are pretentious busywork. Most of us who do communications research, or use its findings, disagree with him. But the dramatic exit has served a purpose. Indirectly, it calls attention to a fact that is ludicrously obvious—that communication is always about *something,* and that in most cases where the communication has real significance it is the something which is important, not the details of transmission and reception. Much behavioral research tries, understandably, to narrow the areas for investigation to manageable size. In the past it has often succeeded to the point where content is just another damn variable and context something that can be ignored because it does not figure in the computations.

There are some signs around, it seems to me, of a general growth of discontent with this kind of pick-and-shovel work in behavioral study. Occasionally one comes across a disenchanted social researcher who wryly classifies himself in the "face-value" school—that is, when you ask people questions, you believe what they tell you. The grim passion for quantification, which reached a point at which every possible element was reduced to numbers and what was left over was called the theoretical framework and put into an equation, seems to be receding. And even the run-of-the-mill researcher is beginning to realize that to call a man "symbol-oriented" and "culture-bound" is not necessarily a complete description of his motives and commitments, or why he talks and acts as he does. There may even be a feeling that there is something larger than the method, more significant than the data, in all science which has as its basic material the human organism. This is a tattered old humanistic refrain, of course, but perhaps we have finally learned enough to understand what it means.

If we are going to develop a more demanding kind of political life for this society, the things which we will be learning about attitude formation and change, about what persuades and what is rejected, will be important. But our conception of ourselves in a world context, our intentions and our actions will be more important. It is to be hoped that these things will be formed increasingly with the help of new knowledge. The new knowledge will have to be supplied, however, by a special kind of man, currently in short supply: the scientist-turned-philosopher, or, at least, the scientist-turned-moralist.

All this has been quite a long way from the gaudy picture evoked by the phrase "control of the mind." It is pleasing to me, at least, that it has to be so, because "control" implies the elimination of imponderables and unknowns. If and when these are reduced to insignificance in our understanding of man, the dynamics of our intellectual life will be enfeebled as surely as political issues in the comfortable society. In light of this, the chase may be more important than the capture, and the unknowns may save us yet.

References

1. Klapper, J. T., *The Effects of Mass Communications,* Glencoe, Ill., The Free Press, 1960, p. 8.
2. Cantrill, H., *The Invasion from Mars,* Princeton, N.J., Princeton University Press, 1940.
3. Bell, D., *An End of Ideology,* Glencoe, Ill., The Free Press, 1960.

Harold D. Lasswell

COMMUNICATION AND THE MIND

It is now customary to refer to the vast network of print and radio-television facilities and activities as "mass" communication. A few years ago scientists and laymen spoke of "public-opinion" media, having the journal of opinion in mind as prototype. The shift from "public" to "mass" reflects more than an extension of the German word for "crowd"; Germans also spoke of "public" and "public opinion." In part the change mirrors the *agit-prop* outlook of political activists, especially in the Communist-Bolshevist camp, intent upon arousing the "masses" to "true class consciousness." The shift also owes something to private businessmen, who learned to use the instruments provided by the "communications revolution" for repetitive impact upon the buying propensities of consumers. In the minds of such modern communicators arose the image of the target of mass-circulation media as a standard *homo sapiens* whose sapience was open to seduction by reiterated declarations of a self-serving character on behalf of creeds or goods.

This repetition often fell short of winning converts and influencing customers. Something had to be allowed for the dynamism of the "people" even when they were "masses." Goebbels was not alone in believing that the highest manipulative skill was to detect rumbles of disaffection before they broke cover, even within individual consciousness, and to provide outlets in harmony with managerial goals.

The stereotyped model of a mass man expressed the manipulator's ambivalent assessment of himself and his object. His ambivalence had something in common with the slave's image of the master whom he controls by perceiving moods before they are expressed in concrete demands, or the approach of the shrewd and dutiful wife and mother who detects the note of fatigue, hunger, or irritation before spouse or child has risen to the full dignity of command. It is no accident, as the phrase goes, that master manipulators display many traits, such as empathy and emotional subtlety, that we defined in our once-"masculine" culture as effeminate or at least weak.

In fact, we are referring to a particular instance of the tie that binds any manipulator to his object. He is limited, even threatened, as well as facilitated by the predispositions of the partner, whether the partner is man, animal, or thing. Think of the impact of the laboratory animal upon the scientist (even to the mannerisms). Consider the sculptor and his marble, wood, or plastic; the mechanic and his motor; the designer and his computer. The matrices of social interaction are man-man, man-nature; and when natural resources are processed into culture materials we have, for instance, man-animal, man-plant, man-edifice, man-tool, and man-machine pairs and multiples.

Deep-seated anxieties are generated in the mind of a manipulator by the act of suborning the independence of a target. In the target object one sees the ego as it might be, and indeed, at the most intimate level of self-appraisal is. In some sense every person is always weak, dependent, and therefore subject to manipulation. Hence some "manipulation anxiety" is the lot of every man. Our civilization is a culture characterized by the manipulation anxieties of all who play a professional role in strategy, and of the millions who perceive, with many gradations of dimness or clarity, that they are strategic targets.

The stereotyped image of a mass man was at first corroborated by many realistic features of the modern communications revolution. The new technology did indeed favor repetition and standardize part of the environment of millions of people. The attention frames of the inhabitants of New York or Podunk were to some degree uniformized by reiterated key symbols, slogans, and images. Urban manufacturers and wholesalers reached out in every direction through the new channels to enlarge territorial markets. Analysis confirmed the interdependence of zones of attention, sentiment, and public opinion, and of such activity areas as markets and arenas. Local audiences found it is impossible not to become involved with the beliefs, loyalties, and faiths of larger communities. Involvement was expressed in public opinion, which was registered in party and pressure-group commitments upon controversial issues.

The standardizing impact of the media was so obvious that important qualifications were ignored or uttered *sotto voce*. Yet, side by side with the general media, other communication networks were building. These channels aimed not at the community in its entirety, but at component elements within communities. Even a superficial inventory shows that every social institution is reflected in the specialized press: political, economic, religious, educational, hygienic, familial, honorific, scientific. The special networks cater to the diverse predispositions found in every locality. They undermine the standardization of life and enable local groups and individuals to find opposite numbers with whom to share values, demands, expectations, and identities. Hence the physicist in an isolated village can keep in touch with his colleagues; the remote cleric can keep informed and speculatively active about theological issues; the village banker can follow trends and consider projections that affect the local market. In principle, the symbol world of the villager can encompass the globe and penetrate outer space. The appropriate generalization would appear to be that diversification, not standardization, is the net effect of the communication revolution.

A moment's reflection suggests that there must be something askew about this picture. As of today at least, the mind of man hardly seems to scale the heights of universality and differentiation. Nor does mass man seem as stereotypically receptive as the original image said he was. In the argot, what gives?

What explains the failure of universalizing processes to attain universality in fact? We account for the strength of restrictive factors by considering the significance of the way in which new patterns are initiated. Potentially universal patterns are parochially introduced. This confers upon local configurations the possibility of limiting a new pattern or of facilitating its spread. The result depends upon the expectations of net value advantage current in these contexts.

Consider communications technology from this point of view. Movable type, for instance, was invented in China and introduced at long last into Europe where we are able to follow its subsequent course of diffusion and restriction. Movable type made it possible to accelerate the production of printed books, pamphlets, leaflets, and periodicals. Steps in this direction were variously appraised in each local environment affected. Scribes and manuscript illuminators often perceived the new technique as a threat to established skills in the communicative arts, and acted accordingly. In this they were joined by connoisseurs of excellence who ridiculed the tastelessness of the new products. Merchants, faced by a flood of advertising from competitors, might lament the innovation, though regretfully aiding its spread by purchasing advertising for themselves. Perceiving that subversive opinions and inconvenient news were disseminated in the burgeoning press, the rulers of the local body politic clamped down upon freedom by measures designed to monopolize or to subject the new media to strict censorship. Ecclesiastical authorities might initially recoil from the tide of print; presently, however, they were reconciled and turned the latest facilities to the purposes of sacred propaganda. Upper classes resented the fact that private libraries were becoming more widely available, thus reducing the privileges of status. Scholars, scientists, and physicians more or less speedily adopted new methods of publication to the needs of enlightenment and health. Not infrequently, families found that ties of kinship were subtly threatened by the competition of remote individuals and groups with whom sons and daughters established contact as a result of new media. In sum, everyone responded to parochially introduced innovations by adopting strategies in which were reflected their expectations about the net significance of the innovation for their present and prospective position in the value-institution structures of society. This was true whether we speak of economic values and institutions; government, law, and politics; churches and other agencies of rectitude; occupational, professional, or artistic skill groups; university, newspress, or other means of enlightenment; social class or caste structures of respect; institutions of safety and health; or family and friendship circles of affection.

We note, incidentally, that an innovation can be commended in universal terms without overcoming local resistance to its further spread. To praise the press as an agency of universal enlightenment is not to perform a universal act, but to use a term of universal reference locally. It is a parochial event, and responses depend upon local predispositions.

Whether an innovation spreads, or, if it spreads, is controlled for purposes which are parochial or universal depends upon the structure of predisposition in the environment where the innovation occurs, and into which it is successively introduced. It moves along a route of potential diffusion to the extent that successive gradients of expectation are favorable. Routes expand into zones of diffusion to the extent that successive gradients within a zone are favorable.

From the beginning of archeological records, the world community has been, and today continues to be, divided into culturally distinct societies who resist the many factors that make for the universalization of an ideology or a system of control that could constitute a truly global structure of public order. The world arena, for instance, remains divided into apprehensive and hostile camps engaged in an arms race of hitherto unimaginable magnitude and danger.

The foregoing analysis does not imply that new instruments of communication, however parochially introduced, have no effect whatever upon the distribution of values and institutions. It is compatible with the analysis to find that the technology of communication has somewhat modified local perspectives and operations. Scholars are generally agreed that the press fostered the rise of the national state as the dominant unit of the modern world. National states rose not at the expense of an effectively functioning world state, but by cannibalizing local units. The focus of attention of villages and towns was standardized to a degree throughout a zone that radiated along routes from a populous center. A large center grew into national dominance. However, at some boundary zone, centers of about equal strength came into contact and were unable to penetrate the other's territory sufficiently to control attention. Obviously, the media fostered translocal centralization, but centralizing processes checked one another at boundaries short of universality. Areas of attention, sentiment, and opinion were limited by predispositions that favored competing zones. Hence the universalizing processes fostered by the media were blocked, with the result that zones of intermediate inclusivity developed.

The communicative components of the social process have formed relatively stable equilibria around metropolitan centers and the capital cities of nation states. To stabilize is to consolidate a network capable of maintaining surveillance of the outside environment of states, of assisting collective action in regard to the environment, and of transmitting selected messages to the rising generation. Every subcommunity possesses a network of communication that performs equivalent functions in reference to other subcommunities constituting its environment within the broader body politic. Furthermore, every group within every community has a network that performs the functions of surveillance of other groups, of mobilization and guidance of group action, and of transmission to those who will be active in the future. We designate component groups according to the value-institution processes in which they perform special roles (power, government; wealth, economic, etc.). It is also true that each individual acquires a network of communication that makes it possible for him to maintain some surveillance of his environment, to formulate and guide his personal policies, and to store information for future use.

Stabilization includes *language,* spoken sign systems employed in all the networks or into which all the *signs* used in transmitting bits of information in any network can be translated. Dialects are differentiated for the use of subcommunities, and argots for specialized groups.

Communicative stability also requires stabilization of *symbols,* namely, systems of expectation, demand, and identification. Shared expectations include common understanding of the past and of the probable course of future events. Shared demands are common preferences and volitions regarding valued outcome of the social process. Shared identifications by identities are the shared symbols of reference to the "self" and "other," individuals and groups of reference which are included with or excluded from the company of the primary ego.

These perspectives, when relatively stable, comprise the *myth* shared by elite elements of the nation state, and by many and presumably most members of the rank and file. The established myth is the ideology; myths not established among the elite are counterideology.

Within any *ideology* we distinguish the *doctrine,* composed of the most general statements of philosophy; the *formula,* or the prescriptions of proper conduct; and the *folklore,* or the popularly accepted versions of norm and experience.

The myth (including ideologies and counterideologies) of any stable nation state is specialized according to the value-institution components of the social process. For example, the power myth includes political philosophy, the legal codes, and popular political lore. The wealth myth includes the doctrines of capitalism, socialism, cooperation and the like, the prescriptions of conduct appropriate to participants in the market structure, and popular economic lore. The rectitude myth includes the theological and ethical doctrines of ecclesiastical organizations, the prescriptions of cannon law, and popular mores. The affection myth includes the philosophy of love and friendship, the prescription of family and fraternal life, and popular conceptions of these matters. The enlightenment myth embraces scientific doctrines regarding nature and society, prescriptions regarding the conduct of scientific and historic inquiry, and popular assumptions about the matter-of-fact structure of the world. The skill myth comprises the doctrines regarding excellence in the arts, crafts, and professions, prescriptions relating to codes of conduct, and popular lore on these subjects. The well-being myth embraces the doctrines regarding psychosomatic integrity and deviation, prescriptions regarding the conduct of those engaged in care, cure, or prevention, and popular lore regarding health, safety, and comfort. The respect myth comprises doctrines of social class and caste, prescriptions that articulate modes of class conduct, and popular images and standards.

That any myth or myth component is stabilized is to be explained, we think, by the maximization postulate in one of its forms. A myth pattern outcompetes an alternative pattern; those who accept it have the expectation of a higher net value position than if they had accepted the alternative. On the value-indulgence side, this is a matter of expected gain or blocked loss, and on the value-deprivation calculus, of expected loss or blocked gain.

To become stable a myth must therefore receive value reinforcements that sustain the system of expectations sufficiently to prevent changeover to competing myths.

It is evident that when we examine a stabilized myth we are describing an equilibrium relationship of extraordinary complexity. A network of channels exists and is regularly used; sign systems serve particular channels and provide a language of reference for dialects and argots; symbol systems comprise comprehensive and specialized myths with ideological and counterideological components; myths are sustained by net expectations of advantage which are supported by a flow of value indulgences sufficient to perpetuate the system of expectation. The implication is that the flow of technique in the social process, as distinguished from myth, is appropriately phased, and hence that the total flow of activity, communicative and collaborative, has achieved stability.

Once a myth or myth component has been stabilized, it is not difficult to see how it is perpetuated from one generation to the next. The socialization sequence through which children and young people pass as they move up the escalator toward adulthood is so organized that the articulation of the myth is "indulged" in terms of many values, and failures of articulation are "deprived" in the same terms. As a simple reminder, to memorize and repeat the Declaration of Independence or passages from the Bible is rewarded by affection, respect, and positive evaluations of excellence and morality (skill, rectitude) and by a continued flow of other benefits (food and other creature comforts associated with well-being, playthings and other evidences of wealth, opportunities for access to further sources of enlightenment, a voice in such decisions as come within the age range). Deprivations follow recalcitrance, and especially adverse remarks about the ideology itself; these are deprivations of well-being (corporal punishment), of affection and respect (expressions of contempt), of rectitude (denunciation), of skill and wealth (denial of play equipment and tuition), of enlightenment (denial of books), and exclusion from consultation in self-government.

Once established, the myth is internalized so that the conscience, as well as the conscious self, provides indulgences for conformity and deprivations for nonconformity. The unconscious system, for example, characteristically imposes feelings of self-righteousness or guilt (rectitude), of pride or humiliation (respect), of love or indifference (affection), of euphoria or anxiety (well-being), of gratification for excellence or negative gratification for clumsiness (skill), of comprehension or disorientation (enlightenment), of impoverishment or enrichment (wealth), of mastery or subordination (power). The internal system is sustained by appropriate balances of value indulgence or deprivation at the adult level throughout the early, middle, and later stages of the career line.

It is evident that a stabilized myth contributes to the stability of a society by standardizing the use of individual minds at successive phases of collective processes. Consider a national process of decision: It passes through phases of intelligence, recommendation, prescription, invocation, application, appraisal, termination. Take intelligence, for example: The formal structures include military, diplomatic, economic, and cultural observation and reporting of the activities of other nation states. The individuals who act as primary observers and reporters, having incorporated the myth, are so modified that they are predisposed to see events through the selective screen acquired in the course of introjecting the myth. The comparative study of intelligence amply demonstrates the uniformities that result from socialization of the child, even to the standardization of error. I include inbuilt errors of perception, such as the chronic underestimation of Japanese flying ability, which reached grotesque dimensions among Western intelligence sources before World War II, and the common and fantastic underestimation of the capabilities of folk peoples to acquire industrial civilization. Even when these misperceptions did not distort observations made by direct observers, they were almost certain to be reinstated at the interpretive stage of processing intelligence reports.

Possibly the most treacherous limitation imposed by myth is upon the imagining of alternatives. This has been conspicuously present among strategists who perform a recommending-promoting function, but it has been present at all subsequent phases of decision. The result is to hedge in the range of recognized courses of action open to legislators, policemen, judges, inspectors, and all other official or unofficial participants in the total process.

The negative side of the uniformities of a stabilized myth are clearly indicated in the foregoing: myth cramps creativity; myth often substitutes misperception for reality. We have seen above that the stabilization of myth at the national level blocked the potential universality of public order and the potential diversification of human achievement on a global plane.

When we review the stabilization of myth in the perspective of man as a biological species, its positive and negative impacts are strikingly confirmed. It appears that the stabilizing of myth is a spontaneous (and partly deliberate) strategy by which mankind has sought to keep man's excess symbolic capacity under control. We are told that the brain is about the same today as it was tens of thousands of years ago when human beings were organized into relatively tiny bands. Small folk societies learned the fundamental strategy whereby man's pluripotentiality can be hammered into the narrow range of patterns that a given society is able or willing to tolerate. The basic strategy is to reduce or impose limitations upon the infant and child. It is generally agreed that an educational process is indispensable to the domestication of man's destructiveness; or, indeed, to the achievement of a genuinely human self; or, for that matter, sufficient social stimulation to acquire language, hence the tools of complicated thought. Nonstimulated infants and children become semiarticulate savages, as Ferdinand of Sicily learned by experimentation some time ago. But once the basic predispositions are modified to conform to the limits of myth (and technique), the individual is sufficiently maimed for the rest of his life to share most of the misperceptions of reality, the parochial identifications, and the established value orientations of the society of which he is part.

In executing the strategy of limitation, the greatest tactic open to small folk societies was and is the management of psychic contagion, which was accomplished by repetitive group participation in myth-expressive rites. Ceremonialization, ritualization, orgiastic dancing, singing, playing, dramatization—all these terms call up component activities whereby the primitive receptivities of man were originally integrated into symbolic, communicative, and collaborative stability. The subjectivities of the individual were disciplined into the mold required to sustain the effectiveness of the cues for the conduction of such collective activities as wars with bands of other men, protomen, and animal bands, the building of lodgings, the collection or domestication of plants and animals, planting and harvesting, care of the young, and disposal of the dead.

In all this there continued to be a fantastic price—the loss of man's unused symbolic capability. In explanation—and implied extenuation—it can be said that, given the shaky texture of social life, it was impracticable for any band, wandering or settled, to cope with the diversities of impulse and idea that kept welling to the surface of man's remarkable brain. Evidently culture had to protect itself against the brain until, by gradual accretion, culture was sufficiently strong and enlightened to permit those identified with patterns of culture to give wider latitude to man's potentialities.

During the first 400 or 500 thousand years man's symbol capacity did, in fact, find impressive expression. He lived in hundreds and thousands of primitive societies, each of which was sufficiently isolated from its fellows to develop somewhat distinctive ways of life. But within any particular band the norm was to insist upon conformity to established patterns; variations crept in by cultural drift rather than deliberate innovation. To evaluate the magnitude of man's early achievements one must examine the impressive sample of folk cultures that exist today or have been laid bare by archeologists.

The human species achieved a formidable leap in culture when it succeeded in inventing cities, an occurrence that came at about the same time in the valleys of the Nile, the Tigris-Euphrates, and probably the Indus. Following V. Gordon Childe, it is possible to convey a sense of the momentous character of this leap in development by taking note of the following innovations associated with the city: the state, or the organization of society on a basis of residence in place of, or on top of, kinship; legal codes; systematic taxation; monumental public works; the art of writing; the beginnings of arithmetic, geometry, and astronomy; and full-time technical specialists, as in metal working.

The human species was now able to express itself by means of a complex division of labor within what might in principle become a universal community. Instead of the mechanism of geographically segregated folk societies, it became possible to release the creativity of man in thousands of new directions, and to communicate, store, and retrieve the enormously accelerated achievements of civilized man.

Even the record of civilized and urbanized man, impressive as it is, has produced no more than partial release of man's capacity. The fundamental strategy of restriction continues. Tactics, however, have altered. We rely less upon the mechanism of psychic infection and ceremony to direct and restrict man's creativity than upon two vast and specialized networks: systems of education and systems of instantaneous communication. It is true that primary, face-to-face groups and situations continue to play decisive roles and that common sentiments are aroused and directed by the networks, but new factors are introduced when primary situations are strung together into complex chains and zones in nation-state and state-coalition areas.

Historically, emphasis has been laid upon the destructive component of human predisposition. To what extent is it possible to show that much chronic and intermittent anger, rage, and negativism are the fruits of frustrations upon capability imposed by the nurturing process? Do recurring drives to use latent capabilities arouse malaise and desperation when they are interfered with? Do modern opportunities to communicate heighten levels of inner stress by appealing to capacities which civilization is not yet adept enough to encourage and express creatively? In this, as in so many respects, our epoch may be seized by anxieties of transition which mark the emergence of more advanced levels of culture.

For the future the question is whether education and communication networks will contribute to a double liberation of man: liberation from parochial loyalty and the expectation of violence, and liberation from the restrictions that spring from the crippling anxieties of elder generations who are uncertain of the adequacy of culture to cope with man's creativity, particularly as encountered in children and young people. A fully consummated communications revolution, if it occurs, will dissolve predispositions that block the way toward universality and diversity. The precautionary struggle of culture against brain will tilt toward realism and creativeness.

We must first puncture the sanguine expectation that it is only a question of time and patience before universalizing trends occur from without. The ground for this expectation is that in the course of man's evolution social and political units have grown larger, and that potential coverage by communication facilities is all-inclusive. We have drawn attention before to the restrictive consequences of the parochial introduction of potentially universal forms and commented upon the subordination of universal possibilities to the purposes of nation states and state coalitions. It remains to show more explicitly that, as political units enlarge, parochializing factors can become stronger, not weaker. Given the meteoric rise of the technology of destruction, it is conceivable—if not, indeed, probable—that universal catastrophe will forestall universal order.

I refer to the tendency to internalize the focus of attention within an expanded and extended body politic. For example, as the Soviet world takes in more territory, the percentage of the population who live part of their lives abroad is reduced. Barriers to travel and to authenticated communication cut down the access of Soviet citizens to the world outside and of people from the outside to Soviet countries. As experience abroad declines, the focus of attention becomes relatively stabilized to conform to the political divisions in the world arena. At this stage parochialism is redefined and intensified by expansion.

A more subtle mechanism is also involved. A "self-reference effect" operates when strangers meet, since novel patterns of behavior disturb or shock the conscious or unconscious components of personality. Hence attention is focused intermittently upon the "self" and the "other," and during the early stages of these adjustments, the distinctive identity of the self is typically reaffirmed and accompanied by assertions of worth or superiority.

It is important to recognize that the long-run result of the self-reference effect differs from the earlier phase, and characteristically brings about an enlargement of self-systems. The mechanism is a temporary and partial withdrawal response which enables the parochial self to become familiar with a widened context, and hence to redefine—and often to amplify—the boundaries of identification.

In this technoscientific age it is appropriate to ask whether instruments of communication can and will be developed that make universal attention compulsory or bring it within the range of voluntary choice, free of serious danger of local detection and negative sanction. Can we imagine receiving and transmitting acts of such microsize and strength that they can be sown everywhere behind nation-state and state-coalition boundary lines—or communication devices of such irresistible strength that they defy "jamming"?

Whatever the future of communications technology, the point within the competence of a social scientist is that diversified foci of attention, whenever realized, foster diversities of demand, expectation, and identity.

In estimating the balance of factors that affect the future we do not underestimate the importance of elements that contribute to the attrition of local fanaticism. The study of religious and secular revolutions has attested to the passage from "ideology" to "phraseology." Whether a utopian ideology draws support from the "internal" or "external" proletariat, the early phases of the movement provide rewards for agitators and organizers of protest. Once an established order is swept aside and a new elite and symbol system are installed, the balance of value indulgence and deprivation changes. Career opportunities favor administrators of civil, military, and police affairs. The phrenetic reiteration of the triumphant myth is ceremonialized, specialized, devitalized. If levels of consumption rise, and the income pattern is graduated rather than bifurcated, fanaticism cools.

We are interested in a more elusive set of factors affecting the fate of fanaticism. The first is the scientific frame of mind. Modern science and technology spread from Western Europe in piecemeal fashion, as might be predicted from the pattern of deferred or diluted diffusion discussed before. Similarly, the scientific approach moves from the scrutiny of physical events to the study of sign and symbol events, hence, in the long run, ideologies are vulnerable to comparative investigation. This is true despite the well-known fact that the person who studies the stars, the atom, or the cell is not necessarily qualified to approach the investigation of symbolic or behavioral events objectively or with ingenuity. The scientific pattern is, however, capable of being universalized beyond the parochial matrix of any specific scientist, scientific specialty, or subset of problems.

At this moment it is not practicable to do more than give a few hints regarding the procedures which are at hand, or which are likely to be reinvented in various contexts to develop the comparative study of ideology. Such procedures dilute or forestall unquestioning devotion to any particular constellation of doctrine, formula, and lore.

A major aid is the analysis of the *manifest content* of utterances that exemplify ideological systems. The path is then clear to discover how manifest content is related to the context of the social movements in which they appear. Some ideologies purport to provide guidance for individuals and groups in solving the problems with which they are faced, it is obviously pertinent to compare ideologies according to such problem-solving questions as these (which I shall briefly enlarge upon), though without making an attempt to exhaust each topic.

1. What value goals are proposed for men in society? Note in this connection that the articulated doctrines in Washington, Moscow, London, and other elite centers is remarkably uniform in its commitment to human dignity as against human indignity; for example, it is against the ideal of a world run by a superrace.

a. Are the value goals justified by reference to a transempirical source—Divine Will, for example—or postulated on grounds of experience? If the latter, what procedures, if any, are proposed for interpreting experience?

b. Are general categories of value specified in terms of institutional practices which are dogmatically affirmed or regarded as open to inquiry? Values are dogmatically specified, for instance, when particular institutional patterns are alleged to be the only patterns by which goals can be fully realized. In contemporary ideologies, "socialism" and "capitalism" are often treated this way, rather than proposed as guesses about the institutional arrangements by which values can be optimalized in various social contexts. Similarly, "presidential government" or the "cabinet system" may be held to be superior "by definition."

2. How is the past presented? For instance, is history viewed as a straight line of evolution toward the goal sought? Is it cyclical and without discernible trend? Is human progress regarded as possible or impossible?

3. How are social changes explained? For instance, what role is ascribed to belief in ideology? Upon what factors is belief said to depend? What social consequences are attributed to belief (or disbelief)?

4. How is the future projected? Is the "desirable" goal said to be "inevitable"?

5. What major policy strategies are proposed? What role is assigned to coercion? How is the decision process to be organized for the making of collective decisions?

The postulational methods of mathematics and logic, when applied to ideologies, describe formal structures with precision and hence enable contextual questions to be raised in definite terms. *Formal questions* include:

1. How many levels of abstraction are employed in formulating the ideology? At the lowest level the terms are given, or are capable of

receiving, operational definitions which can be used to relate the formal system to concrete situations.

2. How many key terms (defined, undefined) are used at each level? A system may be organized by single-term, two-term (either/or), or by multiple-term levels.

3. Are distinctions explicitly drawn between propositions that formulate norms of preference and determination, and propositions that designate events? In this connection ambiguous statements are brought into the open. For instance, a statement may be called "nature's law," and it is unclear whether the maker of the statement purports to make a factual statement or not. If we find that he goes on to complain that nature's supposed law is violated, we classify the statement as normatively ambiguous. Sometimes the factual references are manifest, but further examination shows that the statement maker is using fact-form discourse to affirm a preference. This is designatively ambiguous, as when the future is said to be "inevitable" rather than "probable."

4. In the formulation of normative-prescriptive statements what polarities are used? Prescriptive statements lay down norms of conduct. Analysis shows that they travel in polar opposites which are available as guides (and rationalizations) for choice.

The pertinence of scientific investigation to the task of locating *ideologies in context* is clear enough. When ideology *A* is compared in context with ideology *B*, or subpattern 1 of ideology *A* is compared with subpattern 2 of the same system, the questions are: What factors account for the invention, diffusion, or restriction of each ideology or subpattern? What factors in the social process are affected by invention, diffusion, or restriction?

At this point such verifiable questions arise as under what combination of impinging environmental factors, acting upon what combination of predispositional factors, a given mode of response appears with what probability. For instance, under what constellation of circumstances do individuals (singly or in collective situations) become aware of, and concerned about, resolving contradictory statements in the ideology with which they are identified? When do they ignore contradictory statements of fact or manifest contradictions of prescriptive norm?

We know from the comparative study of the history of religious, legal, and political prescriptions that any syntactic system can be, and probably has been, used to justify contradictory modes of conduct. In limited time-space situations, however, syntactic formulations are applied to concrete issues according to value demands, expectations, and identifications which are localized. All syntactic systems can be interpreted universally; but they are invoked in parochial contexts to yield localized results. All syntactic systems are potentially equivalent (interchangeable) at the most generalized level of abstraction, but competing systems are treated as nonequivalent so long as local expectations are that assertions of nonequivalence yield net advantages to the assertion maker.

Scientific inquiry is continually forcing into the focus of attention the apparent contradictions between an ideology as communicated most generally and as invoked or complied with in concrete circumstances. From the point of view of a nonfanatic, of course, this is a major contribution of scientific inquiry, since it performs an appraisal function that enables individuals acting singly or jointly to respecify value goals for the future. This perpetual confrontation of conventional ideology with the results of carefully defined functional analysis and empirical procedures is a fundamental contribution of science to man and society.

I shall not undertake to review the present state of inquiry around the globe upon the dynamics of ideology. The immediate point is that the spread of modern civilization carries within it propensities to apply the scientific frame of reference to all events, and though parochial factors may combine to defer and distort the application, the predisposition is found wherever science is found. And this is not conducive to the care and feeding of fanatics.

Another predisposition fostered by modern civilization can be identified as a factor favoring universality. There are grounds for suggesting that the civilization of the machine cultivates common experiences that lay the foundation for universal art. Parallel experiences across boundary lines predispose toward transnational epidemics of psychic infection. Despite all barriers, we have evidence that to a degree modern instruments of communication are already a considerable distance along the way toward remodeling the globe into one great village whose villagers share many sentiments that are expressed and strengthened by communicable patterns of esthetic expression.

I have in mind music and dance, and especially jazz, which is not alone in permeating the metallic curtains of the Soviet world, but provides a universal opportunity for identifications to occur between the young people reared in modern civilizations or folk societies. Rhythm, sound, and body movements possess relatively universal appeal, and jazz is the very stuff of epidemic. To the extent that there is withdrawal of involvement with traditional or newly established ideologies, there is likely to be discovery and affirmation of modes of esthetic expression. In a word-sodden world there is latent hunger for freedom from argumentative, hortatory, or even descriptive discourse. The esthetic experience provides withdrawal into moments of ego privacy and composure; without the sense of having lost compansionship, one stays with the orchestra or the "combo" of the "hop." The esthetic experience, as reanalyzed by Cassiver and Suzanne Langer, though entangled with the gut, is likewise of the mind. It is the symbolization of affect, and the symbolic arrangement is perceived as a pattern of style. A temper tantrum is not art, but allusions to a tantrum can become art when allusive symbols and signs achieve style.

We cannot pursue this theme further at the moment, but the immediate point is that parochial barriers are permeable from within and without by esthetic as well as scientific components of a universalizing civilization.

We must not overlook the strategies open to political elites who look upon themselves as threatened by the withdrawal of involvement in the parochialisms upon which much of their power is based. To the extent that withdrawal of involvement creates a power vacuum, it is probable that parochial elements will take advantage of its existence. Under continual provocation, extreme and dangerous strategies may be devised to counteract the universalizing and diversifying effects of communication. Symbolic indoctrination may itself be given up as the principal means of stabilizing systems of public order. Chemical and biological warfare can be waged upon dissenters whose capacity for feeling or expressing opposition would be permanently crippled. This is the somatization of acquiescence. It is not demagogery; rather, it is somatarchy, or rule by biochemicals in place of the manipulation of sign and symbol. Science blindly finds new aids to further blindness—or to vision.

It is not within the present scope of our discussion to foretell the outcome of the incessant struggle of parochial against universalizing factors in the world community. That apprehensive political elites will seek to keep their power positions is to be taken for granted. But elite perspectives undergo transformation. And the universalizing and diversifying potentials of modern communication, though trapped by parochial influences and harassed by elderly apprehension regarding the brain, are perpetually rejuvenated by scientific and esthetic patterns inseparable from the civilization in whose texture they are indissolubly woven.

THE ADVANCE OF CIVILIZATION

This is an actual transcription of the formal but spontaneous panel discussion of the papers immediately preceding. Only minor editing has been done where continuity and clarity required it. The editors feel that the spontaneity of the actual discussion gives a particular value to the panel in this form.

Moderator: Leo C. Rosten
Panel Members: Harold D. Lasswell, William E. Porter, Herbert A. Simon

Prof. Rosten I would like to tell a story to illustrate the role of the social scientist. According to this story, Destiny once came down to an island on earth, summoned before him three men, and said: "What would you do if I told you that tomorrow this island would be innundated by a tidal wave?" The first man said, "I would at once eat and drink and make love and do all the things I have never done before." The second man said, "I would take my loved ones to the sacred grove and make sacrifices and pray and pray and pray so that, when we were drowned, we would be prepared to enter Paradise." The third man said, "I should at once assemble our wisest men and begin to study how to live under water."

I do not mean to suggest that the social scientist is the last man. But the social scientist studies the hedonist, the mystic, and the scientist. He tries to provide relevant insights into why these people are what they are, how they work, and what the implications are of what they do. The good social scientist performs these roles with neutral compassion for the fate of man. We have had, it seems to me, an admirable example of how the combination of detachment and insight can be brought to bear on problems involving the possibilities of the human being both as an individual and in groups. Professor Simon, do you conceive in the computing ingenuities now facing us that in time an artificially constructed instrument can reproduce all the cerebral and emotional activities and the inner life of fantasy which are today considered particular to man?

Prof. Simon I think in answering a question like that a scientist has to make some kind of distinction between the kinds of bets he places, the kind of gamble he makes each day in deciding what should be investigated and what are profitable ways of investigating it. He has to make a distinction between the kind of an assertion that he is willing to make to himself and the kind of assertion that he thinks he can back up with evidence and which therefore becomes part of the public part of science. It seems to me that the motivation inspiring people involved in the kind of work I was describing is the notion that we can explain and understand by this kind of simulation an ever-widening part of human mental activity. Up to the present the greatest progress has been made with respect to the cognitive activity, in which the emotional and attitudinal components are very small indeed. My private bet is that this kind of explanation will extend very far into the area of the emotional and the affective. I can see nothing that has arisen as yet in this exploration which would suggest a boundary line, and I suspect that the exploration will go very far indeed before it meets such a boundary line—if indeed it does. That is really all one has to say about the present. One does not have to speculate about whether the boundary exists, nor does one behave differently in the investigation if he believes it does or does not exist.

Prof. Rosten Professor Porter, in discussing political education you talked with some high degree of preference about developing a livelier political life and a deeper sense of involvement. I want to ask whether we can break through the prevailing mythologies to say that in one sense it may not be desirable to impose upon people the need for political involvement if, in fact, they do not feel they want it. The egalitarian assumption may be worth considering, that democracy is not necessarily the system in which everyone participates politically to the same extent but in which everyone has the choice to do that which he can and wants to do best.

Prof. Porter I suppose that the answer to this question deals essentially with some terribly confused matters. At some point you have to make some commitment to your concept of the function of man. This is in a sense related to Professor Mace's wonderful cats and their biological activities. He made quite a point that these activities were not aimless. The cats had a set of goals all their own, even though these goals did nothing to provide better shelter or more food or necessities. I suppose I have almost a sentimentalist-humanistic point of view, which says that man's intelligence must always function in a context simply because he has it. This is a terribly unscientific observation, but I think scientific investigation more and more pushes us to the point where these values become increasingly important. The society in which there is just enough freedom to permit us all to manage our own little field sounds awfully dull to me.

Prof. Rosten I would like to tell a story to illustrate how the young are crippled by our educational system. I was always a very poor student of mathematics, on the assumption that, after all, if I add 2 and 2 and I get 4, and if Einstein adds 2 and 2 and he gets 4, so what's the use? But it occurred to me, as I watched my children, how ineptly we communicate and educate, and I once said to a mathematician, "Why on earth do you defer the teaching of algebra to the high school level when children are ready for it at about the fourth grade?" He took this as a sign of my surpassing innocence and said, "That is nonsense." I said, "But you do do it. When you teach Johnny his multiplication table you say, 'Johnny, how much is 2 times 2? '4.' Then you say, '4 times 2 equals 8.' You then say, 'Johnny, 2 times what equals 12?' And at that point Johnny is confronted with one of the great inventions of the human mind, the concept of *x*; 2*x* equals 12. But we don't do that. We force him merely to repress the awareness of this tremendous conceptual leap." So I was particularly pleased when Karl Pribram told me that children were being taught set theory at a much younger age than formerly.

Professor Lasswell, would you care to comment about your participation in the famous "people machine" used in the Presidential election campaign?

Prof. Lasswell My participation in this enterprise, which has been correctly characterized by Professor Porter, is part of my concern for making the latest information available to the community—on the basis of which strategies can be calculated and goals clarified. There are great possibilities now to improve the information inflow available at the focus of attention of people of our community. The problem is to make the same flow of information available both to those who desire to manipulate and to those who are targets of manipulation. This is a continuing gradation: some of us spend a part of our time manipulating others; the rest of the time we are manipulated by other people. This means that we may wish to move our society in the direction of making available to those who have the purpose and the initiative the same stock of common information in the most compact and best time position. This is one reason for my concern for active participation in this type of innovation.

Prof. Porter Some students are interested in the idea of the legal control of obscenity; that is, the basis upon which, without violating our presumably strongly held tenets of freedom of expression, law can be made to control the publication of openly obscene material in any kind of logical way. One of the superficial arguments always raised early is the causality and the provocation—delinquency and so on. But there is no evidence that this is true at all. Is there a defensible idea that a culture has a right to defend its ethical standards?

Prof. Lasswell One of the most important interpretations of this question would be that the decision-making process in a culture like ours may very well include the question, "What manner of man in what sort of social process do we want to achieve through future years?" And if we ask that question, one of the subsequent questions will be, "What is the relation of your definition of words like 'obscenity' to the characterization of the manner of man and the manner of interaction, the social context of the man that you accept?" First, let us consider definitions in terms of the way you talk about the goals and events, and then the way you talk about the immediate events. I would say that if you construe "obscenity" as certain patterns then it is quite clear that every community could say, "We do not want human beings or a social process characterized by certain forms of expression. Under these circumstances it would be entirely good sense to say: "Our objective is an obscenity-free man. We want a man who does not need obscenity." Conversely, if you define obscenity in a more interesting way—as some people do—the problem is, "How much obscenity do you want your man to enjoy?"

Prof. Rosten On obscenity, I know few ways of indicating the parochialization of attitudes and the extent of certain values better than the story of the model who came to the artist's studio. She had come to be painted in the nude and she started to undress. However, the artist said, "Don't bother to undress. I have a frightful headache. Let's just have some coffee and you can come back tomorrow." So she put all her clothes back on, and she and the artist were having coffee when footsteps were heard. "Oh goodness, my wife," said the artist. "Quick, take off your clothes." I take it that Professor Lasswell would like a society in which *some* obscenity may be clothed or unclothed, according to the way people are inclined.

Prof. Simon A question has been stirring in my mind since I listened to Professor Porter's remarks. It seems to me that one of the big themes that has been running through almost all the papers here has been the relation between man's reason and man's emotion. We fear control of the mind or other constriction of reason, although our fears have been much allayed by what has been said about mass communication. We somehow raise reason to some level of eminence in the mind. I thought this came out in Professor Porter's talk in another way, when he was speaking about the effect of televising a political campaign, the public's reaction to political events, and the problem of political choice. I wonder if he would care to enlarge on the question of why it is best for us to judge political campaigns in terms of what are called "issues," rather than in terms of the reaction of one's body chemistry to the personality characteristics of a particular candidate when we see him on the screen. I would also like to ask Professor Porter whether he thinks our judgments on issues are more reliable predictions of the policy that will be followed by a government under a particular President that our judgment of a candidate based on close-range assessment of his reactions as a human being to a variety of unforeseen situations.

Prof. Porter One reason I assume there is something virtuous in the rational analysis and choice among alternatives is that essentially I am an old-fashioned man of the eighteenth-century rationalist school. I think there is a better answer in the fact that these face-to-face kinds of reactions are so often idiosyncratic in nature. Consequently, I believe that in the process of argument and rational examination we arrive at something approximating the truth which *does* have some universal application. When we make a judgment on a different basis, however, we are more superficial. Our judgment may be related to something totally irrational, so that our chances of arriving at the correct answer are fewer. This, of course, raises the problem of what is the right answer —which in a sense is Professor Simon's question. But in terms of trying to estimate how certain kinds of political figures will react in a situation, as he points out, we are making a choice between how they're going to react ad-lib when we judge them on the basis of their personality, or how they are going to react in terms of the basic patterns of their thoughts and essential points of view.

Prof. Rosten I can't resist adding a historical footnote. Franklin Roosevelt was elected in 1932, partly on the basis of a balanced budget. What struck me in the television debates during the last presidential election campaign was that, in the effort of each candidate to present an appealing persona, Mr. Nixon made the fatal error of trying to show that he was the superior by acting as if he were equal. The fact that the public did not learn something about how men act under stress suggested certain conclusions about personality structure.

Prof. Lasswell I wonder if Professors Porter and Simon think that there are some better ways of organizing our communication efforts than those we have made use of to date? We are very much impressed by the mass media of television, the press that is aimed at very wide circulation, and so forth. I wonder whether or not any of our work to date makes it possible to think creatively about new channels of communication or new combinations of information flow that will make available to more participants in our society that which is clarifying to them and also pertinent to the body politic.

Prof. Porter I think there must be such possibilities. I should like to see the mass media themselves work closely with behavioral scientists who are studying the formation of public opinion and similar issues. I should like to see social scientists deliberately construct a certain amount of their material so that it would really provoke. A great body of research indicates that it is possible to construct such material. There is the problem of transmitting the kind of information which Professor Lasswell was talking about—information coming out of Mr. Kennedy's "people machine." It is a most exciting concept to me that not only the presumed manipulators but also their targets would have access to the same kind of information. We should get our mass media to make a commitment for this concept. I think there is also a great place for the role of government in the establishment of certain kinds of mass communication which do not receive adequate attention under the present system.

Prof. Rosten I am always interested by the defense of mass media. I was once questioned by a group of students about the limitations of the press. I said, "Wouldn't you much prefer a system in which people vote?" They said, "Of course." I said, "Well, go to a newspaper or magazine stand and watch the voting. Each time you buy a magazine you are voting for one against another." The limitation, however, is that you can select only from among those which are available. The real answer to those who are too sanguine about the state of the press is that in many ways it is as good as we have talents for at this stage. In that wonderful formulation of *Alice in Wonderland,* "It isn't so much that the public likes what it is getting but that it necessarily is getting what it likes."

From the Floor Professor Porter, will you comment on the increasing complexity both of the issues about which the public is to make decisions and of the consequences of these decisions? Is it possible that this very complexity destroys the public's ability to take sides, to find an acceptable pro and an acceptable con?

Prof. Porter I would say in reply that the great critical issues are very often not terribly complex, although they may have complex manifestations, questions about what to do in detail; for example, a reassertion of immediate trouble in Berlin might be too complex to handle. At the heart of this problem, once scientific information is fairly stabilized, I think there is a whole range of problems where the basic decisions are essentially quite simple, even though their ramifications can be complex.

From the Floor Professor Simon, at the end of your paper you implied that man's dignity and stature should not seem diminished by any explanation of his mental processes or behavior in mechanistic terms; his dignity does not, and should not, rest upon mystery. Upon what do you feel this dignity does rest, if it indeed exists?

Prof. Simon When I refer to the dignity of man, I think I am just using a brief term to refer to the set of views we have about ourselves as individuals, as members of a species, and as people who live in a very large and complicated universe. I think I refer there to the set of beliefs that we hold about this, the basic beliefs which seem to make the whole activity valuable, meaningful, and pleasurable to us.

From the Floor The law sets boundaries, as parents set boundaries for their children. That is in a sense right; it gives stability to a society and also is a haven for the timid. But I think at the same time we should respect those who responsibly go beyond the boundaries of the accepted, so that these boundaries may ultimately be extended.

Prof. Rosten This is not unlike Mr. Koestler's comments on the sacredness of the individual's mystical experience, or nonconventional, nonconforming mentation.

Prof. Simon I agree with the comment that we always struggle with this balance between demand for conformity and permission for creativity.

Prof. Rosten I am reminded of one of the many apocryphal stories involving Winston Churchill. One of the war criminals, a German General, was being tried, and it leaked out that Mr. Churchill had contributed £1,000 sterling to his defense. When asked how he, the arch enemy of the Nazis, could contribute to the defense of them, he gave an explanation which I consider to be on a level with a statement of John Stuart Mill. He said, "I do not have the slightest indication as to whether General So-and-So is innocent or guilty of the appalling crimes for which he is being tried. That is not why I gave the money. I made the contribution to ensure that English justice would never have anything to be ashamed of."

Prof. Porter Professor Simon, I want to refer to the point you made earlier in this panel discussion, that you see nothing to indicate any barrier between what you might roughly call the creative end of Mr. Koestler's spectrum and the mechanical end with which you are now working. Doesn't the program which is put into these instruments in effect represent perception? It is the result of perception in the human being. If we assume that with infinite elaboration these machines are essentially capable of all these mental activities, doesn't this imply that the human organism is also limited to those things which he can take into his perceptions?

Prof. Simon Yes.

Prof. Rosten Would you not agree, Professor Simon, that in that context Professor Lasswell's statement about the widening of the parochial outlook and the breaking through the myths of the comparative systematic analysis represents, if nothing more, the widening of the capacity of human production in communication as well as in perception? Don't you agree, in other words, that people will actually perceive more if taught and encouraged properly?

Prof. Simon Every advance in knowledge which has really radically changed man's understanding of his relation to the universe has been a widening, and it has also often been a very painful change in that perception. The revolution that took the earth out of the middle of the universe and put it as a planet of the sun was a radical modification of man's outlook. The revolution that made man a species that evolved from other species was such. Any steps that we take toward explaining, whether by biochemical or other means, what goes on in the human head *does* change man's concept of where he fits in the world. If you believe that knowledge is freedom in some sense, this is more than a slogan. It does mean more freedom; it does not mean an absence of the problem.

Prof. Rosten I cannot resist pointing out that it was not until the end of the nineteenth century that artists dared to do what children had always done but had had knocked out of them by realistic parents and art teachers. This was to put color into shadows. We can no longer look into a landscape or a bowl of fruit, as people did before the Impressionists. It was not until Cézanne that someone had the boldness to say: "Why do you always have to look into a picture? Why can't the picture seem to be coming toward you in the reversal of perspective?" If this is true in the crude and so-called obvious phenomenon of visualization, think of how much more this is true in terms of conceptualization and the organizing of fantasy in the interplay between fantasy and reason.

I would like to conclude this meeting with a story which illustrates man's capacity to be unpredictable in relation to the experimenters, whether pharmacologists or computer designers. A man took his son to a psychiatrist and said, "This boy needs help." The psychiatrist said, "I shall give him a very simple test." He drew a circle on a blackboard and said, "Now, son, what do you think of when you see the circle?" And the boy said, "That is two rhinoceroses making love." The psychiatrist, who was a dialectical materialist, said, "What do you think of when I draw this circle?" And the boy said, "Oh, that is peachy; that is two elephants making love." The psychiatrist turned to the father and said, "Your boy is seriously disturbed," and the father said, "What do you mean? It was you who drew all those dirty pictures."

PART FIVE

RESTRICTION AND FREEDOM OF THE MIND

Chairman: John B. deC. M. Saunders

At the close of the general sessions, the participants in the symposium were divided into six panel groups, each to serve as a focal point for discussion of the issue that had occupied so much of the time and attention of the symposium, restriction and freedom of the mind. The panels were chosen so as to provide a variety of disciplinary backgrounds for each discussion group, and to make available a variety of viewpoints on the questions likely to be raised. Following discussion of restriction of the mind, the composition of the panels was rearranged for further discussion concerning freedom of the mind.

Because of the length of the discussions, it is not possible to publish them in full, but each panel has been recorded, abstracted, and edited for consistency, and the printed summary follows. It cannot, of course, be expected to demonstrate that rigorous arrangement of fact and ideas that is expected in a formal presentation, but the editor feels that the significance of the thought that emerged from these discussions more than outweighs the disadvantage inherent in committing to writing comments which were delivered *ad hoc.*

The summaries were made possible by the combined efforts of a number of persons. Paul Clifton edited the material. The actual recordings were arranged by the following:

Robert R. Alford, Teaching Associate, Department of Sociology, University of California, Berkeley

Malcolm A. Brown, Clinical Psychologist, State Medical Facility, Vacaville, California

Price Charlson, Ph.D., Assistant Professor, Department of Philosophy, University of California, Berkeley

Donald G. Langsley, Clinical Instructor in Psychiatry, Langley Porter Neurological Institute, San Francisco

David Matza, Assistant Professor, Department of Sociology, University of California, Berkeley

Gerald A. Mendelsohn, Assistant Professor, Department of Psychology, University of California, Berkeley

RESTRICTION OF THE MIND

The discussion in this first panel centered on two main topics:

1. A difference in viewpoints about the mind-brain relation, expressed by Professor Simon's thesis of the human potentialities of machines, on the one hand, and by Dr. Penfield's proposition of the uniqueness of man, on the other

2. The implications of our affluent society, an amplification of Professor Mace's thesis

Recorder: Malcolm A. Brown
Panel Members: C. A. Mace, Wilder Penfield, Herbert A. Simon

Professor Mace opened the discussion with the opinion that the human mind should be restricted to a performance of the functions that machines could not do. He was not himself disturbed by the possibility that machines might one day be able to do everything that minds could do today. He cited the simple case of how much more profitable it was to do elementary mathematics on paper rather than in one's head. By the same token, he argued, there should be no strong objection to handing over to machines, a greater number of problems, especially more difficult tasks. He issued a warning, however, that increasingly efficient machines should not be permitted to deprive human beings of the need to think; no one should become so dependent upon machines as to lose his faculty for asking questions.

Professor Simon replied that his concern with automatic computing machines, although avowedly different from Dr. Penfield's concern with an understanding of the mechanisms of the brain, was nevertheless directed toward satisfactory substitute goals. He expressed his longstanding interest in the question of exactly what division of labor human beings should make between the functions that human minds could perform and those that man-made machines could do. He, for one, was reluctant to relinquish the full use of his own mind. In expressing his appreciation of Professor Mace's observations about placing too great a reliance upon machines, he alluded to the possible atrophy of both human muscle and human brain capacity, after the manner of the domesticated cat, should machines ever become predominant.

Dr. Penfield expressed his astonishment at Professor Mace's belief that machines would one day be able to do everything that the human mind could do. The computer was surely not the first mechanical instrument invented by man that was expected to take over all of man's basic functions and skills. One ability possessed by man would never be replaced by machines: the power to construct new computers to perform bigger and better tasks. Expressing the opposite viewpoint, Professor Simon rejoined that he was postulating the very proposition that Dr. Penfield argued could never be achieved. Developing his thesis of the uniqueness of man, Dr. Penfield asserted that no machine could ever assume the same capacity for initiative that is characteristic of man. In a lighter vein, he went on to say that, although it was not inconceivable that a machine could acquire a sense of humor, he nevertheless doubted that a computer would ever be able to perform the unpredictable caprices of a woman. Did Professor Simon seriously believe that computers might one day direct the scientific evolution of new species? Replying, Professor Simon said that he had implied precisely that proposition in his paper in the symposium. Carrying his argument one step further, he then referred to the probability that a new biological mutation from the species of man would one day come into existence that would take the form of a mechanism with the properties of self-subsistent organisms.

Professor Mace then asked the other two panel members to enumerate the tasks that could not be performed by machines, and to explain why machines could not perform them. There were certain problems, for instance, that could not be performed by machines owing to the absence of information—for example, what would Khrushchev's next move be? Moreover, every machine built to date had to have its logical and mathematical procedures built into it by human beings. Finally, the very nature of novelty presupposed that there were certain situations that were inherently unpredictable. This principle was the basic presupposition behind the theory of emergent evolution.

Professor Simon asserted that there were machines already built that could modify their own responses in the course of making an adaptive reaction to their changing environment. These machines could simulate human thinking inasmuch as they neither performed in a predetermined mechanical fashion nor were they given to sheer aimless trial-and-error groping. Through their modification of their own adaptive reactions, they [thus] simulated man's symbol-manipulating mental faculty.

When Dr. Penfield objected once again that no machine could possess the capacity for initiative characteristic of man, Professor Simon replied that our human capacity for initiative was as much predetermined by our biological cells and genes as the actions of computers were predetermined by built-in mechanisms. He cited, for example, the case of a machine built at IBM by Arthur Samuels, which started out in the morning learning how to play checkers and by evening was capable of playing checkers better than Samuels. He went on to say that many machines already possessed the capacity to develop their own sensory organs through repeated exposure to a changing evironment. He described the tortoises produced by Grey Walter, which were able to steer themselves around a room and to renew their fuel supply whenever it ran down by returning of their own accord to the plug-in electrical circuit.

To develop Professor Simon's thesis of the human potentialities of machines, Dr. Penfield then asked him to reiterate how the three levels of explanation contained in Simon's paper—information processing, neurological processing, and chemical processing—were analogous to the mental functions of human beings. Professor Simon replied that human behavior could ultimately be described in terms of those programs whose patternings functioned at a more or less microscopic level of existence. According to such a view, mind and brain were indistinguishable from one another, and it was the agencies of implementation, wherein the patternings of these programmings consisted, that had the only determining significance. In other words, Professor Simon was endorsing a mechanistic interpretation of human behavior that reduces the mind-brain problem to a materialistic monism.

Professor Mace pointed out that Professor Simon was espousing a behaviorist concept of human experience, and hence one that restricted human behavior to those factors that could be directly experienced by the senses. Such an account excluded the possibility that a human being could experience pain, because pain was an aspect of human behavior—like so many other subjective psychological phenomena—that was not directly observable to the objective senses. Animals were not mere automata devoid of feelings, as Descartes believed they were. Professor Simon responded that he did not share Descartes's belief, and that he did believe that animals experience things that machines did not.

In response to a question from the audience, Dr. Penfield elaborated upon his viewpoint regarding the mind-brain relation. He believed that brain action, which essentially consisted of electrical potentials moving through the brain, always accompanied mental activity. There was no evidence that any mind or spirit could function without concomitant brain activity. A dualistic view that totally separated mind and brain, consequently, must be maintained until the day came when our knowledge of the brain was so great that we could reduce all mental phenomena to specific brain actions. Dr. Penfield referred to his experiment with the man who could not utter the word "butterfly" when presented with one for identification. He was unable to say the word because of an impairment to that part of his brain corresponding to and making possible the ability to name a concrete object conceptually—even though he was perfectly capable of recognizing the object. Professor Simon interjected that he could reproduce verbal asphasia in his EPAM machine. Dr. Penfield retorted that the machine could produce nothing more than an automatic, rather than a genuinely conceptual, response.

Professor Mace, supporting the viewpoint of Dr. Penfield rather than that of Professor Simon, questioned whether any machine could perceive color. On the one hand a machine might be able to discriminate between any gradation upon the color spectrum; on the other, it remained questionable whether it could experience the same qualitative sensations accompanying an experience of a colored object as perceived by a human mind.

The remainder of the session was devoted primarily to a discussion of the many problems raised by Professor Mace's analogy of the domesticated cat and our affluent society of today and tomorrow. Professor Mace said that his original interest in the domesticated cat was stimulated by his personal involvement in some empirical research dealing with the nature of ultimate enjoyments as expressed by the average person. These memorable experiences often took a most urbane and nonphysiological form—such as the time when a girl first went to the Sadler's Wells Ballet, or the occasion when a girl's father returned home after a long spell in the hospital. This empirical research demonstrated the extraordinary complexity of our everyday motives and illustrated, he felt, the ridiculousness of the attempt to reduce our basic motives to the rudimentary ones of sex, hunger, survival, and the like.

Dr. Penfield observed that the majority of people had a distinct drive toward altruism and the concern and primary consideration for the well-being of others. Wholeheartedly agreeing, Professor Mace went on to specify that the third basic human motive in an affluent society—that is, in addition to the motives of play and the cultivation of the arts—is altruistically to help other people. Dr. Penfield commented that the greatest satisfaction a man can know is the successful accomplishment of the lifelong task he has set himself.

Professor Simon questioned the prevalence of melancholy in our modern affluent society. He was inclined to feel that its origin could be traced to a basic lack of meaning in daily living characteristic of those whose wealth had left them with too much leisure. He also wondered about the significance of status seeking in an affluent society. He believed that status seeking could be likened to the snake in the Garden of Eden tempting us to a level of aspiration so far above our present circumstances that we were unable contentedly to accept our existing situation. In an affluent society, he felt, most of the people should be able to be moderately successful most of the time, and to be reasonably happy, they should aspire to an average of about 10 per cent more income than they presently earn. Unless they could anchor their aspirations within reasonably attainable limits, they would never be able to return to the happy innocence of the Garden of Eden.

Professor Mace expressed the view that a gradual transition to a genuinely affluent society would assuredly occur in the future. He felt that people were nowadays too inclined to become overanxious about the dangers of life in general and about the dangers of our modern civilization in particular. The present-day concern over the presence of status seeking in a democratic society had been, he felt, exaggerated. What it really represented was a kind of motivation to power that had gotten out of hand for the moment. In reality, however, societies were and must be hierarchical, and the average person had a relatively clear picture of how high up the hierarchy he expected to go. Sharing Professor Mace's optimism about the approach of a genuinely affluent society, Dr. Penfield applauded the merits of social competition. He pointed out that in ancient Greece there emerged from socially fostered competitive standards a conception of excellence of individual achievement that became an intrinsic cultural end in itself.

The discussion in the second panel took place among a philosopher and moralist (Father D'Arcy), a psychiatrist interested in psychopharmacologic research (Dr. Cole), and a psychologist interested in the relation of chemical change in the brain to learning (Dr. Krech). The questions put to the panel members by the audience dealt primarily with the following three issues:

1. *The replacement of the brain by machines*
2. *Dualism-monism, the mind-brain relation*
3. *The danger of control of the mind*

Recorder: Donald G. Langsley
Panel Members: Jonathan O. Cole, Martin C. D'Arcy, S.J., David Krech

The audience wanted to know not only whether computers could replace the brain, but whether these machines could perhaps even outmatch man's thinking capacity. Dr. Krech commented that scientists often employed models to understand various phenomena, and the use of the computer as a model might simulate certain simple or even complex thought processes. However, such a model neither replaced the brain nor necessarily showed us how it worked; a model much closer to the anatomy, chemistry, and physiology of the brain would be necessary to understand the brain itself. A computer simulating various feats performed by the brain could hardly be considered the equivalent of the human mind.

Members of the audience then asked: "How does the creative mind operate?" "How does the research scientist get his ideas?"

Dr. Cole replied that the creation of new scientific theories resulted from the synthesis, within the brain of the scientist, of his own observations and deductions. Instead of using cluster-computer techniques, the observer acted as his own computer. Dr. Krech felt that there was no such thing as one scientific method. He pointed out that the scientist used any method that worked, and that the "productive scientist combines the intuition of the poet with the persistence of the bookkeeper." In other words, his intuition preceded the testing by scientific methodology. Dr. Cole felt that both aspects of scientific creativity were important and best combined in one person.

"Is there a creative source from which scientists get their ideas?" a member of the audience asked. The overtones of the question, of course, were whether the creative source was from within or without. Dr. Krech and Dr. Cole both commented that information reached the human brain from a variety of sense organs and that it all had to be creatively synthesized; often the resulting idea was expressed as an intuitive "hunch" comparable to the analogy of the diver assisted by the underwater chain, mentioned earlier in the symposium. Both felt that the creative process came from within. Father D'Arcy expressed his belief that there was more to creativity than the central nervous system. He cited the art critic Gombrich, who said that inspiration comes not only from reality but from inner selection and addition. Father D'Arcy felt that the mind also grew by expectations and desires; the nervous system carried on the "mind's instructions."

The audience then asked: "Are the mind and the brain the same thing?" "If the mind is something more than the brain, what is the mind?" One member of the audience, commenting on the need for consistency in the study of human beings, suggested that Father D'Arcy's position was more consistent from the level of the cell to the level of the individual. Another member of the audience asked for the comments of the panel on the question of dualism versus monism. The scientist and the philosopher did not agree in this area: the position of the scientist was that no one person could study or necessarily understand the sum total of human behavior, whereas the philosopher believed than one person was perfectly capable of comprehending the over-all picture, provided he had the knowledge to distinguish between the woods and the trees.

Dr. Cole felt that a study of human behavior demanded a study of discrete aspects, on the analogy of the cell under the microscope. While Father D'Arcy agreed that the first principle of investigation was to divide up in order to master, he cautioned that in dividing up to measure parts, one must be careful not to lose sight of the whole. Dr. Krech responded that a legitimate question for the scientist might be "What is brain?" rather than "What is man?" He offered, however, to take the alternative position, and pointed out that in studying an onion one may peel away successive layers until finally one comes to "nothing." Dr. Krech argued, "I belong to this 'onion' school of science." He pointed out that any scientific system consistent with many facts had a high probability of being wrong. He suggested that the world was too complex to be explained by a single universal philosophy encompassing all data. "Puzzlement is what the scientist lives on, and currently business is booming." Dr. Krech viewed the job of the scientist as "taking apart what nature has put together."

Many questions from the audience implied an apparent fear that the scientist would one day be able really to "control the mind"; many members of the audience believed that thought control already existed or that complete control of the mind was imminent. None of the panelists shared such fears. The two scientists agreed that complete control of the mind by drugs or any other procedure known to science was not possible at the present time, and neither scientist expected to hear of it in the near future. Father D'Arcy felt, on philosophical and religious grounds, that man and the mind were more than the brain, and that the mind could not really be controlled.

Dr. Krech pointed out that to attain complete control of the mind, we should have to know more about social, psychological, neurological, biochemical, physiological, and anatomical characteristics than we do at present. "What we call mind is a function of innumerable factors. By the time we get that much knowledge we shall also have achieved freedom from worry over control of the mind." Father D'Arcy related that before coming to this symposium he had gone to see a pharmacologist whose philosophical outlook he found very comforting. The pharmacologist's concept of the interrelation of body and soul (self) was that it might be possible temporarily to effect changes in the mind, but that no matter what changes drugs might make in temperament or disposition, existence itself was not changed.

A member of the audience raised the question as to whether or not technology might eventually destroy the world. Dr. Krech replied that he did not believe in any magical drug control of the mind. He suggested that thermonuclear warfare was by far a greater concern than thought control. Father D'Arcy pointed out that he was not so sure that people would want to go on wishing for life without a philosophy which would provide serenity of soul.

Another member of the audience asked whether control of the mind, crude as it was now, could be perfected. He questioned whether or not there should be limitations on the uses of drugs, and whether scientists would draw the line. Dr. Krech and Dr. Cole both stated that they know of no scientist who wanted control of the mind. Dr. Krech said, "I know of scientists who want to understand more about the mind and to cure the diseased mind. The understanding of atomic physics is child's play compared with the understanding of child's play." He went on to explain the difficulty of studying all the complex variables of human behavior. Dr. Cole felt that the mind would be extremely difficult to control in any case, but that if control were to be achieved, there would be many factors involved besides drugs.

Another question from the audience was whether drugs might obtund creativity in mentally ill creative people. Dr. Cole commented that if a person were so sick as to require some of the present-day psychopharmacologic agents, he might well also be so sick as to impair his creative ability.

A final comment from the audience suggested that the choice of the word "control" in the present consideration of the mind was perhaps unfortunate, and that actually we had been discussing chemical, cultural, philosophical, and moral *influences* on the mind. A member of the audience pointed out that there were many aspects of our culture, as well as our ethical and philosophical points of view, which influenced the mind but that we do not fear these. He suggested that a more appropriate study than that of complete control of the mind (repugnant as such a concept was) might be a study of the various factors which influence behavior.

The third panel was a further attempt to bridge the gap between the two cultures of science and the humanities through a discussion of restriction of the mind. The following questions were examined by a panel consisting of a historian (Professor Hughes), an essayist-novelist (Mr. Huxley), a psychiatrist-psychologist (Dr. Pribram), and a medical historian (Provost Saunders):

1. *The nature of mind*
2. *The restriction of imagination by reason in a rational society*
3. *The relation of drugs to the creative process*
4. *The role played by drugs in a sane society*
5. *The restriction of freedom on the individual mind by the conformist pressures of society*

Recorder: Price Charlson
Panel Members: H. Stuart Hughes, Aldous Huxley, Karl H. Pribam, John B. deC. M. Saunders

Provost Saunders, in opening the discussion of problems associated with restriction of the mind, emphasized the magnitude of the subject, the numerous sides it presented, and the difficulty even of interpreting such a topic as the nature of the mind, its boundaries, and the play of influences upon it. Influences that were, in a sense, parts of the mind included the structure of society; war, moral, political, and religious institutions; and the symbols and ceremonies of a given civilization and period of history. These influences might be called parts of the mind because they impinged upon our motives and behavior. Moreover, the mind was dynamic; as times changed, the nature of the mind might also be said to change.

The problem of the restriction of imagination by reason in a rational society was analyzed by Professor Hughes. In his paper—prepared beforehand—Professor Hughes had, he said, failed to discuss the danger—emphasized by Mr. Huxley—of the restriction of phantasy and imagination in the contemporary world. Amplifying his theme, he said he sensed a threat to imagination in the development of rational procedures in logic and in the sciences, with the accompanying tendency of social institutions to suppress the imaginative activity which characterized childhood. He suggested that we might learn a great deal about freedom of the mind from observation of children playing with words. Their talk was too often stifled by adults, and this suppression of their verbal play stifled a possibility for speculation. The problem facing us was how to maintain a rational, technical civilization, yet still foster the human imagination.

Reason and imagination were not at all incompatible, suggested Mr. Huxley. He characterized the imaginative life in Wordsworth's terms: the child saw life as an exciting dream. Unfortunately, education tended to grind this imaginative view out of the child; however, education could be reorganized. The problem, according to Mr. Huxley, was to discover how to move freely between the two worlds of reason and imagination.

Dr. Pribram suggested that the problem had been brought one step closer to its solution; at least we now recognized its existence, for until Mr. Huxley and others pointed it out to us, we did not even see a problem. A better word for "imaginative communication within a society," Dr. Pribram thought, might be "communion." But although the experience of communion in society had its merits, it had been feared, and with good reason, because of two characteristics: communion was contagious and it was a fleeting condition. Proper restraints were needed, even though it might be valuable to encourage phantasy.

The problem, the panel members agreed, was how to encourage phantasy in this controlled manner. When did this childlike quality of imagination begin to give way to rationality, and why do some people retain the gift of imagination throughout life? It was also agreed that, in some fields of research at least, imagination was needed just as much as reason, and that in many men interest in both was retained throughout life—for example, mathematicians were frequently also musicians. Nevertheless, it was conventional to suppose that logic and imagination were incompatible.

Professor Hughes pointed to the "intuitive leap"—like the sudden ignition of a flame—characterizing genuine scientific discovery, and he suggested that this imaginative leap in the dark was followed by the rational, scientific testing of the insight to determine its value. Machines might lift the burden of some of the scholarly drudgery from our brains—as they had taken some of the physical load from our shoulders—thereby leaving our brains free to perform more imaginative work. Machines would thus help to implement imaginative activity in the practical adult world of everyday reality.

Dr. Pribram commented that Professor Hughes seemed to suppose that phantasy was always pleasant. On the contrary, phantasy was painful much of the time and involved a great deal of effort. So-called busywork was one form of protection against the strain of imaginative activity. Furthermore, imaginative activity might be going on during busywork.

To Dr. Pribram's repeated caution that phantasy was fleeting, Mr. Huxley replied that the experiences were valuable in themselves, and that we need not evaluate a way of life solely by the creative expressions that it left behind. It was conceivable, he argued, that a situation could exist in which a society could have a maximum of valuable experiences, yet leave nothing permanent for the historian. On the other hand, he agreed that not all the results of creative work were good. Once imagination has done its best, we must decide what part of its production is worth keeping.

Provost Saunders raised the question of whether we could stimulate the creative process to produce results of high quality and whether drugs could be used to this end. Dr. Pribram replied that discipline and preparation were needed if the use of drugs was to produce the desired kind of experience, and that the effect of drugs depended upon expectations set up in the organism. Mr. Huxley emphasized the unpredictability of the creative result.

The discussion then shifted to the question of what part drugs could play in a sane society. The panel considered the advisability of proscription of drugs by physicians. Although it was agreed that the banning of drugs carried with it the danger of criminal exploitation—that is, the need for drugs would be used basely for motives of profit—the psychological aspect of drug taking seemed very complicated. Coffee and alcohol, and the ways these functioned in different societies, served as analogies. It was agreed that the attitudes taken by society toward a given drug are very important in measuring the effects of the drug upon behavior.

The discussion then moved to matters of social restriction of the mind. Professor Hughes asked what could be done in the "cold war" compatible with our open society. His own answer was that we should do less, rather than more, in the "cold war," unless we were willing to change the gentle and tolerant character of our society. Its essentially unaggressive quality was not easily made compatible with heroism and war. We should, he suggested, make freedom the issue.

Professor Hughes and Dr. Pribram then discussed whether it would be better to make an issue over freedom or to permit issues to be blurred and haphazard. Dr. Pribram thought that making an issue of freedom would risk leading to a rigidity of policy, and possibly to war, whereas a piecemeal raising of issues permitted give and take on all sides and relieved tensions. Professor Hughes argued, on the other hand, that we and the Communists agree in principle about freedom. What was needed was a recognition on the part of the Communists that freedom was feasible in practice. He cited the modification in viewpoint of the Roman Catholic Church, through the centuries, from intolerance to tolerance; and he attributed this change of heart to the constant criticism of the Protestants.

Mr. Huxley, considering the opposing pulls of social restriction and freedom, remarked that it was characteristic of a technical civilization to require its citizens to be "organization men," and that this state of affairs, while unfortunate, was unavoidable. Dr. Pribram saw the problem of freedom in society as an individual decision. One could choose whether to be free in public or in private. One could live publicly in a conformist situation, and yet in private have one's own thoughts. Internal freedom might involve the use of drugs. The attainment of external freedom sometimes demanded a change of the environment.

Professor Hughes suggested that history showed the existence of three basic kinds of society: traditionalist, individualist, and conformist. Traditionalism and conformism differed in that members of a traditionalist society, unlike members of a conformist one, felt no tension in the situation, but accepted it uncritically. The individual enjoyed greater freedom in our own times, he said, than in most previous periods of history. Dr. Pribram added that the individualist was not freer than the traditionalist; he was tyrannized by the self, rather than by society. His conformity was "inner-directed." The ideal goal, all members of the panel agreed, was the achievement of a balance between freedom and restriction, both individual and social.

The members of the fourth panel consisted of a psychologist whose description of his experiments with the effects of isolation on the individual aroused great interest in the symposium (Professor Hebb), an author who has been especially concerned with the problem of the relation of the individual to society (Mr. Koestler), and an author with a wide knowledge of many behavioral aspects of contemporary society (Professor Rosten).

Much of the discussion centered on the general problem of the relation of the individual to society, and in clarifying some of the more important of the ideas discussed in the symposium, these panel members analyzed the following problems:

1. Obscenity

2. Prejudice and tolerance, with special emphasis on the effects of isolation on the individual

3. The information requirements of a complex organism

4. The effects of advertising on the mind

5. The significance of myths for a society

Recorder: David Matza

Panel Members: Donald O. Hebb, Arthur Koestler, Leo C. Rosten

Mr. Koestler pointed out that the definition of obscenity was relative, not absolute, and that what was defined as obscene depended completely on the conditions that happened to obtain in a society at any given time. A man serving a prison sentence who read a description of a meal consisting of choice wines and foods would feel that such a passage was utterly obscene. Similarly, in a society in which freedom of sexual relations existed but in which eating was surrounded by taboos, a description of a meal in a novel might well be analogous to some of the sexual incidents in *Lolita*. Mr. Koestler thought that we could take obscenity to mean a whetting of appetites the satisfaction of which were debarred by custom or law.

Professor Hebb made the point that before an obscenity could be said to exist, the element of desire for the forbidden fruit must be added to the arousal of anxiety just mentioned. Obscenities, he felt, lay at the border between the forbidden and the permitted. The variation in the definition of obscenity was another example of the ambivalence that was characteristic of human species; what was obscene to some was not to others.

In a further discussion of prejudice versus tolerance Professor Rosten asked Professor Hebb, "Did I understand you to say that the major determinant of prejudice was a kind of innate fear of the stranger rather than anything that is learned?" Professor Hebb replied that the common assumption was that prejudice was rooted in economics and that patterns initiated in economic rivalry were then transmitted through the mechanisms of learning. The evidence seemed clear that these sorts of assumptions were unwarranted. Although an element of learning certainly existed, the learning might take place very quickly and might be based on incidents that it was hardly possible to avoid. It was difficult, if not impossible, to teach children the avoidance of things far more dangerous than the taking on of an attitude of prejudice. He did not think that it was the completely strange thing that invoked fear and hostility; rather it was something that combined the familiar and the strange. In summary, he felt that our reaction to things that were different or strange was primarily natural rather than learned.

Widening the discussion to the social sphere, Professor Rosten raised the phenomenon of what he called "reverse prejudice"—that is to say, "the prejudice of tolerance." He illustrated his meaning by reference to his membership in a committee which was to appoint a man to an administrative position. One man mentioned as a possibility was a Negro. Professor Rosten reacted adversely to the nomination because he felt the man was not sufficiently intelligent. He went on to say that, although his unfavorable reaction was purely on the grounds of the man's low intelligence, he was nevertheless accused by other members of the committee of being prejudiced against the man because of his color, which was untrue. "This is what I mean by reverse prejudice."

Professor Rosten commented further that the degree of reaction to the strange and unknown varied markedly between individuals. For example, his son—the elder child—as an infant reacted to the strange with a great deal of anxiety, while his daughter, rather than withdrawing from the strange, seemed delighted by the approach of the novel. Agreeing with the proposition of individual variation, Professor Hebb asked whether that did not just imply what he termed "a different zone of risk" for each child.

Mr. Koestler, while agreeing that there were individual differences, asked if the generalization could not be made that no one could withstand the permanent withdrawal of those forces that affirmed identity. Professor Hebb objected that from a practical point of view research could not be pushed that far. He referred to the isolation studies that he had carried out. In these experiments, the perceptions of the subjects were cut off so that they could not explore their environment. Although some students were motivated by financial reasons to persevere with the experiments for as long as possible, not one could tolerate the isolation for more than 5 days, and only a few could withstand it for that long.

Returning to the subject of prejudice, Mr. Koestler expressed the opinion that it involved an ambivalence between fascination with the new and fear of it. Prejudice was caused not by simple novelty, but by a distortion and mutilation of the familiar. The "monster" could be taken as a prototype of this distortion: it involved a mutilation of a familiar or habitual object—for example, an adult with a duck's head, or a dog with a cat's head. Raising the topic of isolation again, Mr. Koestler remarked that the "out-of-body" experiences referred to in Professor Hebb's experiments were the type of hallucinations sought after by mystics. The mystic's quest was to shut out the world. To do this, he tried to close off all bodily orifices. The aim of these meditative techniques was to attain the condition produced in the isolation experiment. Professor Rosten inquired how a yogi would react to Professor Hebb's isolation experiments. Could experience and training teach one to withstand pressures of that sort? Professor Hebb thought that such an ability might be inculcated, but wondered how long it would last. Mr. Koestler said that after about 15 years of experience, a yogi could go into a trance for about 36 hours.

Professor Rosten then related a personal experience to substantiate Mr. Koestler's observations regarding fear of monsters. He told of his consultation with psychiatrists to obtain relevant psychiatric knowledge for use in children's stories he was writing. Jointly they agreed to invent a situation in which a child was to have a sibling. The resulting story written by Professor Rosten included a dream in which the child imagined his anticipated sib to be a fascinating and exotic playmate—a "rampatan"—who soared through the air and was in all respects an enjoyable figment. Children loved the story and asked to hear it again. Mothers who were not pregnant similarly approved of it. However, for pregnant mothers the story aroused a host of anxieties regarding possible deformities in their anticipated child. The point he was making, said Professor Rosten, was that the unfamiliar recombination of the habitual was reacted to quite differently by people in differing contexts.

Professor Rosten then raised a related question: although one of the papers had pointed out that societies minimized the introduction of the novel, must we not increase tolerance of departures and deviations in order to increase our capacity for change? This problem was related to the importance of social restrictions that applied in all societies. Professor Rosten asked Mr. Koestler to amplify his earlier point, distinguishing between two sorts of religious elements—dogma and mysticism. In response Mr. Koestler said that his point was that scientists had frequently been motivated by utterly unscientific quests—by superstition or mysticism. He quoted Kepler as a case in point and said that we must never interfere with the irrational beliefs of individuals; these irrationalities might have highly fortunate consequences. The attitude to dogma, however, should be quite different. Dogma prevented one from pursuing what interested him, whatever the motivation. For instance, we must allow an atheist to be an atheist, although atheism might turn out to be an even more irrational assumption than theism. Using the model propounded by Simon and others interested in the analogies between mind and electronic computer, we might think of atheism as involving the following assumption: a human being was "programmed," but there was no "programmer." At any rate, we should never interfere with the private sphere of human activity—though, of course, he added, we always did. Professor Rosten made the point that, even in the community of intellectuals, limitations were placed on human freedom. New ideas were often unwelcome, he said. His view was that a simple and useful model of the truly civilized man was one in which men insisted on the capacity to tolerate intolerable ideas.

Professor Hebb then asked Professor Rosten whether he would tolerate nazism, fascism, and a proposal of incest. Were there not limits to what could be tolerated? Wasn't the sound culture the one that propounded certain restrictions and allowed freedom beyond those limits? Defining his position on the question of tolerance, Professor Rosten said that he would tolerate anything—particularly in the political sphere—that remained in the realm of words. The organization of violence, on the other hand, was quite a different matter. This was, of course, overly simple. He said that in regard to more complex incidents we should do well to recall the rule of thumb regarding the different consequences of yelling "Fire!" in a crowded theater as contrasted with doing the same in less dangerous circumstances; whereas the latter would be permissible, he thought, the former would not.

A member of the audience, commenting that the brain seemed to function in a relatively disorganized manner when it was cut off from a patterned flow of information and that this situation seemed to be truer of higher forms than of lower ones, asked whether information requirements become different as organisms become more complex. Mr. Koestler replied that he thought a principle of that sort certainly held true in the case of societies. Japan, for example, was cut off from international relations for about 250 years. The results, he suggested, were just those that a neurologist might have predicted. Professor Hebb was not sure how far one could press the analogy. The needs of a society certainly did become different when that society became more complex. He felt that, at certain levels of complexity, the introduction of nonstability might become necessary.

A member of the audience asked the panel to comment on the effects of advertising on the mind. Was there considerable restriction or control? Professor Rosten revealed the interesting fact that studies showed the effects of advertising to be quite modest. The success or failure of a single advertisement, or of an entire advertising campaign, was virtually unpredictable. Little was known about the criteria that determined or influenced success or failure. Similarly, in Hollywood's attempts to manufacture or create new stars, there was virtually no way of predicting the outcome. Many stars reached great heights without being expected to do so, and on the other hand, many of the most elaborately planned attempts to "engineer" a new star were complete failures.

Putting a question to the panel regarding Dr. Lasswell's discussion of myths, a member of the audience asked the panel members to comment on what they thought a mythless society would be like. Mr. Koestler thought that such a society would be stimulus-starved.

Professor Hebb felt that myths integrated a society and that many of the sources of human identity were rooted in myth. Professor Rosten said that myths performed important social and psychological functions and added that life would be impossible if we always told the truth.

Complimentary viewpoints were expressed in this fifth panel by a histologist doing basic research in genetics (Dr. Hydén), a clinical scientist (Dr. Kety), and a law scholar (Professor Lasswell). Considerable interest was aroused by the discussion in Dr. Hydén's paper of the constituents of brain cells and drug effects on the brain. Genetical topics analyzed ranged from possible new forms of life to transfer of memory traces, drug behavioral effects, and the question of positive changes in the brain produced by drugs. The subjects discussed were:

1. Recent advances in genetics

2. The value of freedom of the mind

3. The effect of mental freedom on scientific inquiry, including the intriguing question of the apparent inconsistency of scientific progress in Russia despite restriction of freedom

4. The comparative efficiency of totalitarianism and a free society

5. Creative freedom in Russia

6. The limits to the amount a man can learn

Recorder: Gerald Mendelsohn
Panel Members: Holgar Hydén, Seymour S. Kety, Harold D. Lasswell

The discussion began with comments from Dr. Hydén on some implications of recent work in genetics. He pointed out that the Weiss experiments indicated that DNA had a controlling function in the synthesis of cell constituents, specifically the constituents of brain cells. Since the nature of the DNA molecule was unique for each species, these findings raised the possibility of phylogenetically determined memories. Dr. Hydén made it clear, however, that this supposition was only speculative.

Asked by Dr. Kety whether, if he were designing a human organism, he would like to build in a mechanism for transmitting memory traces, Dr. Hydén replied that the action of such a mechanism would not be unlike that of DNA as described by him. Both men agreed that such transmission would be of relatively gross characteristics. Certainly, whether phylogenetic memories were possible or not, the genetic inheritance set a capacity for the brain, which was restricted according to its substrate.

Continuing in this vein, Dr. Kety commented that it seemed a pity that acquired memory traces—such as those of outstanding men, for example, Einstein—could not be transmitted to other individuals. Although man might possess some ability to behave without learning—that is, instinctively—the overwhelming proportion of information was acquired. Some acquired information could be passed on verbally, but not to the extent that one might wish. Dr. Kety agreed with a comment from a member of the audience, however, that empirical transfer would limit the freedom of each successive generation and so would be undesirable. This answered, in a sense, the question of why we did not find in nature a provision for genetic transmission of learning: this would have led to less experimentation and a slower development of the species.

Speculation on possible new forms of life then followed. Dr. Hydén pointed out that homo sapiens was only one of many possible special cases of life; the human being was animated, could speak, and could interbreed. Assuming that another type of animated organism existed with similar capacities, the biological expectation would be constant aggression between the two species. What, then, would be the result of the simultaneous existence of two such types? Professor Lasswell said the possibility of creation of a new form of life was a contingency that some workers had in mind. What were the alternatives in envisioning the design of future life? Did we want life at all? Or was the highest level of life the ability to renounce the compulsion to live? Assuming agreement on the desirability of life, should we follow divine precedent and create new life in a form as close as possible to man's present image? Or, transcending this limitation, should we create something better? If we took this last course, what were the possibilities? He agreed with the implication that, if other nonhuman forms of complicated life were to be created, antagonism between those forms and man would follow. The problem, in short, was whether we wanted to deal with this new form of life.

The theme of several questions from the audience was how we could make changes in human beings on the basis of our present knowledge of genetics and pharmacology. There was general agreement among the panel members that positive changes in the brain (or "mind") could not be produced by means of drugs. Dr. Kety said that, although we had to accept the obvious fact that drugs could influence mood, attention, and motor activity in a gross way, human behavior was much more affected by stored experiential information. He could not visualize a drug which could work positive changes by putting in stored information; however, it was clear that there were many mechanisms which did exert effects on behavior via experience. Though we might worry about the feared threat of drugs to freedom of the mind, the danger they presented was highly theoretical, particularly when compared with social and cultural restrictions. Forces tending toward conformity—loyalty oaths, for example—could influence freedom of the mind and exert a far more potent effect on behavior than any drug. In response to a question, Dr. Kety expressed the opinion that the threat of losing one's job produced changes in behavior far more subtle than those effected by any pharmacological substance.

Discussing the genetics of the problem, Dr. Hydén examined the possibility of transmitting changes through the use of drugs. Experiments in Holland and France, he mentioned, had shown that somatic mutations could be achieved before fertilization, but that the observed changes were in body cells, not in reproductive cells; in other words, such mutations were not transmittable. Chemical substances did exist which could induce mutations or increase their frequency, but it was also known that most of the mutations which could occur in a species had already occurred in the past 5 million years. The answer to the question posed, then, was that it was very unlikely that we could produce a transmittable change by the action of drugs.

Questions relating to his paper were answered by Dr. Hydén; the behavioral effect of the drug he had described aroused the greatest interest. Psychiatrists who had used the drug, Dr. Hydén reported, found that it made patients more suggestible; however, this was clearly a preliminary statement based only on clinical impressions, and there was little definite to report as yet. At least another 6 months of work by the psychiatrists was needed to obtain a better understanding of the behavioral effects of the drug.

The Western belief that freedom of the mind was good and restriction bad was then examined. In response to a question from Dr. Kety, Professor Lasswell commented that there were two approaches to this issue. The first was that of the "custodians" of culture. Their response was trans-empirical: it stressed the will of God or some similar metaphysical category. The argument centered on the assumed belief that God created man to perform a divine purpose which man, because of his finite nature, cannot fully comprehend. Part of this assumption was that man was given freedom in various spheres, and consequently, restriction of those areas of freedom was contrary to God's will.

The second line of argument was empirical. This approach pointed to man's knowledge of the consequences of restriction as revealed by history. The men who believed in freedom maintained that the consequences of restriction were unfortunate in terms of the utilization of human potentialities. A caste system, for example, imposed limitations on the upper orders of the hierarchy as well as on the lower. Professor Lasswell concluded that by and large, although much of the information we possessed was unsatisfactory, nevertheless the sound information we did have tended to confirm the proposition that freedom was good.

Scientific rationale—based on biological speculation—Dr. Kety added to Professor Lasswell's two humanistic arguments to provide a rational trinity in support of the Western belief that freedom was good. Dr. Kety argued that creativity and the freedom to experiment were perhaps built into the nature of life. Reproduction involved the mixing of genetic patterns, leading to new individuals—each different not only from one another but from his ancestors as well. By this kind of experimentation, the species improved and competed adaptively. Moreover, mutations produced new individuals with unpredictable traits. Most of these changes were maladaptive, but sometimes a hardier product emerged. Dr. Kety felt that, in general, the freedom of opportunity to experiment led to improvement of the species.

What effect did restriction of the mind exert on scientific inquiry? This problem was raised by the following intriguing question from a member of the audience: "Thought is restricted in the Soviet Union, yet Russian science is reputed to be at least as advanced as ours. How can this apparent contradiction be resolved?"

This apparent inconsistency had puzzled Dr. Kety, too, he said. Though his reflections were impressionistic, since he had never visited Russia, he quoted Lysenkoism and the adulation of Pavlov in Russian neurophysiology as examples of limitations on biological science instituted for political purposes. The views of both these scientists were used to support the theory of dialectical materialism, and consequently it was heresy to disagree with either of them.

Dr. Hydén felt that, while Dr. Kety's impressions correctly described the situation of a few years ago, a remarkable change in the direction of greater freedom of thought had occurred during the past 5 years.

"Did the quality of science improve as the degree of freedom increased?" asked a member of the audience. Dr. Hydén's reply was that it was difficult to answer this question since the rate of accumulation of information in all parts of the world was exponential. Dr. Kety pointed out that we had not learned to evaluate science itself in the way we did the data produced by science. There was no good evidence to demonstrate a correlation between a greater degree of freedom and the quality of research. As the head of a department, he felt that, in the United States, the best work was done by scientists who were free to choose the areas of investigation they preferred. In other societies, though, it might be that a good man could work to equally good advantage on an assigned project.

Professor Lasswell pointed out that sociological factors significantly affected scientific levels of attainment. We were handicapped in obtaining data in this field by political restrictions; for example, it would be extremely difficult to obtain such information relating to Russian science. A further handicap was the unwillingness of many scientists to try to understand the factors which made a difference. Thus we were forced to use anecdotal data to make judgments. We deserved to be better informed about the class factors, specialized interests and other influences affecting levels of attainment in science. We also required a better empirical base from which to generalize about scientific creativity.

Addressing himself to Prorfessor Lasswell, Dr. Kety said he feared totalitarianism was more efficient than democracy in getting a specific job done. Consequently, should one be concerned that in the next 50 to 100 years totalitarianism would make such superior headway in educating people for technical occupations, regulating the national economy, and so forth, that it might win the competition with freedom?

Professor Lasswell replied that there was no basis for asserting that totalitarianism was a more efficient system. Although it was commonly assumed that the motivations of the elite were highly focused in such regimes, the "totalitarianism" of the twentieth century was really the product of revolutions in which a few people make the decisions. Thus a problem existed in differentiating between rapid revolutionary change and totalitarianism. We assumed that the terms "communism," "socialism," "capitalism," "totalitarianism" had empirical referents. This was not the case, and the problems of applying such labels were very complicated; thus such a term as "a more totalitarian regime in China" was scarcely admissible in a critical sense. Such a term was a "dialectical gimmick" rather than a worthwhile variable.

Although supporting Professor Lasswell's general position, Dr. Kety feared that freedom of the mind might not possess the strength to withstand the challenge of a different approach which had a more determined purpose and, moreover, was less deeply concerned about the ultimate fate of mankind. Though he wished otherwise, he was still not convinced that the assumption of the superior efficiency of totalitarianism was false. Professor Lasswell responded with an example based on his participation at sessions in which different kinds of people met for a period of mutual reconsiderations of their positions. Despite their differences in background and the limitations of time, they were able to agree on some basic principles, and particularly, to share in the presumption against coercion in favor of middle levels of freedom.

Some light was thrown on conditions in present-day Russia by a member of the audience. He said that according to a Russian refugee of his acquaintance, the Soviet system was like our own except that it had a higher degree of specialization. The people on the upper levels felt that they had as much freedom as Americans, but those on the lower levels might not have as much independence as in the United States. In general, though, all levels of Russian society were content.

The relation of art to science, especially in Russia, was the subject of a further question from a member of the audience. It was asserted that basic research in the arts was strictly controlled in Russia. Since, according to Mr. Koestler, creativity in the arts involved the same faculties and the same approach to life as in the sciences, could the panel extrapolate from this state of artistic affairs in Russia to the state of scientific affairs? Dr. Kety agreed with the premise that the same factors underlay both artistic and scientific creativity. But science was pragmatic, and as such, had objective criteria of evaluation, while the standards of art, bound up as they were with culture, were more subjective. Thus it might be unrealistic to make comparisons between Russian and American art. Further, though Soviet science and art were restricted by the government, Western artists had been subjected to restrictions which, if not as obvious, were perhaps as important; financial support of an artist was just as important as social support.

The question on which the panel closed its discussion was directed to Dr. Kety. He was asked whether he would conclude that the more one knows, the less one can learn. His initial response, that we do not know the capacity of the brain, was seconded by Dr. Hydén, who added that the number of memories a man could acquire during a lifetime would have to be small compared with the capacity of his biological system. Turning to the involvement of creativity in the question, Dr. Kety pointed out that it was assumed that creativity consisted of giving new forms to information that had been previously learned. If information was, in fact, the raw material for creativity, the more one knew the greater the chance for creativity.

In the sixth panel the differing viewpoints of a sociologist and political scientist (Professor Lipset), a psychiatrist and psychologist (Dr. Miller), and a professor of journalism (Professor Porter) were heard in a discussion of the following topics:

1. The "feelings" of computers

2. The use of mass communications media for political purposes

3. The reporting of scientific conferences by the popular press

4. Dr. Penfield's work on the recall of "memories" by the application of electrodes to the brain

Recorder: Robert R. Alford

Panel Members: Seymour M. Lipset, James G. Miller, William E. Porter

Professor Simon's assertion that a computer could actually "feel" was the subject of a question put to Dr. Miller by a member of the audience to the effect that this statement sounded like something out of science fiction. Dr. Miller replied that the issue became metaphysical, not scientific, when a question was couched in those terms. Most of the computer programs which simulated human behavior dealt with cognitive processes; this emphasis would continue because computers were simply rational machines. The problem could not be dismissed by saying that, of course, computers could not "feel." The only scientific way of learning about the inner feelings of either a human being or a computer was by analogy. The subjectivity of computers could not be penetrated any more than could the subjectivity of human beings other than oneself. Alfred North Whitehead believed that every living thing, down to the amoeba, had subjectivity, and that it was impossible to divide material objects neatly into living and nonliving objects. Therefore, it was difficult to know where subjectivity—and, hence, feeling—began and ended. It was probably safer to assume subjectivity in everything.

The idea that a computer could "feel" was merely an analogy; it was convenient to assume that there were processes going on inside the computer to which we did not have direct access. Anatol Rapoport had made a neat statement of this dilemma of subjectivity in a reference to the existence of free will. According to Rapoport, if a person predicted his own behavior, then behaved in the way he predicted, he concluded that he had free will. If that person predicted another person's behavior, and that other person behaved in the way the first person predicted, then the first person would conclude that the other person's behavior was determined. Yet there was, in fact, no logical difference between the basis for the two predictions. When a machine appeared to act as if it was "making up its mind," it was actually difficult to know what was really going on inside.

Dr. Miller went on to say that affective processes, on the other hand, were different from cognitive processes. Could the computer simulate emotional processes, that is, could they "feel," in the present analogy? To the extent that emotions could be described as neurological processes, we could simulate those processes with the computer. The nervous system is extremely complex, being composed of sympathetic and parasympathetic branches in complicated relations with the endocrine system. Neurological and chemical information go through the various systems, the cortex, the hypothalamus, and so forth. This total neurological picture tells us how emotions are *mediated*. There is a "traffic flow" of information. The complicated flux which is emotion could be simulated by the computer. We did not know precisely whether computers "felt"; all we did know was that we had simulated in the computer processes that were analogous to neurological processes in the human.

Could one find the linkages between emotions and the mediating mechanisms? In other words, could the *intensities* of emotions be simulated? These questions were put forth by Professor Porter. Dr. Miller replied that nothing was yet known about the linkages, that we did know that certain drugs produced fear, but we did not know how the drugs were linked to the emotion, if indeed the distinction between the neurological processes and the "emotion" was possible.

A member of the audience asked whether a computer exhibits elementary self-awareness, as seemed almost to be implied. Dr. Miller replied that surely the questioner recognized that we all projected our own emotions to others. In so far as the computer was concerned, we simply did not know what went on inside. Professor Porter recalled a *Time* magazine article which had discussed the "moods" of computers, explaining how they became "tired" and demonstrated other apparently "human" characteristics.

What role could an agency such as Radio Free Europe play in disseminating public information? Did its association with government make it a mere propaganda agency? These questions were put to Professor Porter, who replied that, in his view, any means of access to information was good, whether or not it was sponsored by government. The idea of control by government was repugnant to some people because it implied the possibility of thought control; nevertheless, the possible influence of the mass media in influencing public opinion must not be overemphasized. In

Britain, the BBC introduced the Third Programme in the hope that good taste would spread throughout the population via the radio, but in fact, the situation did not work out that way.

Professor Porter was asked whether Radio Free Europe was directed to follow a definite propaganda line; he replied that he was not sure. Certainly it did adhere closely to a State Department position. According to law, it must get approval of its policies, since its broadcasts so closely reflected the United States's position.

The next question was put to Professor Lipset: President Kennedy used computers to simulate the voting predispositions of the electorate. Was not that approaching the kind of manipulation that interfered with freedom of the mind? Professor Lipset explained that this computer (called the "people machine") simulated the voting habits of the total population. Past attitudes and various population characteristics already known to affect voting behavior were fed into the computer. There was no moral or political danger in such a machine, he felt, *provided* that all sides had access to the information. If both the manipulators and the manipulated knew what was going on, it then became a public matter. A monopoly of information held by one side, however, was bad. Dr. Miller stated that many surveys of buying habits were kept secret. No information was released either to competitors or to the public. Was that legitimate? Professor Porter said that he did not object to this practice in its application to business. The political realm might be different, but he did not believe that it was really possible to hide anything in politics except in a totalitarian situation. Dr. Miller was asked if he remembered a *Harper's* piece on the religious issue in the last Presidential election campaign. Nixon had agreed with Kennedy's evaluation of the religious issue, and tried to reduce its salience, because he agreed that it could only help Kennedy. Dr. Miller countered that that was not true in the 1928 Hoover-Smith campaign. In that election, the religious issue helped Hoover. This showed that the issues determining the role of mass communications (and the direction of its influence) shifted according to the climate of opinion at the time. They probably had so little direct effect that secrecy did not matter.

Professor Lipset added that, in any case, the "people machine" included too few variables because of the pressure of time. Also, it only included data on the Eisenhower years; those elections might not have been sufficiently representative of stable political loyalties to make accurate predictions. In the next campaign, probably both sides would have access to such information as was available.

Dr. Miller asked whether the denial of Kennedy's press secretary,

Pierre Salinger, that Kennedy used a "people machine" was because of public attitudes about possible manipulation. Professor Lipset felt that the simulation of public attitudes could easily be labeled manipulation, although Nixon was unable to make an issue of it because the Republicans had relied on market researchers. Dr. Miller pointed out that the very term "people machine" was "loaded," since the term itself implied manipulation.

Professor Lipset said that American politicians were actually behind European ones in their use of such "modern" campaign techniques as computers. Chancellor Adenauer of West Germany was in direct contact with West German public-opinion agencies, and would even adjust a speech in accordance with discovered reactions to another speech made a few days before. The German pollsters estimated that a shift of 10 to 15 per cent of public attitudes might be due to Adenauer's sensitivity to the winds of opinion. A questioner asked whether this was not manipulation. Professor Lipset's view was that it was not illegitimate manipulation; it was simply responsiveness.

Professor Porter was then asked whether he thought mass communication was really adequate for the job it must do. He replied that certain popular attitudes must exist before the mass media were effective. Professor Lipset added that the more people knew, the harder they were to manipulate. In areas of life or knowledge where little was really known, or where the knowledge was not diffused, a monopoly on communication channels could really decisively affect opinion. The shifts in American opinion about Tito's regime in Yugoslavia were a case in point, because little about the regime was actually known by the average person, and the picture presented by our press was almost uniform at any given time. It was relatively easy for the typical image of Tito to change from an anti-fascist hero during the Second World War (when he was seen as the "George Washington" of Yugoslavia), to a vicious Stalinist, to the hero who broke with his Russian masters.

Dr. Miller contended, however, that the matter was rather more complex than that. Political parties utilized verifiable *facts,* not mere fictions; but they chose to emphasize one set of facts rather than another. This could not be described simply as manipulation. Professor Porter felt that the implication of this situation was that mass media had real importance in chaotic times when public opinion was not stabilized. Of course, by the time the chaos existed, it was too late for the mass media to do anything about it.

In this discussion of the impact of something familiar or accepted upon public opinion, Dr. Miller said that the voices of Edward R. Murrow and

Arthur Godfrey were the "official" voices scheduled during World War II to announce an enemy attack to the nation. They were chosen because it was felt that they would be *believed*. Professor Lipset said that this problem of the relative trust in different media or persons was an important one, and one we knew little about. No one seemed to know why Europeans seemed to trust the BBC announcers more than the Voice of America announcers. Professor Porter felt that faith in the BBC was a historical legacy. In 1940 and 1941, the BBC had told the truth about bomb damage in England and about other war news when no one else had. The BBC announcers would have been believed even if they had spoken in thick Hungarian accents, because they spoke the truth.

A member of the audience commented that the unemotional tone of voice cultivated by BBC announcers could be used for many purposes, once its credibility was established. The same calm voice, the audience member contended, carried many fictitious stories for military purposes. Professor Porter agreed that he had no doubt of that either.

Dr. Miller asserted that the press coverage of the symposium had been irresponsible. Many major differences of opinion that did not exist had been reported purely to make headlines. He felt that some of this irresponsibility might be because of low professional competence on the part of newsmen, and that it was as vital to raise the salaries of newsmen as those of teachers. Endless discussions of the ethics of the press seemed to do no good. Robert Hutchins, when at Chicago about 10 years ago, conducted a conference on this problem which proposed some detailed recommendations, but these had not been implemented. Taking up this point, Professor Porter said that the report of the Hutchins conference was a standard work in schools of journalism, but had had no perceptible practical effect. Then, referring to the question of the symposium and the press, he said that 10 years ago such a symposium would not have been made available to reporting by the press, partly because physicians wanted to avoid personal publicity. The real question was whether it is worthwhile to have a symposium such as this reported at all at the price of some inaccuracy.

Dr. Miller responded that the reporting of scientific conferences in the newspapers could be dangerous. At an SPSSI conference some 5 years ago, he was quoted out of context and was attacked by the Bishop of Wichita on the basis of that erroneous quotation. There did not seem to be the same kind of climate of feeling about controversial scientific findings now, however. Symposia such as this mainly set up agendas for future scientific action. Press coverage, even if irresponsible, could help to prepare public opinion for developments to come. Defending the press, Professor Lipset contended that the last paragraph of Dr. Penfield's paper, in which he speculated on "control of the mind," was the only "glamorous" part of his talk, so that one could not blame the press for treating it in a sensational manner. Dr. Miller commented that historically scientists had always been more conservative about the implications of their work than might be indicated by what they were actually doing. They had always been cautious about predicting the path and speed of the development of science. Actual developments had moved much faster than their predictions indicated.

Dr. Miller was asked by a member of the audience to comment on Dr. Penfield's work on bringing back memories by applying electrodes to the brain. Describing Dr. Penfield's previous work by way of background, he explained that Dr. Penfield dealt with the brain correlates of psychomotor epilepsy. Removal of part of the frontal lobe sometimes relieved epileptic conditions. This was one indication that it was possible to discover the areas of the brain controlling different aspects of behavior. The possible implication was that one could take out or put in complex memories. An example of the kind of control which was possible occurred in one of Dr. Penfield's papers. When Dr. Penfield touched a spot in the brain of a man undergoing a brain operation, the man grunted. After the man voluntarily produced the same sound, he was asked by Dr. Penfield about the difference between the two situations. The man said, "It felt as if the sound was drawn from me when you did it. I could do it too if I were on *your* side of my brain." "Where," Dr. Miller asked, "does that leave us in our concern with control of the mind?"

FREEDOM OF THE MIND

In this panel, in the absence of a prepared topic by the panelists, the modus operandi *of the group was to discuss questions from the audience. If any generalization can be made about the panelists and their responses, it would be that each of the three panel members exhibited interests and thinking beyond the boundaries of his particular discipline. Dr. Cole is a clinician engaged in research and the administration of research on clinical application of psychopharmacologic agents. Dr. Hydén is a basic scientist interested in cellular physiology and chemistry. Professor Mace describes himself as a philosopher and psychologist. The audience, aware of the diverse backgrounds and training of the three panelists, spent a great deal of time asking questions on the motivations and make-up of scientists in particular and people in general. Four general topics were discussed:*

1. *The nature of the scientist*
2. *The nature of people in general*
3. *The nature of the mind*
4. *The neurochemical work of Dr. Hydén on the brain and mind*

Recorder: Donald G. Langsley
Panel Members: Jonathan O. Cole, Holgar Hydén, C. A. Mace

Professor Mace opened the discussion by asking the other two panelists if they felt the need of a philosophy of science. Dr. Hydén said he felt that scientists studied certain problems not only out of pragmatic necessity such as the need to cure, but also for the sake of curiosity and in an effort to learn more about the meaning of life. Speaking as a clinician, Dr. Cole said that he felt his work was to cope with pragmatic problems in order to satisfy his own private set of values and for the good of scientific endeavor. He also noted that he was kept so busy that he had little time to think about the philosophy of science. Professor Mace, a motivational psychologist, felt that there certainly were innate driving forces consisting of a private system of values, and quoted Stephen Leacock's story about the college student whose curriculum consisted of divinity, Arabic, and music. Leacock chuckled, "Surely you're not going to be an organist in a mosque?" The student replied, "No, these are the courses that fit into my timetable."

A member of the audience asked if a sense of values limited the scientist's mind or freed it. Professor Mace felt that scientists on the whole were moral people who did research because they liked it. He expressed the personal conviction that if the world were going to be saved it would be done by the educated and motivated segment of the population. Dr. Cole felt that, in the absence of an absolute set of ethical values, each scientist had to develop his own. Dr. Hydén expressed the view that it was difficult to put definitive values on biological phenomena. He gave the example of evolution: some individuals over the long run perished in this evolutionary struggle, and if one said that this was bad, this view might be extended to the generalization that evolution was bad. Dr. Hydén felt that one could not look at it this way; evolution, he thought, was not only a fact that had to be accepted, but also, he suggested, the forces behind it were in the long run productive. Dr. Hydén's point of view seems to have been that whatever the drive, the end result might well be useful in the case of scientific investigation.

Dr. Hydén then asked Professor Mace how he felt about the need for neurotic anxiety in the motivation of the scientist. Professor Mace felt that a little bit of instability had some psychological advantages and that this might well play an important role in creativity.

Another point raised by the audience was the question of nonscientific controls, such as cultural values or external agencies, and whether or not such external agencies might eventually control and dictate research. None of the panelists shared this fear, and Dr. Cole pointed out that, although this concern existed, the other extreme would be to say that anyone with scientific training or a doctorate was thereby entitled to tools of his trade, that is, support for any and all research interests. This, too, was an illogical extreme. Professor Mace felt that in any effective scientific endeavor the scientist had the right to choose his own area of research.

Although questions about human behavior in general were scattered throughout the panel discussion, most of them were directed to Professor Mace, whose subject in the symposium had been motivation of behavior. Dr. Hydén asked what the effect on behavior would be if we could alter genetic characteristics by a greater degree of manipulation of genes. Professor Mace felt that human beings had considerable variability and that genetic variation would be just one more factor. In regard to whether or not social stratification was biologically determined, he stated that there was little evidence for this (except such situations as pecking order in chickens) and that the biological factors were outweighed by sociological considerations.

Dr. Cole asked how the 11-plus exam in Britain influenced social class. Professor Mace was of the opinion that there were class differences in intelligence, but that education in its availability to all classes would be one of the determining factors in changing class structure.

Dr. Cole, in speaking about the question of inhibition of motivation, pointed out that although some drugs were primarily depressants, they might, by depressing inhibitory factors, also increase freedom of behavior.

A member of the audience asked if the exercise and appreciation of sensory experience would make people creative. Dr. Cole felt that the clinician often wished to inhibit the input of seriously disturbed people (schizophrenics) because these people were oversensitive. Professor Mace felt that new ideas and techniques should be tried. Dr. Hydén felt that any exercise led to a biological change in the use and an increase in the efficiency of the mechanism to a point, the limiting point apparently being genetic endowment.

One questioner asked if acceptance of a credo such as communism might free or restrict the mind. Professor Mace expressed the opinion that this was analogous to a religious conversion, which produced both freedom and inhibition. He offered the thesis that communism would thrive not in the affluent society, but in penurious groups.

Dr. Cole asked if the suicide rate were not higher among affluent societies. Professor Mace replied that Sweden might be an example of higher suicide rate, but cautioned that a single statistic did not prove a point. Dr. Hydén pointed out how careful Sweden was about its statistics, and Dr. Cole suggested that this might mean only that in Sweden suicides were counted more carefully.

One question from the audience concerned the effect of the welfare state on motivation. Professor Mace felt that one of his studies of young people who leave school showed a general raising of the sights under the welfare state. Youngsters who previously had felt that they never could go to a university now aspired to go. He pointed out that studies of many groups showed that most people wanted about 10 per cent more salary than they presently had. He was optimistic that people would not be too complacent.

It would be inconceivable that a symposium on restriction and freedom of the mind would not raise questions of definition, and the question of definition of the mind came up repeatedly among the speakers in the symposium as well as among various panels. One member of the audience asked, "What is the inherent nature of mind—cells, awareness, or what?" Professor Mace expressed the opinion that for the most part people felt that the mind and the brain were not necessarily synonymous terms. Many psychologists were happy to talk about the mind in terms of brain, but he felt that this was a change in the use of the word. He was willing to accept the proposition of determinism in mental processes and physical activities, and stated that he was prepared to believe that his wants were determined by constitution and environment. He wished, however, to distinguish between mind and brain, although allowing that at present these terms were difficult to define with precision.

Another question from the audience suggested that perhaps we were forced into a dualistic approach because in the study of man we were both observer and observed. Professor Mace felt that psychology was the only science in which the scientist was a part of the subject matter. He suggested, however, that there were some things that a person could report in himself better than someone else and refused to agree that we should discard subjective evidence. Dr. Hydén discussed the inherent dualism in the perceptual experience, citing the example of perception of color. He pointed out that one could analyze light waves and define in electrical and chemical terms their effect on the sense receptors and central mechanisms, but this did not give a real definition of what color was.

In view of Dr. Hydén's fascinating report of his work on proteins, RNA, DNA, and a drug which affected levels of RNA, it was not surprising that many questions arose about this work and its implications. Dr. Hydén amplified somewhat and noted that his neurochemical work had begun as a side line while he was looking for a model of memory. He said that in his initial experiments with rats, cells of the phylogenetically older parts of the central nervous system were treated with the drug and showed an increase in amount of RNA per cell. An even greater surprise came with the finding that the composition of the RNA was different. He commented that the changes were most marked among glia cells. He suggested that when one could show that in 1 hour the composition of RNA (important as a template in protein formation) was changed, that perhaps the drug ought to be tested to see if it had any effect on behavior. He reported that in testing the drug clinically his psychiatric colleagues had found that it produced increased suggestibility. Dr. Cole asked Dr. Hydén whether he felt that this biochemical shift of the RNA continued upward or leveled off. Dr. Hydén replied that, as in all other biological processes, there would be an adaptive effect.

One member of the audience asked Dr. Hydén to elaborate on whether the RNA or the protein molecule was the information-storing agency. Dr. Hydén stated that he felt that it was difficult to separate RNA from its proteins; in the cell one had to look at DNA and RNA. DNA and nucleosides must be present for the synthesis of RNA. He felt that the permutations and combinations of different arrangements of RNA in its highly polymerized forms permitted storage of vast amounts of information—something on the order of at least 10^{15} items. He suggested that RNA, as the first substance to be modified by incoming information, would then affect the structure of subsequent proteins formed. From the standpoint of energy he felt that it was difficult to see small portions of RNA as transmitting information and that in this area proteins did a better job.

There were also questions from the audience about the relation of serotonin to brain function. One questioner asked if Dr. Hydén's work referred to serotonin or a serotonin inhibitor. Dr. Hydén implied that this had not been tested but that other psychotropic drugs had not changed the RNA. Dr. Cole felt that the evidence concerning serotonin in mental illness was still foggy. In reply to a question about the relation of serotonin to schizophrenia, he commented that since 95 per cent of serotonin was from the intestinal tract, it was difficult thus far to determine its activity in the brain.

This discussion, which revolved around the questions of faith and moral values, took place among a Jesuit priest (Father D'Arcy), a psychologist (Professor Hebb), and a professor of journalism (Professor Porter). The questions discussed were:

1. The distinction between scientific faith and religious belief

2. Moral values in a society, and the relation of the individual to that consensus

Recorder: Price Charlson
Panel Members: Martin C. D'Arcy, S.J., Donald O. Hebb, William E. Porter

Father D'Arcy opened the discussion with the statement that religious belief was inseparable from the Western tradition. It was difficult to understand how those who did not affirm a religious belief could hold that the mind was free; he said, in particular, that it was difficult to understand how materialists were able to support the hypothesis of freedom of the mind. He emphasized that he was speaking as a philosopher, not primarily as a religionist.

Professor Porter acknowledged that we had lost certain insights through secularization. Professor Hebb distinguished between religion and the kinds of belief and faith that nonreligious persons might have, yet he doubted that a man could exist without faith and beliefs. He suggested that one might at least argue that a pure, naked faith could be found better represented among scientists than among religionists. Professor Porter said that in American culture a religion-in-morality had replaced traditional religious observations.

The faith of the scientist in truth, Father D'Arcy argued, was an incomplete faith: faith involved a belief in persons, as well as in principles. The tenets of a true faith included belief in free will, belief in a valuable progress, and belief in the immateriality and the immortality of the soul. Expressing the scientific viewpoint, Professor Hebb characterized the faith of science. He listed among its tenets the belief in an orderly universe, the belief in a human mind able to deal with the problems presented to it in the pursuit of knowledge, and the belief in the limitlessness of the mind's capacity to solve problems. He denied that there was any conflict between religion and science. Although he found it difficult to define precisely the difference between religion and science, he suggested that the two fields differed not in the nature of the thought but in the nature of the assumptions. Nor did he believe that a materialistic approach to the world denied the freedom of the mind. Modern conceptions of the nervous system assumed that we were creative machines, not clocks. Human beings originated ideas which were not derived from experience. Hence, free will was not ruled out by a monistic philosophy, which need not be—and in the light of modern discoveries should not be—a simple materialism. We did not know what matter was; and the assumption that thinking mind and matter were incompatible involved the assumption that we already knew what matter was.

Father D'Arcy replied that we certainly did know enough about mind and matter to realize that they were different. Animals did not have souls; they were not able to choose freely between good and evil, even though they might select between alternative courses of action. Freedom involved not merely a selection, but a recognition of good and bad—and the freedom to choose on the basis of this recognition. Professor Hebb said that the faith of a scientist was better characterized as a set of working assumptions which the scientist did not set out to confirm because all his work rested upon such tenets as were already listed. But the human mind, he said, could not answer certain questions—and these were the traditional religious ones; indeed, the answers that the mind *was* able to understand *were not* answers to these questions. The distinction between scientific faith and religious belief could possibly be found in this area.

Turning to the freedom of the mind in society, Father D'Arcy asked whether the words "liberty, equality, and fraternity" had any meaning from a mechanistic point of view. He suggested that these words derived their meaning from the belief that the human being was made in the image of God. He was, however, willing to omit the phrase "the image of God," as he hoped to come to agreement with those who, without being religious, held a classical humanist position. Professor Hebb replied that every custom and every belief excluded other customs and beliefs—and so restricted the freedom of the mind. Every part of the education of children, in any society, inculcated thought control. He wondered how many of us would be willing to have children grow up without any such inculcation of moral and other ideas, so that they would be completely free later to decide every issue for themselves. Unquestionably, no society did this, and the problem appeared to be one of determining at what point to leave conformity. Regarding thought control, Professor Hebb further suggested that a society that was despotic was only less successful in inculcating its ideas, for such a society depended upon violence and coercion. A democratic society was only more successful than a despotic society in imposing its set of values, because it managed to inculcate these ideas without external coercion.

To Father D'Arcy, this sounded like moral relativism. He maintained that some things were known to be right and others wrong by the light of reason. Moreover, it was clear that an important distinction had been overlooked. All children were brought up in some society and took on the customs and beliefs of their parents, and every society surely enjoyed equal success and suffered approximately equal failure in this regard. Parents and children might, of course, disagree about the application of moral rules. However, one could not imagine the situation which Professor Hebb described—a situation in which children did not have a predetermined set of moral values inculcated upon them, but were left to make their own decisions about right and wrong when they grew up. If no beliefs were taught to them, what basis would they later have for making their own decisions?

The panel members agreed that, in order to survive, every society must be based on a commonly agreed set of moral values; however, the panel failed to agree on the proper source of this consensus.

This panel consisted of a clinical scientist (Dr. Kety), an author (Mr. Koestler), a neurosurgeon (Dr. Penfield), and a medical historian (Provost Saunders). In addition to amplifying the views expressed in their papers, these authors discussed the following questions:

1. *The social conditions that are necessary for freedom, and the ways in which these conditions could be achieved*
2. *Free will*
3. *The production of mediocrity through mass-communications media*
4. *The relation between human input and output*
5. *The relation between science and faith, including the conflict between the criteria used in science and in one's own personal life*
6. *The common factors underlying creativity in both art and science*
7. *The nature of an open mind*
8. *The recall of experiences as a result of direct stimulation of the brain, as an amplification of Dr. Penfield's paper*
9. *Monism versus dualism*

Recorder: Gerald A. Mendelsohn
Panel Members: Seymour S. Kety, Arthur Koestler, Wilder Penfield, John B. deC. M. Saunders

To open the discussion, Provost Saunders asked the panel what social conditions were necessary for freedom and how these conditions might be achieved. Dr. Kety's feeling was that to preserve true freedom of the mind even those beliefs we considered axiomatic must be critically examined. On this basis we must even ask why freedom of the mind was a desideratum. Pursuing this argument, Dr. Kety summarized two lines of reasoning given earlier by Professor Lasswell, the transempirical approach and the pragmatic approach. The former implied that since man was created in the image of God, human freedom and dignity were divine "axioms." The latter contended that there had been greater productivity and progress where freedom had prevailed. To these two rationales he then added his own, an extrapolation from the data of evolution to the mental sphere. An important aspect of nature was experimentation, his argument ran; this experimentation led to unique constellations of genetic patterns and, in extreme cases, to mutations. The survival of these patterns and mutations was a function of their ability to adapt to difficult circumstances of life. It was through these processes that evolution occurred. Similarly, progress in the mental sphere could occur only under circumstances in which there was freedom to generate new ideas, which were in turn subjected to ruthless critical examination and to the competition of other ideas. By this rationale, he reasoned, one could support the transempirical faith in freedom with historical and biological considerations.

Mr. Koestler agreed with Dr. Kety but added some "subjective addenda." He would like, he said, to see several freedoms guaranteed: freedom from platitude in all fields of experience; freedom from the organized, legalized, and political lie, whether public or private in origin; freedom from the half-truths so characteristic of mass-communications media; and freedom from exaggerated freedom, from anarchic freedom, for example, pseudo-Zen. Dr. Kety suggested an addition to this list: the freedom to be in error, that is to say, the freedom not only to express the truth but also to be gloriously wrong.

Approaching the topic from quite a different viewpoint, Dr. Penfield denied that there was such a condition as "freedom of the mind." There could be no mental activity without brain action, he argued, and in the sense that the mind was dependent upon the action of brain, it could not be free. If we turned our consideration to the means by which the brain could be controlled from without, however, we must conclude that there was no scientific method of forcing the brain to any constructive idea. Although punishment, drugs, brainwashing, and so forth might destroy or blur brain action, there was no external means by which the brain could be spurred to positive activity.

Dr. Kety concurred with Dr. Penfield in the mechanistic view suggested by his opening comments, but he pointed out that we had no proof of the correctness of this position; it was only the most heuristic position. The belief that mental activity was determined by brain action did not detract from human dignity or deny consciousness. However, freedom must be reinterpreted in the light of this position. The mind of each of us was determined by complex, individual experience, and thus each of us was unique and each idiosyncratic in behavior. In this sense, perhaps, we were free—free to generate new behaviors, free to generate random activity and random noise. Restraint lay in forcing this complexly determined mechanism to conform to a less complex process. The notion of free will did not need to be introduced to justify freedom of the mind. Moreover, the mechanistic view of life fostered a feeling of compassion and humility in regard to judgments about other people.

The problem of free will occupied the panel for some time. Mr. Koestler commented that it might be honorable to avoid the problem entirely since 2,000 years of philosophical effort had contributed little to its solution. He went on to say, however, that while he knew he was not free, he felt he must act as if he were. He agreed with Dr. Kety's comment that the mechanistic position did not necessarily restrict values, nor was it incompatible with the desire for freedom from external domination. But Mr. Koestler added that, although the mechanistic view might encourage tolerance of others, we could not extend this same tolerance to ourselves. The other person was a mechanism, but we must judge our own behavior more sternly. To the axiom, "To understand all is to forgive all," should be added the corollary, "To understand oneself is not to forgive oneself."

Did the communication by the mass media of identical material to millions of people foster mediocrity rather than variety of experience? This was the next question put to the panel by the moderator. The panel agreed with the case for mediocrity.

Provost Saunders then posed the question of whether a common input leads to a common output. Dr. Penfield replied that it was difficult to know what the input really was in human affairs. However, if one maintained that input controlled output, one was truly a hard-core mechanist. The assertion in question, he continued, was the basis of the Marxian position on human behavior. It was important to realize, however, that science had proved nothing in regard to philosophical assumptions about the mind, whether they were Marxian, religious, or for that matter, deterministic. A mechanistic view of life was a faith just as much as was belief in dualism or in God. The tacit assumption that science had already proved a hypothesis about God was not true; indeed, the hard fact was that there was no place in science for propositions of faith.

These reflections of Dr. Penfield's led to a consideration of the nature of science and its relation to matters of faith. Dr. Penfield reiterated that there was no place in science for unprovable hypotheses, only for those which could be proved or disproved. Although Dr. Kety agreed with Dr. Penfield, he suggested, nonetheless, that he had a mechanistic working hypothesis, for his whole career had been spent in looking for the roots of behavior in physical and chemical factors such as neurons—not in spirits or demons. Dr. Penfield replied that a good scientist must spend his life proving that the brain accounts for everything, but he must not assume that he has proven the point.

Provost Saunders then asked whether one could draw the conclusion that scientists worked with hypotheses but that the individual expressed his personal life as an assumption. The panel agreed that both hypotheses and assumptions were made in science, but whereas the former could be tested for truth, the assumptions were accepted as true. Science therefore attempted to reduce assumptions to a minimum. The view of Mr. Koestler was that this conflict between the scientific life and the personal life led to a dualism in which, as a scientist, one had to apply criteria such as heuristic value and verifiability, but in the private sphere one did not apply the same criteria. Within science itself, moreover, one could verify a prediction but not the theory on which it was based. Disagreeing, Dr. Penfield asserted that one could certainly hope to verify a theory. In rebuttal, Mr. Koestler pointed out that the Babylonian theory of astronomy could be used to predict eclipses with great accuracy, though the theory itself was unprovable. Degrees of verifiability therefore had to be considered in one's thinking. The reply of Dr. Penfield was that science must have small hypotheses to prove or disprove; if a scientist disproved several predictions based on a given over-all hypothesis, then he dropped that hypothesis.

"Is not science an act of faith?" asked Provost Saunders. "Is not science in reality a spiritual position?" Dr. Penfield vigorously disagreed. Mr. Koestler, however, asserted that the assumption by science of regularities was, in fact, an act of faith. Dr. Penfield replied that science was an approach which began with Hippocrates's insistence that nothing in nature or in disease was produced by the gods or by spirits. The scientist must devote himself to a program of objective observation in which untestable hypotheses has no place. The panel, including the moderator, did not agree that the Hippocratic tradition was the only origin of the scientific method. Mr. Koestler, for example, suggested that there were antecedents of science in certain mystical traditions. Provost Saunders proposed that the necessity for consistency that was characteristic of Egyptian thought was a possible root of scientific inquiry. One could argue, in fact, that the necessity to be consistent within oneself might also be a rationale for belief in freedom of the mind.

The common factors underlying creativity in both art and science, considered in Mr. Koestler's paper, were next discussed by the panel. The moderator asked Mr. Koestler what he meant by the assertion in his paper that art was not cumulative. Mr. Koestler replied that the same eternal truths were reiterated again and again by art; only the forms changed—the costumes and the levels were all that were different. Moreover, our experience of a given work of art was different each time we viewed it. In the emotionally neutral realm of science, however, there was a cumulative process. Science never restated truths; rather, it moved upward to new syntheses, in pyramid fashion. The distinction between art and science might thus be made that art contained an emotional experience as opposed to the integrative experience of science. Yet it must be kept in mind that there was no hard-and-fast boundary between art and science. Sometimes we lost sight of this truth because of the present cold war between the two cultures of science and humanities—a cold war based not only on mutual contempt, but also on mutual feelings of inferiority. This antagonism between science and the arts had not always been the case: Poincaré, for example, claimed that what guided the mathematician was an artistic impulse. The panel agreed that there were basic similarities between artistic and scientific creativity.

The driving forces behind creativity were next considered. Dr. Kety pointed to an inferiority complex in creative people. Anne Roe, in her study of outstanding scientists, found a high incidence of physical disability in the childhood of her subjects, a fact which led to the hypothesis that they learned to compensate for physical limitations by intellectual achievement. Dr. Kety continued that he had been impressed by the need for approbation and esteem on the part of particular artists he had known. This was often expressed as egotism and conceit, while beneath it was a need to indicate to themselves and their friends how much they were appreciated as artists. Mr. Koestler remarked that the same applied to scientists, but Dr. Penfield felt that the good scientists he had known had not been conceited and that they were well aware of how little they knew. He concluded that one evidence of greatness in a scientist was an open mind.

Provost Saunders asked what constitutes an open mind. Dr. Penfield replied that a person with an open mind expected to be taught and accepted nothing on the basis of authority alone. This statement was seconded by Dr. Kety, who added that science was open-minded in that it made few assumptions and, in fact, abhorred assumptions. They might be made as a point of departure, but they must be tentative and must be subjected to ruthless critical examination. Mr. Koestler cited Ernest Jones's description of Freud as an extremely skeptical and yet extremely gullible man. There was general agreement that the creative person, the genius, could generate and entertain a great number of constructs and could also attack each one of them vigorously. While agreeing with the general notion, Provost Saunders suggested that perhaps the word "randomness" might be more appropriate than "gullibility" in describing this aspect of the creative process. In response, Mr. Koestler pointed out that in the example of Edison searching for an appropriate filament material he saw an approach to invention that was very systematic rather than random. Thus we must conceive of a continuum between random and systematic approaches. Perhaps the ability to change one's frame of reference, randomly or systematically, was essential to creativity.

One query from the audience led to considerable discussion: Dr. Penfield was asked whether, in the recall of experiences resulting from direct brain stimulation, there was a reliving of the remembered situations. He replied that there was; the patients experienced their memories just as they had the initial incident, with no alteration of effect and occasionally with accompanying motor phenomena. Mr. Koestler pointed out that prior to these discoveries of Dr. Penfield's we had thought that the memory system was selective and efficient, but now we were faced with the rather frightening suggestion that every one of our experiences was retained. He wondered, however, whether it was possible that the memories elicited belonged to a special class of memories characterized by emotional significance or special value, such as a psychiatrist might uncover. Dr. Penfield replied that there were different kinds of memories—voluntary memory, generalized memory, detailed memory, memory for words—each of which was likely to have a different underlying mechanism. The memories he elicited differed from normal memories in their vividness, but they were generally of rather commonplace events. The events experienced by the patients concerned elaborate visual and auditory phenomena, but since the stimulation had been close to auditory and visual areas of the brain, this was quite understandable. The commonplace nature of the memories elicited led to the guess that much of our experience, perhaps even our whole waking life, was recorded.

Mr. Koestler asked Dr. Penfield whether the memories were part of a continuous record comparable to a motion picture or whether they were more like selected snapshots. Dr. Penfield replied that the former was the case; something was always happening in these memories, some activity was always taking place. Moreover, repeated stimulation at a single point elicited the same sequence every time. For instance, if a patient recalled a song each time he was stimulated in a particular area, the song began at precisely the same place in the music. There was really little that was unique about these memories, he continued, although patients usually had not recalled them before. They did resemble memories produced by patients during epileptic seizures, and, in fact, on occasion the memories evoked by stimulation had previously occurred during seizures. One final point that Dr. Penfield stressed was our inability to select or in any way to influence what was elicited by stimulation.

What is the meaning of monism and dualism—two words employed repeatedly in the symposium? This was the final question asked, and came from a member of the audience. Dr. Kety, speaking as an "unreconstructed dualist," said that most human beings were aware of both a material world and an inner world of sensation. We learned, then, that there were two kinds of entities—consciousness, on the one hand, and the material world, on the other—and that the latter could influence the former, for example, via drugs. One argument for monism—that advanced by Berkeley—asserted that our only evidence of the existence of the material world was sense data, that is, the data of consciousness. Another position asserted that consciousness was an artifact of the material world, and that the reductionism of the monistic position was the product of a desire for parsimony. Dr. Kety maintained, however, that it was possible to hold that both the material world and consciousness existed. He found it difficult to explain consciousness solely in terms of matter, or matter in terms of consciousness. The panel expressed general agreement with Dr. Kety's statement.

This discussion, which centered on the general question of the ability of the human brain to solve problems, took place between a psychiatrist-psychologist (Dr. Miller), a historian (Professor Hughes), and a professor of law and political science (Professor Lasswell).

The panel members discussed four main problems:

1. The capacity of the brain to store memories

2. The ability of man to cope with and control his environment

3. The need to formulate solutions now to the anticipated social problems of the future

4. Freedom of human choice

Recorder: Malcolm A. Brown

Panel Members: James G. Miller, H. Stuart Hughes, Harold D. Lasswell

Professor Lasswell opened the discussion by posing the primary question that brought him to the symposium: Did the panel members think that the more knowledge we had the less we knew? His own observation was that nature lacked that regard for the future without which human beings could not plan and develop their own social potentialities. His conclusion was that human beings must therefore assume this responsibility for themselves.

Responding, Dr. Miller referred to the experimental research of McCulloch and Pitts and Jenkins and Sallenbach, who attempted to estimate the extent of the human brain's capacity to store knowledge. The first group of researchers had discovered the great facility of specific memories within the brain to store duplicate and successive memory traces and their patterned interconnections. The second group of researchers had gone on from there to hypothesize that forgetting, with the passage of time, was not so much the wearing away of memory traces as it was the action of countless new memory traces forcibly pushing out and supplanting the older ones. This would seem to indicate, he argued, that it was entirely possible that there was a limit to the capacity of the human brain to remember experiences. To the extent that this was true, education became primarily a matter of controlling the mind in the sense that education, by fostering the cultivation of irreversible habits, restricted the mind's capacity for assimilating the widest range of alternatives available to it. It was not so desirable that the child should be encouraged to expose itself to every possible kind of experience because of its limited memory capacity.

Professor Hughes agreed with Dr. Miller that most education represented a kind of constriction. However, he felt that there must be a way to cultivate social restriction in the child and, at the same time, to permit his mind to develop freely. This must be the case, Professor Hughes argued, if it was true that a really well-trained mind was capable of exercising itself with complete freedom within its special province of knowledge. Dr. Miller rejoined that there still remained a limit to the rate at which the brain could assimilate new information. A good illustration of this limit was the unrealistic way in which many of us bought books, thereby accumulating a large library—the bulk of which we never read. He questioned the worth of the efforts of Robert Hutchins and Mortimer Adler at the University of Chicago to instill 1,300 million words and 102 ideas into the memories of their students.

Dr. Miller, pursuing the question of information-input overload, pointed out that the maximal use of our human capacities was recently brought to the widespread attention of the public and scholars alike as a problem to be squarely faced because of the recent appearance of the computer. It was his opinion that education during the future was going to change from a process of obtaining information directly from the teacher to a process of obtaining from the teacher the various strategies by which to cope with information-input overload. He outlined seven different types of strategies: (1) omissions, (2) errors, (3) queueing, (4) filtering, (5) approximation, (6) multiple channels, and (7) escape. Professor Hughes heartily seconded this prediction, declaring that it was already his teaching practice to coach students in how to beat the rules of the game, so inundated were they with required texts for each course.

A member of the audience offered the following definition of freedom: the confidence of an organism in its capacity to adapt to its environment. Professor Hughes responded negatively to this definition, taking issue with any kind of crude naturalistic model of behavior to explain man's behavior. He felt that there was a difference between the beast who coped with his environment and man who transformed his environment. Dr. Miller felt that this definition of freedom really placed the emphasis upon the subjective aspect of the individual's adjustment to his environment. In actual fact, Dr. Miller went on, the input-output model of behavior that he personally adhered to was still applicable to such a definition of freedom. This model presupposed that inside the organism there were various subsystems, and within these subsystems there were various stresses, excesses, and tensions, in constant operation. Freedom of the mind could be explained according to such a model of behavior, in terms of a stress-defense ratio. The organism-environment relation was thus reduced to a relative accommodation between the quantitative output of inner stresses, excesses, and tensions within the various mechanical subsystems, on the one hand, and the quantitative input of integrating sensory stimuli, on the other. This stress-defense ratio became modified to a threat-defense ratio when the brain allowed the information stored up from past experiences to substitute for the internal stresses themselves in the form of word symbols and signals which thereafter functioned as warnings of impending threat. Hence, the more desirable our psychic mechanisms of defense, the more freedom of choice was permitted to our symbol-manipulating minds.

"Has man made progress since the dawn of civilization in his ability to cope with and control his environment?" asked a member of the audience. Dr. Miller replied that if the thesis of Benjamin Whorf was correct—that our thought processes were determined in large part by the verbal categories and words that we used in daily speech—then man today did possess a more effective ability to cope with his environment than did his primitive ancestors. Professor Hughes remarked that the English language was the most highly developed language in the world, not so much because of its grammatical complexity but by reason of its syntactical looseness and voluminous vocabulary. Sharing Dr. Miller's sympathies in part, he went on to question the worth of the "great books" program at the University of Chicago, feeling that it was primarily an expression of the forced overloading of books that plagued America's system of education. He felt that more time and effort should be given to the active contemplation of a few well-chosen and personally esteemed books, so that a student might be encouraged to take the time to link the significance of what he was presently reading with what he already knew. When a member of the audience rejoined that the basic purpose behind the 102 ideas of the great-books program was to furnish the skeletal means by which the student could make his own higher synthesis of knowledge and wisdom, Professor Hughes replied that the individual student's personally selected inventory of the greatest ideas and books was preferable as a means of effecting a higher synthesis within his mind.

Professor Lasswell then raised the question of whether human beings normally felt more, rather than less, handicapped as a result of the accumulation of their encounters with problem-solving situations. He looked upon the social problems confronting us today in terms of their implications for the future, saying that these implications ought to be anticipated in a reasonable manner, and we should make some active attempt to control them. An illustration of such a problem with implications for the future was Dr. Kubie's prediction that molecular substitution and its control would make possible within the next 200 years the indefinite prolongation of man's life. Professor Lasswell was strongly of the opinion that we must anticipate these social problems of the future if we are not suddenly to find the freedom of our minds restricted by unanticipated developments. For instance, if the usual kind of biological reproduction of the human species should be eliminated, there might be a real danger that our style of living would become so stereotyped that we would be unable to meet emergent natural situations of threat, so removed would we have become from our biological capacities.

A member of the audience inquired whether there was a need for a new professional discipline to formulate the solutions to the anticipated social problems of the future. Professor Lasswell was quick to assent that a spontaneous recruitment of volunteers was needed today to achieve this very goal, whether formed into a new professional discipline or acting independently. He went on to criticize the seminar techniques presently employed to make decisions about social problems; what was needed instead, he suggested, was the technique of the planetarium. A planetarium, he continued, was a single environment that was capable of simulating all the galaxies and solar systems in the heavens above. In the same manner, he suggested, we needed to apply this technique to the future problems of our American society, rather than confining it to the map rooms of military headquarters. Dr. Miller stated that a computer simulation of social processes along the lines of the planetarium technique was presently being undertaken at Systems Development Corporation in Los Angeles. He also pointed out that no official policy maker had yet consulted these planetariumlike research projects before making major national decisions.

Can freedom best be analyzed according to a subjective consciousness of choices or in the more objective dependent of one's recognition of them? This question was raised by Dr. Miller, who was inclined to favor the latter alternative. He cited the experimental psychological investigations done over the years on the nature of problem solving and concept formation. This research had revealed that the foremost activity involved in both these mental processes was classification of the data into comprehensive categories. Invariably he noticed that the subjects of the concept-formation tests would reach a point at which their method of classifying the objects presented became a mystery even to themselves. For similar reasons, the primary role of the psychotherapist—performed by advice, objective analysis, or suggestion—was to indicate to the client those areas in which there were a greater number of alternative solutions to a pressing psychological problem, and hence to indicate a greater latitude of freedom of choice than the client had hitherto been aware of. However, Dr. Miller continued, insight into these additional alternative solutions did not always result in improved behavior or promote a greater freedom of the mind. This would suggest the limited influence of conscious choice as a determinant of one's real mental freedom.

A member of the audience expressed the opinion that feeling was the basis of choice and human freedom. Professor Hughes, speaking for historians, felt that subjective definitions were acceptable, provided they were not contradicted by objective phenomena. Professor Lasswell observed that our American tradition was prone to conceive of freedom in terms of a context-analysis point of view; that is to say, so pragmatically oriented was our national tradition that it preferred to hire those concrete procedures by which we might come to realize specific situations or contexts of freedom, rather than to attempt to define the principles upon which freedom was supposed to be founded. Generally speaking, it was true to say, he believed, that our American culture deprecated overly prescriptive definitions of key metaphysical concepts.

This discussion—one of exceptional interest—took place among an author whose works on the effects of mescalin, the future of mankind, and other topics have attracted widespread interest (Mr. Huxley), a psychologist (Dr. Krech), and a scientist whose paper on the "thinking" capacity of electronic computers provoked considerable discussion (Professor Simon). The topics discussed by these speakers, largely in response to questions from the audience, were:

1. *The beneficial role of experience in the development of the individual*
2. *The basis of our fear of "thinking" electronic computers*
3. *The springs of human creativity in an affluent society*
4. *Mr. Huxley's experiments with mescalin*
5. *Creative outlets for "everyman" in contemporary society*
6. *The nature of scientific inquiry*
7. *An analysis of the reasons for the popularity of the present symposium*

Recorder: Robert R. Alford
Panel Members: Aldous Huxley, David Krech, Herbert A. Simon

Dr. Krech was asked to comment on the view, put forward in the symposium, that both human beings and computers required exposure to a wide range of experience in order to function in a "normal" fashion. Replying, Dr. Krech stated that sensory deprivation affected the biochemical composition of the brain; this was shown by research on rats. In research carried out in his laboratory, he and his colleagues had employed male litter mates to minimize genetic differences. At weaning (25 days) one rat was put in isolation. His brother was put into a large case with nine other rats, where he was trained by the experimenter and subjected to "environmental complexity." At the end of 80 days, the brains of both rats were chemically analyzed. The two rats showed a predictable difference in the activity of brain enzymes. This was a biochemical change, related to the efficiency of transmission of neural impulses. The implication was that environment determined almost everything about this rat, including the functioning of his brain. By analogy, one might assert that play and other stimulation of children were as necessary for full development—in this basic physiological sense—as food. Moreover, the effects of isolation of the rat were not completely overcome by restoration of the normal environment at some point; traces were still found in the brain.

Isolation affected human beings in a somewhat different way, argued Mr. Huxley. There were many religions of self-isolation, he observed. When men cut off external stimuli, they recombined their previous experiences in many strange ways, such as hallucinations and visions. Speaking from his own considerable experience with computers, Professor Simon made the point that computers as well as men needed rich sensory experiences before they could feel the effects of "isolation" in that way.

There seemed to be a paradox in this problem of the relation of isolation to freedom of the mind, asserted a member of the audience: to produce a free mind, we had to stimulate a person, but were we not controlling a person by determining which stimuli he received? People isolated themselves to change their bodies and minds, to produce visionary experiences, to obtain a feeling of unity with the universe, replied Mr. Huxley. This approach was only one out of many different Eastern philosophies, however.

Some other philosophies argued that Nirvana must be rejected until all sentient beings had been helped along the road. Mr. Huxley's personal view was to side with the latter tendency in Oriental philosophy.

Professor Simon made the point that the question used the word "freedom" in several senses: the paradox of the necessity of both stimulation *and* isolation was, he suggested, a semantic one. Mr. Huxley asked, "Are we talking about freedom *from* . . . or freedom *to* . . . ?"

In reply to a question, Mr. Huxley expressed the opinion that Professor Simon's computers were not necessarily bringing us closer to the "Brave New World"; it depended on how they were used. Research did not dictate a given form of society.

Professor Simon was asked about the "ah-ha" experience in the computer to which he referred in his paper. In human beings, he replied, the "ah-ha" experience concerned problem solving. Although problems were sometimes solved by trial and error, on other occasions the answer was suddenly perceived in an intuitive flash of deduction, even though all the steps of deduction had not been thought through. What seemed to happen was that the problem was solved on the more abstract level, with the details filled in later. The computer had the same experience of a sudden perception of a pattern at an abstracted level.

In response to a question put by Dr. Krech, about 30 of the 150 members of the audience raised their hands to indicate some kind of fear of the idea of a thinking computer. Attempting to explain why this question disturbed people, Professor Simon first emphasized that he identified himself with human beings, not with machines; he underscored the fact that he was on the side of people. Then he went on to explain that we usually thought of human beings as *special* creatures—whether on a religious basis or some other basis—and suggested that whenever someone implied that something was *like* a human being this feeling of uniqueness was threatened and we worried.

The panel was asked whether they would agree that the computer had the potential of destroying certain aspects of man's abilities. Mr. Huxley said that he would not agree. Before we had printing, he went on, man had to rely on his memory. Now we had encyclopedias, and it could be argued that man's ability to memorize had atrophied, that in a sense, a human ability had been compromised. People were also less skilled in the physical act of writing words now because of the introduction of typewriters and other technical devices, but there was really no loss, only the saving of appalling amounts of labor. He added, nevertheless, that he personally sympathized with this feeling of loss and impoverishment.

The following question was from the audience: "There appears to be a paradox in the situation that man functions best in a free society, yet, when freedom leads to an affluent society, creativity is stifled. Does our very success threaten our freedom of the mind?" Dr. Krech did not agree that the affluent society discouraged creativity. The psychologist Abraham Masloa had investigated levels of need satisfaction in human personality development and asserted that unless physiological needs—food, shelter, and so forth—were satisfied, "higher" levels of needs—such as creativity and love—did not manifest themselves. Satisfaction, not frustration, of primary needs produced a creative person. Following this line of argument, Masloa said—and Dr. Krech agreed—that an affluent society did not stifle creativity. The great artists of the past were not starving and ill-housed, contrary to the common belief about the connection between suffering and creativity. Mr. Huxley, a creative artist himself, agreed with Dr. Krech's statement. The Renaissance artists, he said, were feted by dukes and princes who seem to have had an uncanny ability to patronize the very artists whose work had survived. Mr. Huxley regretted that the same taste did not prevail among our modern political leaders. Dr. Krech quoted the old Hebrew saying, "Where there is no wealth, there is no learning." A rabbi in the audience, in turn, quoted the quick reply, "Where there is no learning, there is no wealth."

A member of the audience hazarded the opinion that maybe the source of creativity was kinds of disturbances other than physical frustrations. Psychic frustrations, for example, sometimes caused a flowering of creativity: Beethoven composed some of his greatest works after he was deaf; Freud was hounded most of his life. Dr. Krech added the point that affluence created only the *conditions* for creativity; it was not in itself the mainspring of creativity.

The question of the implications of Masloa's deprivation hypothesis for child rearing was raised by a member of the audience. How did one prevent children from becoming spoiled if one satisfied their every physical want, hoping that "higher" needs would emerge? Dr. Krech stated that parents must not only provide all physical needs; they must also stimulate other levels. Spoiling took place when only physical needs were stimulated. Mr. Huxley said that the too-affluent child in our culture was loaded down with a plethora of mechanical playthings. A child must also work with a hammer and wood; he must be stimulated to activity, not allowed to remain passive.

A member of the audience then asked at what point satisfaction of needs changes into indulgence. Dr. Krech was not certain that he knew where to draw the line. Which elements were negative and which positive was an important but fruitless question. Possibly some of the most wasteful aspects of our affluent society would yet turn out to be some of the most important. But this was only speculation, he added.

Mr. Huxley was asked to describe the effects he had experienced in his work with mescalin. Was a greater freedom of the mind really achieved with a limited sensory input? Mr. Huxley replied that although no one could live permanently in a mescalin state, it was an extraordinary experience. It was a state of "fortuitous grace," he said, in theological language; it produced experiences which might be extraordinarily helpful in understanding the world, in producing new creative insights, and in relieving the fear of death.

But was not this sense of freedom the result of restriction of sensory input, countered a member of the audience, and therefore somewhat contradictory to what was discussed earlier about the need for maximum sensory input, that is, for the most complex stimulation—as in the case of Dr. Krech's rats? Disagreeing, Mr. Huxley said that he did not think the two situations were contradictory. The mescalin experience relied upon previous sensory experience to make it meaningful. And more fundamentally, what we perceived as stimuli depended largely upon our ability to conceptualize. If the mescalin experience heightened the ability to conceptualize, then sensory abilities were heightened, not restricted. Continuing the questioning about mescalin, a member of the audience said that among the pharmacologists who had spoken there seemed to be an axiom that there was no drug that *extended* thought processes; "Does mescalin?" he asked. Replying, Mr. Huxley said that he did not understand the meaning of "extended." He suggested that we engage in any kind of experience in order to perceive things in a new and more interesting way, to find a new way of doing things. However, this might not be "extending" thought processes in the questioner's sense.

The same member of the audience then went on to ask whether one did not get from mescalin this ability to "focus" upon certain experiences at the price of other mental abilities? One had something much better to do than solve problems when one was under mescalin, responded Mr. Huxley. "What would be one's reaction if he were making love and someone asked him to take a Rorschach test?" he asked. "Would it be an indication that his mental abilities were restricted if he replied that he had something better to do?"

Decrying the use of much creative talent for commercial ends, a member of the audience expressed the opinion that ideas, it seemed, had only marketplace value in our society. How could we change the valuation placed on ideas? A creative elite was needed, the questioner argued, which was adequately supported. The real problem, countered Professor Simon, was the need to provide opportunities for the creative expression of the average man in our society. The creative elite fared well enough already.

Dr. Krech was asked to describe the future direction of his research work. Replying, he made the point of the often unexpected nature of the development of scientific investigation. The question, he said, was impossible to answer specifically. When a scientist started his work in his laboratory he did not know what was going to happen. To tie a scientist to a plan, he said, was *really* a restriction of freedom of the mind. Professor Simon agreed that a research scientist found it impossible to adhere rigidly to a predetermined plan; it was necessary to modify the direction of one's work as new conclusions were reached.

Dr. Krech then brought up the question of the tremendous interest shown in the subjects discussed in this symposium—as proved by the high attendance. Mr. Huxley, who has often written on these topics, expressed the opinion that the whole subject of control of the mind was fascinating and alarming. Computers, drugs, and manipulation had a sinister ring, he argued. "Then you think that people came to this symposium as they would have gone to a horror movie?" asked Dr. Krech. Professor Simon expressed the opinion that the program was carefully designed as a projective device. There was great variety in it, he said, but all the participants had focused upon a central problem: freedom and control of the mind.

Pursuing the question of the motivation inspiring attendance at the symposium, Dr. Krech asked specific members of the audience, picked at random, why they were there. He obtained the following answers:

1. I cheated; I was paid to come.
2. I am an M.D., interested in science and self-improvement.
3. I wanted to hear and see famous people. Also, I am a teacher and thought I should get some ideas about creativity to use in the classroom.
4. I felt that I could learn something about my fellow man. Man has advanced little in knowledge of himself; we must change man's values.

Mr. Huxley repeated his previous analysis that not only were the topics of enormous importance, but in addition, there was a sinister glamor about these matters. The next "glamor sciences," suggested Dr. Krech, continuing the motivational analysis, would be the behavioral sciences. A conference on atomic energy by contrast, would not now be so popular. People had begun to realize that the sciences of man must be promoted, and prestige would begin to accrue to those sciences, he argued. A member of the audience pointed out that the man in the street, not just the technical man, attended this symposium.

[*Editor's Note.* An informal poll of the occupational composition of the audience at this panel discussion revealed the following statistics: about one-third were doctors; one-fourth were teachers of various kinds; one-fifth were research scientists (not included in the first two); and the remainder came from the "lay public."]

To conclude the discussion, a member of the audience asked each member of the panel to give, in turn, his impression of what had actually been gained from these discussions. The view of Mr. Huxley was that there had been extremely creative features in many speeches and discussions in the symposium. The bridging of the gap between, on the one hand, men from the humanities—historians such as H. Stuart Hughes, psychologists such as C. A. Mace, and political scientists such as Harold Lasswell—and on the other, men from medical and other scientific disciplines, had resulted, he felt, in much fruitful discussion.

Professor Simon felt that the chief point reemphasized by the discussions was the difficulties encountered by people or groups who tried to change or manipulate the human spirit. Much evidence had been presented to show that controlling the human mind was extraordinarily difficult.

Winding up the discussion, Dr. Krech said that he had not only gained new knowledge, but he had also had some of his existing beliefs confirmed. However, what had impressed him the most about these meetings, he said, had not been the speeches or discussions by the faculty, but the tremendous interest shown by so varied and highly skilled an audience. The reasons for this great interest in the behavioral sciences would provide him with much food for thought in the following weeks.

Several topics implied, but not actually discussed, in papers in the symposium were dealt with in this panel discussion. These topics included:

1. *An explanation of the original rationale which inspired the symposium*
2. *The desirability of avoiding confusion between (a) the cure of illness by pharmacology and (b) manipulation of the normal person*
3. *The vulgarization of psychiatric knowledge*
4. *Freud's psychoanalytic approach*

5. An interpretation of the argument of Mr. Koestler's paper
6. The impact of social pressures on the individual

Recorder: David Matza
Panel Members: Seymour M. Lipset, Karl H. Pribram, Leo C. Rosten

The original purpose of the symposium had been to confront pharmacologists with representatives of the social sciences and the humanities, said Professor Lipset, who explained that his role was primarily that of suggesting names for speakers. His understanding, he went on, was that many pharmacologists were beginning to feel that ultimately they could foresee a time when many mental and even social problems could be alleviated by drugs. The initial aim of the symposium, as he understood it, was to subject this view to the scrutiny and criticism of humanists and social scientists. Somehow, in the course of the symposium, or perhaps in the preparation of papers for it, the original rationale had become obscured. This sort of optimistic pharmacological view was, in fact, never expressed. This viewpoint raised many questions and problems. For example, the discovery of drugs that had the capacity to reduce tensions could conceivably make the finding of underlying causes of various problems irrelevant. The sorts of questions that were not discussed because of almost universal caution and good will at the symposium could, he felt, have been fruitful and stimulating. Such questions might have included: How low a level of tension do we want in our society? Do we not want to maintain a certain level of tension? There was virtual unanimity among the speakers on these points, he said. They agreed that, while we knew something about the brain and mind, and while we were likely to learn more, this did not really constitute an ability to change or control human behavior. He thought that, in a way, there was perhaps too much politeness, too much scientific caution. The scientific dreams did not come through. Scientists were typically overcautious in their predictions of subsequent developments. They usually overestimated the time it would take to arrive at certain discoveries.

Dr. Pribram thought that there had been a tendency during the symposium to get two problems confused: the cure of illness as contrasted with the manipulation of the normal person. The pharmacologist wished to cure the ill. He did not want to apply the new techniques to the normal person. In brief, he desired to restore the abnormal to the community of normal persons. This goal was far different from that of restriction of normal behavior. Like the humanist, the pharmacologist wanted to maintain and extend human freedom.

Professor Rosten, returning to Professor Lipset's point, asked whether we had not had a vulgarization of psychiatric knowledge resulting in an overemphasis on goals such as group popularity. People who preferred isolation to intimate social relations with a group ought to be encouraged rather than discouraged, he felt, provided they were not destructive. This type of contemplative isolation produced the creative person or the mystic. Similarly, the idea that the purpose of life was happiness seemed a narrowing view. It meant the reduction of tension and conflicts which were themselves valuable and creative. We must encourage not-so-rational behavior. The role of the pharmacologist and the psychiatrist was to remove unnecessary suffering, not all suffering. Freedom, to be meaningful, involved the right to be irrational if no one else was hurt.

Professor Rosten commented that it was unfortunate that there was little discussion at the symposium of psychiatry as a method of controlling or influencing the mind. Surely it represented one sort of intervention in human activity. However, it was difficult to engage in a scholarly or scientific conversation with a psychoanalyst. Somehow their training seemed to set them apart from most other researchers. Few psychoanalysts knew how to formulate a problem in a way in which their theories or assumptions could be tested; nor could they formulate it in a manner permitting fruitful discussion with a nonpsychoanalyst. For instance, if a patient agreed with an analyst's interpretation of a dream, then the proposition was confirmed. If the patient disagreed, the psychoanalyst was still right; the patient was merely resisting. How did the psychoanalyst know?

The absence of a psychoanalytic point of view at the symposium was in itself rather interesting, remarked Dr. Pribram. Professor Simon, he felt, had come closest to a psychoanalytic point of view. The similarity between the approach of Professor Simon and that of Freud was missed, however, unless we asked: What was Freud trying to do? Freud, we must recall, was a neurologist of the Würzburg school. Freud and the other members of that school were interested in the problem of thinking; they were concerned with the processes by which thought took place—but they found these processes to be highly elusive. Their technique consisted of confronting a subject with a problem and asking him to verbalize his attempt to solve the problem. Freud, steeped in this tradition, contributed a great deal to the solution of the problem posed by the Würzburg school. His insight was that if one simply allowed a patient to externalize his thoughts, saying whatever came into his mind, one would gradually expose the layers of the thought process. This approach closely resembled that of Professor Simon, who compared the computer with the students, using this method as a technique of unraveling the processes involved in thinking.

Professor Rosten disagreed with this view. Freud, he said, did not encourage thinking about a specific problem. He had allowed his patient to talk freely about anything. Simon, on the other hand, was concerned with ego activity and cognitive problems. Dr. Pribram, in response, admitted that the problems facing Freud's patients were more complex than those to which Simon's computers and students were subjected. But Freud was a better "computer engineer" than most. Even though the problem was more complex, Freud's patients were faced with something like a specific problem awaiting solution.

Professor Rosten objected that the patient was often unaware of what his problem was. It seemed to him that Freud's fundamental insight was that human behavior, although irrational, was not random; it was patterned. His work constituted an attempt to classify and analyze the irrational in human behavior. Dr. Pribram countered that Freud had not been dealing with random events. He was concerned with the discovery of the hidden order in human activity.

The view of Professor Lipset was that, although Professor Simon's objectives might be similar to Freud's, their logic was quite different. Returning to his original point, he raised a question about the pharmacologist: Dr. Pribram had pointed out, he said, that the goal and the potential of pharmacology were to deal with sick people and not to tamper with the normal. But what was "normal"? One of the major consequences of psychoanalysis had been to *expand* the definition of what we took to be sick people. New categories of illness came into being as a result of Freud's discoveries. What was a normal level of anxiety or tension? What were the effects of medical and scientific developments on our definitions of normality? These questions posed interesting social problems. Did the alleviation of tension or anxiety result in a diminution of creative energy? Whether it really did or not, many artists certainly believed that it did.

Dr. Pribram said that there clearly had to be some instituted social control on the uses to which these drugs might be put. However, we must remember that all these developments were still only possibilities. The tenuous state of our knowledge regarding these matters, he thought, had been correctly stressed during the symposium. Professor Lipset made the point that we should also remember that if and when these drugs appeared, they might have positive rather than negative consequences. Reducing tension might facilitate, rather than hinder, genius.

Professor Rosten thought that this was already the case. The psychoanalytic technique probably facilitated, rather than hampered, creativity. Although during the actual period of analysis there was likely to be some diminution of creativity, after the completion of the process there was probably an enlarging of whatever talents one possessed.

A member of the audience asked a panel member to give his interpretation of Mr. Koestler's paper. Replying, Professor Rosten said that Koestler had been interested in the state of trance and that he had also been working on the method of discovery, particularly as it involved irrational motivation, as in the case of Kepler. Thus he became interested in the general problem of creativity. His argument was that creativity in the arts and sciences involved highly similar processes. Creativity involved breaking through conventionally dissociated gestalts and integrating these previously unconnected frames of reference. The creative person managed to associate what was previously thought unconnected. Once perceived, these discoveries, or associations, seemed remarkably simple. Freud was a good example. What was amazing was the length of time it took human beings to see the obvious. By the time we were socialized, perception was so remarkably selective in most of us that it remained for the genius to see connections that had been trained out of the average person.

What effects did political and economic pressures have on the freedom of the citizen? Was not the individual in our society subjected to distinct pressures to conform? These questions were asked by a member of the audience. Professor Lipset expressed the opinion that this problem was highly complex. Clearly, in any society there were fixed choices and assumptions, and in no society was there complete freedom. Furthermore, these assumptions were not random or completely arbitrary. They typically operated to perpetuate the system. There is a consensus in society which serves to rule out many alternative points of view or paths of action. The problem was the degree of freedom that could be tolerated by any ongoing social system which must perform a variety of tasks somewhat effectively if it were to be maintained. The Soviet Union thought of the United States as having a totalitarian society because the free choice existing in our society did not include the choice of their system. In point of fact, we do rule out this possibility. In regard to a child's religion, too, there were certainly restrictions on individual freedom. The problem was that if we were completely free, there would be a breakdown of ongoing social institutions. Every society allowed a greater or lesser latitude for freedom within the limitations placed on the choices of the population.

The point, said Dr. Pribram, was that freedom could come only with structure. We did not want the absence of structure—that is, the chaos of anarchy; rather, we wanted some divergence in the structure. Professor Rosten added that as we became freer we learned more about areas of which we were previously unaware. Our expectations changed in the process of becoming free. Emancipation provoked higher aspirations regarding freedom than had existed before its attainment. There was a kind of moving equilibrium by which the word "freedom" took on new and additional meanings. This was sometimes a dangerous process, since it might instill the notion that all human problems were capable of final solution. Some eternal human problems might be mitigated, he thought, but we possibly would never achieve anything like a final solution. Such problems included, for instance, the problem of the young versus the old, the problem of rebelliousness, and the problem of aging. There would always be conflicts and difficulties in areas such as these. The important thing was to handle and cultivate discontent, not to obliterate it once and for all.

In a sense, Professor Rosten thought, the theory of democracy had been traditionally misread and misstated. It did not call for a final solution to all problems or for equality. There was a natural aristocracy of talent. The just and effective society provided the maximum opportunities for the continuing solution of problems and for the continuing individual quest for self-fulfillment. Men in the arts and sciences, moreover, should not ignore the fact that talent and creativity might take a variety of paths. For example, a great deal of creativity appeared in modern business activity; the substance of the business executive's tasks might not be dramatic, but this should not obscure the creativity he brought to these tasks.

In the United States, stated Professor Lipset, a great deal of talent had been recruited into business activities. It was alleged that in England and on the Continent there was not such great recruitment of talent into these pursuits because of aristocratic traditions which frowned on business activity. Some had given this as a reason for the decline of English supremacy in the economic sphere.

The United States had contributed a great deal to the precept of equality of opportunity, he continued. It was interesting to note that the first workingman's party appeared in the United States in the 1820s, and a fundamental part of its platform pertained to the implementation of the precept of equality of opportunity by a system of public education in which the child was taken from his family context in order to minimize whatever advantages might accrue to the youngster born of wealthy parents. This proposal would still be considered highly radical, but it tackled a fundamental problem in instituting a system of equal opportunity. On the other hand, at least in the United States, every family attempted to transmit whatever privileges it possessed; thus whatever inequality existed tended to be reinforced by the family system.